STATIONARY RANDOM PROCESSES

HOLDEN-DAY SERIES IN TIME SERIES ANALYSIS

Gwilyn M. Jenkins and Emanuel Parzen, *Editors*

Yu. A. Rozanov

STATIONARY RANDOM PROCESSES

Translated by

A. Feinstein

HOLDEN-DAY

San Francisco, Cambridge, London, Amsterdam

This book is translated from *Statsionarnye Sluchainye Protsessy*, Gosudarstvennoe Izdatel'stvo Fiziko-Matematicheskoi Literatury, Moscow, 1963.

Library of Congress Catalog Card Number: 66-29909
Printed in the United States of America

TRANSLATOR'S PREFACE

This translation has benefited, in comparison with the Russian original, by the inclusion of certain improved results connected with the factorization of rational spectral densities, which were communicated to me by the author, as well as by the correction (by author and translator) of various minor errors, mainly of a typographical nature.

It is a pleasure to thank the author for his considerable assistance in these matters.

A. Feinstein

AUTHOR'S PREFACE

In recent years new developments have taken place in the theory of stationary random processes. Many papers, devoted to linear forecasting of multi-dimensional stationary (in the wide sense) processes, have brought this portion of the theory close to a final definitive form. Considerable attention has been focused on various kinds of ergodic properties of stationary (in the strict sense) processes which arise in connection with the applicability of the central limit theorem to these processes. This book, which originated in a course of lectures on the theory of stationary processes given by me at Moscow University in 1959–1960, is devoted to these questions.

This book is intended for the mathematically qualified reader, but the basic results which it contains (particularly those relating to rational spectral densities) should also be intelligible to the engineering reader who is interested in applications of the theory of stationary processes.

In writing this book I have benefited considerably from various remarks by my friends. To all of them my sincere thanks.

I consider it my pleasant duty to express here my deep gratitude to my teacher Andrei Nikolaevich Kolmogorov.

Yu. A. Rozanov

CONTENTS

STATIONARY RANDOM PROCESSES

I

HARMONIC ANALYSIS OF STATIONARY RANDOM PROCESSES

1. Definitions. Examples

Let Ω be some measurable space of elements ω (elementary events) with a σ-algebra $\mathfrak{U}$ of ω-sets, on which there is defined a probability measure $P(d\omega)$. We will call any complex-valued function $\xi(\omega)$, defined on Ω and measurable with respect to the σ-algebra $\mathfrak{U}$, a *random variable.* By a *random process* $\boldsymbol{\xi}$ we will understand a family of random variables $\xi(t)$, depending on a parameter t (time), which takes on either all integer values (the case of discrete time), or all real values (the case of continuous time). To emphasize the dependence of each of the $\xi(t)$ upon ω, we will occasionally use the notation $\xi(t, \omega)$.

A random process $\boldsymbol{\xi}$ is said to be *stationary in the wide sense*, if its mathematical expectation $\boldsymbol{E}\xi(t)$,

$$\boldsymbol{E}\xi(t) = \int_{\Omega} \xi(\omega, t)P(d\omega) , \tag{1.1}$$

is a constant, not depending on t, and its *correlation function* $B(t, s)$,

$$B(t, s) = \boldsymbol{E}\xi(t)\overline{\xi(s)} , \tag{1.2}$$

depends only on the difference $t - s$ (it is of course assumed that $\boldsymbol{E} \mid \xi(t) \mid^2 < \infty$).

Example 1.1. Let Φ_p, $p = \overline{1, m}$, be a family of random variables, with the property that

$$\boldsymbol{E}\Phi_p = 0 , \qquad \boldsymbol{E} \mid \Phi_p \mid^2 = F_p = < \infty$$

for all $p = \overline{1, m}$, and

$$\boldsymbol{E}\Phi_p\overline{\Phi}_q = 0$$

for $p \neq q$.

Consider the random process $\boldsymbol{\xi} = \{\xi(t)\}$ of the form

$$\xi(t) = \sum_{p=1}^{m} e^{i\lambda_p t}\Phi_p ,$$

where the λ_p are some real numbers. The mathematical expectation of the $\xi(t)$ is equal to zero, and the correlation function $B(t, s)$ is given by

$$B(t, s) = \sum_{p=1}^{m} e^{i\lambda_p(t-s)}F_p .$$

We see that $\boldsymbol{\xi}$ is stationary in the wide sense.

Example 1.2. Let $\zeta = \{\zeta(t)\}$ be a two-sided infinite sequence of uncorrelated random variables, i.e., such that

$$\boldsymbol{E}\zeta(t_1)\overline{\zeta(t_2)} = 0$$

for $t_1 \neq t_2$, and

$$\boldsymbol{E}\zeta(t) = 0 , \qquad \boldsymbol{E} \mid \zeta(t) \mid^2 = 1$$

for all t. Suppose that the sequence of complex numbers $c(t)$, $t = 0, \pm 1, \pm 2, \ldots$, has the following property:

$$\sum_{t=-\infty}^{\infty} \mid c(t) \mid^2 < \infty .$$

Obviously, the series

$$\xi(t) = \sum_{s=-\infty}^{\infty} c(t - s)\zeta(s)$$

converges in mean square, and $\{\xi(t)\}$ is a wide-sense stationary random process, since

$$\boldsymbol{E}\xi(t)\overline{\xi(s)} = \sum_{-\infty}^{\infty} c(t - s + u)\overline{c(u)} .$$

Two wide-sense stationary processes $\boldsymbol{\xi}_1 = \{\xi_1(t)\}$ and $\boldsymbol{\xi}_2 = \{\xi_2(t)\}$ are said to be *stationarily correlated,* if their *joint correlation function*

$$B_{12}(t, s) = \boldsymbol{E}\xi_1(t)\overline{\xi_2(s)} \tag{1.3}$$

depends only on the difference $t - s$.

Example 1.3. Let the processes $\boldsymbol{\xi}_1 = \{\xi_1(t)\}$ and $\boldsymbol{\xi}_2 = \{\xi_2(t)\}$ be as in Example 1.1,

$$\xi_k(t) = \sum_{p=1}^{m} e^{i\lambda_p t}\Phi_{p,k} \qquad (k = 1, 2) ,$$

and suppose that the random variables $\Phi_{p,k}$ have, in addition, the property that

$$\boldsymbol{E}\Phi_{p,k}\overline{\Phi_{q,l}} = 0$$

for all $p \neq q$ and $k, l = 1, 2$.

Let $F_{kl}(p) = \boldsymbol{E}\Phi_{p,k}\overline{\Phi_{p,l}}$. Then

$$B_{kl}(t, s) = \boldsymbol{E}\xi_k(t)\overline{\xi_l(s)} = \sum_{p=1}^{m} e^{i\lambda_p(t-s)}F_{kl}(p) .$$

We see that the functions B_{kl} depend only on the difference $t - s$, i.e., the stationary processes $\boldsymbol{\xi}_1$ and $\boldsymbol{\xi}_2$ are stationarily correlated with each other.

We will call a family of n stationary processes $\boldsymbol{\xi}_k = \{\xi_k(t)\}$, $k = \overline{1, n}$, which are stationarily correlated with one another an *n-dimensional stationary process* and will write it in the form of a column-vector

$$\boldsymbol{\xi} = \{\xi_k(t)\}_{k=\overline{1,n}} .$$

Let $\boldsymbol{\xi} = \{\xi_k(t)\}_{k=\overline{1,n}}$ be an n-dimensional stationary process, and let H_ξ be the linear manifold spanned by the variables $\xi_k(t)$, $k = \overline{1, n}$, $-\infty < t < \infty$, closed with respect to convergence in mean square. If we identify random variables which differ only with probability zero and introduce a scalar product of elements $h', h'' \in H_\xi$ by putting

$$(h', h'') = \boldsymbol{E}h'\overline{h''} ,$$

then H_ξ becomes a Hilbert space; we will call it the *space of values* of the process $\boldsymbol{\xi}$.

Example 1.4. Let $\boldsymbol{\xi}$ be the stationary process described in Example 1.1. The random variables Φ_p, $p = \overline{1, m}$, can be found from the system of linear equations (assuming the numbers $e^{i\lambda_p}$ to be distinct)

$$\sum_{1}^{m} e^{i\lambda_p t}\Phi_p = \xi(t) , \qquad t = \overline{0, m-1} ,$$

whose determinant is a Vandermonde determinant. It is obvious that these variables belong to H_ξ. Since the values $\xi(t)$, $-\infty < t < \infty$, of the process $\boldsymbol{\xi}$ under consideration can be expressed linearly in terms of the Φ_p, $p = \overline{1, m}$, the space H_ξ coincides with the linear span of these variables.

Let us remark at once that although we have defined a wide-sense stationary process as a collection of random variables $\xi(t)$ satisfying conditions (1.1)—(1.3), almost all of the considerations in the first part of the book remain equally valid for functions $\xi(t)$ with values in an arbitrary Hilbert space H, whose scalar products $B(t, s) = (\xi(t), \xi(s))$

satisfy the requirement of stationary (1.2) (in the multi-dimensional case, (1.3)).

2. Random measures and integrals

Let us recall certain results from measure theory (see, for example, Halmos[*]†).

A system R of sets Δ is called a semiring if, first, together with any two sets $\Delta_1, \Delta_2 \in R$, the intersection $\Delta_1 \cap \Delta_2$ lies in R, and, second, for any sets $\Delta, \Delta_1 \in R$ such that $\Delta_1 \subset \Delta$, there are a finite number of sets $\Delta_2, \ldots, \Delta_m$ in R such that the sets $\Delta_1, \ldots, \Delta_m$ are disjoint and have union Δ: i.e., $\Delta = \bigcup_{k=1}^{m} \Delta_k$.

The simplest example of a semiring of sets on the real line is given by the system of all semi-intervals $[a, b)$ which are closed on the left and open on the right (or conversely).

Suppose that there is defined, on a semiring R, a finite σ-additive measure F, i.e., a positive set function with the property that

$$F(\Delta) = \sum_k F(\Delta_k) \tag{2.1}$$

for any set $\Delta \in R$ which is the union of disjoint sets $\Delta_k \in R$, $k = 1, 2, \ldots$. As is known, the measure F can be extended, preserving its σ-additivity, to the smallest σ-algebra containing all the sets in R. For example, if R is the system of all semi-intervals $[a, b)$, then the measure F can be extended to all Borel sets on the line.

Let us mention the following simple fact, which is a consequence of the very method of extending the measure F. Suppose that Δ is an arbitrary measurable set (i.e., a set in the smallest σ-algebra containing R) such that $F(\Delta) < \infty$. Then for any $\varepsilon > 0$ there is a set Δ_ε which is the union of a finite number of disjoint sets $\Delta_1, \ldots, \Delta_m$ from the semiring R, such that the F-measure of the symmetric difference $\Delta \circ \Delta_\varepsilon = (\Delta - \Delta_\varepsilon) \cup (\Delta_\varepsilon - \Delta)$ does not exceed ε:

$$F(\Delta \circ \Delta_\varepsilon) \leq \varepsilon . \tag{2.2}$$

Suppose now that we have a complex random variable $\Phi(\Delta) = \Phi(\omega, \Delta)$ defined for each set Δ of some semiring R of subsets of an interval $[a, b]$ (which can be finite or infinite) of the real line.

Suppose that Φ is additive, i.e., with probability 1‡

$$\Phi(\Delta_1) + \Phi(\Delta_2) = \Phi(\Delta_1 \cup \Delta_2) \tag{2.3}$$

† The symbol [*] refers to the appropriate item in the list of general references in the bibliography.

‡ From now on we will not distinguish between random variables which are equal to one another with probability 1.

if Δ_1 and Δ_2 are disjoint, and, moreover, that

$$F(\Delta) = \boldsymbol{E} \mid \Phi(\Delta) \mid^2 < \infty , \qquad \Delta \in R . \tag{2.4}$$

Suppose further that

$$\boldsymbol{E}\Phi(\Delta_1)\overline{\Phi(\Delta_2)} = 0 \tag{2.5}$$

for any disjoint Δ_1 and Δ_2. In this case the set function F, defined by (2.4), is obviously additive:

$$F(\Delta_1) + F(\Delta_2) = F(\Delta_1 \cup \Delta_2) \tag{2.6}$$

if Δ_1 and Δ_2 are disjoint.

We shall call a random set function Φ with these properties a *random measure*.

If the relation

$$\Phi(\Delta) = \sum_k \Phi(\Delta_k) \tag{2.7}$$

holds for every set $\Delta \in R$ which is the union of disjoint sets $\Delta_k \in R$, where the series converges in mean square, we will call the random measure *σ-additive*. In this case, the corresponding measure F will also be σ-additive. Obviously the converse is also true: If F is σ-additive on R, then the random measure Φ has the same property.

We will denote the closure (in mean square) of the linear set spanned by the random variables $\Phi(\Delta)$, $\Delta \in R$, by H_Φ.

Theorem 2.1. *Let Φ be a σ-additive random measure defined on a semiring R, let F be the set function on R defined by* (2.4), *and let $\mathfrak{M}$ be the σ-ring generated by R. Then Φ can be extended to a σ-additive random measure defined on the ring of all sets in $\mathfrak{M}$ with finite F-measure.*

Proof. The measure F defined by (2.4) is σ-additive and can therefore be extended in a unique way from the semiring R to the σ-ring $\mathfrak{M}$.

For a set $\Delta \in \mathfrak{M}$ of the form

$$\Delta = \bigcup_{k=1}^{m} \Delta_k , \tag{2.8}$$

where the Δ_k belong to R and are nonintersecting, we define $\Phi(\Delta)$ by

$$\Phi(\Delta) = \sum_{k=1}^{m} \Phi(\Delta_k) .$$

For any two sets Δ' and Δ'' of the form (2.8) we have, by virtue of (2.4) and (2.5),

$$\begin{aligned} \boldsymbol{E} \mid \Phi(\Delta') - \Phi(\Delta'') \mid^2 &= \boldsymbol{E} \mid \Phi(\Delta' - \Delta'') - \Phi(\Delta'' - \Delta') \mid^2 \\ &= F(\Delta' - \Delta'') + F(\Delta'' - \Delta') = F(\Delta' \circ \Delta'') . \end{aligned}$$

Property (2.2) of a measure F allows us to choose, for any set $\Delta \in \mathfrak{M}$,

$F(\varDelta) < \infty$, a sequence of sets $\varDelta_n$ of the form (2.8) such that $F(\varDelta \circ \varDelta_n) \to 0$ as $n \to \infty$. Then

$$\boldsymbol{E} \mid \Phi(\varDelta_n) - \Phi(\varDelta_m) \mid^2 = F(\varDelta_n \circ \varDelta_m) \to 0$$

as $n, m \to \infty$. From this it follows that the sequence of random variables $\Phi(\varDelta_n)$ has a limit in mean square. We define $\Phi(\varDelta)$ as this limit; i.e.,

$$\Phi(\varDelta) = \underset{n\to\infty}{\text{l.i.m.}}\, \Phi(\varDelta_n) .$$

It is easy to see that this limit does not depend upon the choice of the sequence $\{\varDelta_n\}$, $F(\varDelta \circ \varDelta_n) \to 0$, and that the set function Φ thus defined is a σ-additive random measure with values in H_Φ. ▮

Remark. It is obvious that for any random variable h, $\boldsymbol{E}|h|^2 < \infty$, the set function F_h defined by

$$F_h(\varDelta) = \boldsymbol{E}\Phi(\varDelta)\bar{h} \tag{2.9}$$

is a σ-additive complex-valued set function on the ring of sets $\varDelta \in \mathfrak{M}$ such that $F(\varDelta) < \infty$.

Let us now define integrals with respect to a σ-additive random measure Φ defined on the Borel sets of an interval $[a, b]$ of the real line (a and b may assume the values $-\infty$ and $+\infty$, respectively).

We will call a complex-valued measurable function $\varphi(\lambda)$ defined on $[a, b]$ a *simple function*, if it assumes at most countably many different values φ_k (on the sets $\varDelta_k$, $k = 1, 2, \ldots$, respectively). We will say that a simple function $\varphi(\lambda)$ is *integrable*, if the series

$$\sum_{k=1}^{\infty} \varphi_k \Phi(\varDelta_k)$$

converges in mean square. We define the *integral* of $\varphi(\lambda)$ with respect to the random measure Φ as the sum of this series:

$$\int_a^b \varphi(\lambda)\Phi(d\lambda) = \sum_{k=1}^{\infty} \varphi_k \Phi(\varDelta_k) , \tag{2.10}$$

Let the measure F be defined, as earlier, by (2.4). Then

$$\begin{aligned} \boldsymbol{E}\left| \int_a^b \varphi(\lambda)\Phi(d\lambda) \right|^2 &= \sum_{k=1}^{\infty} |\varphi_k|^2 \boldsymbol{E} \mid \Phi(\varDelta_k) \mid^2 \\ &= \sum_{k=1}^{\infty} |\varphi_k|^2 F(\varDelta_k) = \int_a^b |\varphi(\lambda)|^2 F(d\lambda) , \end{aligned} \tag{2.11}$$

from which it is apparent that a simple function $\varphi(\lambda)$ is integrable with respect to the random measure $\Phi(d\lambda)$ if and only if

$$\int_a^b |\varphi(\lambda)|^2 F(d\lambda) < \infty . \tag{2.12}$$

If $\varphi(\lambda)$ is the limit in mean square of some sequence $\varphi_n(\lambda), n=1, 2, \ldots,$ of integrable simple functions, i.e.,

$$\int_a^b | \varphi(\lambda) - \varphi_n(\lambda) |^2 F(d\lambda) \to 0$$

as $n \to \infty$, then by (2.11)

$$E\left| \int_a^b \varphi_n(\lambda)\Phi(d\lambda) - \int_a^b \varphi_m(\lambda)\Phi(d\lambda) \right|^2 = \int_a^b | \varphi_n(\lambda) - \varphi_m(\lambda) |^2 F(d\lambda) \to 0$$

as $n, m \to \infty$. Thus the sequence of random variables $\int_a^b \varphi_n(\lambda)\Phi(d\lambda)$ has a limit in mean square, which we shall call the integral of the function $\varphi(\lambda)$:

$$\int_a^b \varphi(\lambda)\Phi(d\lambda) = \lim_{n\to\infty} \int_a^b \varphi_n(\lambda)\Phi(d\lambda) \tag{2.13}$$

(it is obvious that the limit in (2.13) does not depend upon the choice of sequence $\varphi_n(\lambda), n = 1, 2, \ldots,$ converging to $\varphi(\lambda)$). Relation (2.13) defines the integral, with respect to the random measure $\Phi(d\lambda)$, of all functions $\varphi(\lambda)$ satisfying condition (2.12), and (2.11) holds for these integrals. Moreover, if $\varphi(\lambda)$ and $\psi(\lambda)$ are any two measurable functions for which (2.12) is satisfied, then

$$E\int_a^b \varphi(\lambda)\Phi(d\lambda) \int_a^b \overline{\psi(\lambda)\Phi(d\lambda)} = \int_a^b \varphi(\lambda)\overline{\psi(\lambda)}F(d\lambda) . \tag{2.14}$$

Suppose now that the random measure Φ is such that

$$E | \Phi(\Delta) |^2 < \infty$$

for any interval $\Delta = [a', b']$, where $a' > a, b' < b$, but

$$\lim_{\substack{a'\to a\\ b'\to b}} E | \Phi(\Delta) |^2 = \infty . \tag{2.15}$$

If a function $\varphi(\lambda)$, defined on the interval $[a, b]$, is square integrable with respect to the measure F defined by Φ,

$$\int_a^b | \varphi(\lambda) |^2 F(d\lambda) < \infty ,$$

then it is integrable with respect to the random measure Φ on any interval $[a', b']$, $a' > a, b' < b$. It is easy to show, by means of (2.11), that the random variable $\int_{a'}^{b'} \varphi(\lambda)\Phi(d\lambda)$ converges in mean square to some limit as $a' \to a, b' \to b$. We shall call this limit the integral of $\varphi(\lambda)$ with respect to Φ on the interval $[a, b]$:

$$\int_a^b \varphi(\lambda)\Phi(d\lambda) = \lim_{\substack{a'\to a\\ b'\to b}} \int_{a'}^{b'} \varphi(\lambda)\Phi(d\lambda) . \tag{2.16}$$

The integral which we have defined has all of the usual properties. Namely,

$$\int_a^b [c_1\varphi_1(\lambda) + c_2\varphi_2(\lambda)]\Phi(d\lambda) = c_1 \int_a^b \varphi_1(\lambda)\Phi(d\lambda) + c_2 \int_a^b \varphi_2(\lambda)\Phi(d\lambda) \; ; \qquad (2.17)$$

the set function

$$\Psi(\Delta) = \int_\Delta \varphi(\lambda)\Phi(d\lambda)$$

is a σ-additive random measure; moreover, integrals of type (2.16) satisfy (2.14).

Example 2.1. Suppose that Φ is a random measure defined on the Borel sets of the real line, and that

$$\boldsymbol{E}\Phi(\Delta) = \begin{cases} m, & \text{if } \Delta \text{ contains the point } \lambda = 0; \\ 0 & \text{otherwise.} \end{cases}$$

Consider the integral

$$\xi(t) = \int_{-\infty}^{\infty} e^{i\lambda t}\Phi(d\lambda) \, ,$$

where the parameter t assumes all real values. The $\xi(t)$ constitute a random process, and it is easily verified that

$$\boldsymbol{E}\xi(t) = m \, , \qquad \boldsymbol{E}\xi(t)\overline{\xi(s)} = \int_{-\infty}^{\infty} e^{i\lambda(t-s)}F(d\lambda) \, ,$$

where $F(d\lambda) = \boldsymbol{E} \mid \Phi(d\lambda) \mid^2$. Thus, the random process $\boldsymbol{\xi} = \{\xi(t)\}$ is stationary in the wide sense.

Example 2.2. Let $\zeta(dt)$ be a random measure, defined on all subsets of the line $-\infty < t < \infty$ with finite Lebesgue measure, such that

$$\boldsymbol{E}\zeta(dt) = 0 \, , \qquad \boldsymbol{E} \mid \zeta(dt) \mid^2 = dt \, .$$

Let $c(t)$ be some square integrable function:

$$\int_{-\infty}^{\infty} \mid c(t) \mid^2 dt < \infty \, .$$

Obviously, the integral

$$\xi(t) = \int_{-\infty}^{\infty} c(t-s)\zeta(ds)$$

exists for any t. It is easily seen that

$$\boldsymbol{E}\xi(t) = 0 \, , \qquad \boldsymbol{E}\xi(t)\overline{\xi(s)} = \int_{-\infty}^{\infty} c(t-s+u)\overline{c(u)}\,du \, .$$

Thus, $\boldsymbol{\xi} = \{\xi(t)\}$ is a wide-sense stationary random process.

We now proceed to the integration of random functions.

Let $\boldsymbol{\xi} = \{\xi(t)\}$ be a random process whose values have finite second moments:

$$\boldsymbol{E} \mid \xi(t) \mid^2 < \infty$$

for all t. We will say that $\boldsymbol{\xi}$ is *separable in the wide sense*, if its space of values $H_{\boldsymbol{\xi}}$—the closed linear set generated by the set of all random variables $\xi(t)$—is separable (i.e., contains a countable everywhere dense set of elements).

A wide-sense stationary process $\boldsymbol{\xi}$ is, for example, obviously separable in the wide sense if its correlation function $B(t)$ is continuous at $t = 0$; in this case

$$\| \xi(t) - \xi(s) \|^2 = \boldsymbol{E} \mid \xi(t) - \xi(s) \mid^2 = 2[B(0) - \operatorname{Re} B(t - s)] \to 0 \qquad (2.18)$$

as $t - s \to 0$.

Further, we will say that a random process $\boldsymbol{\xi} = \{\xi(t)\}$ is *measurable in the wide sense*, if for any $h \in H_{\boldsymbol{\xi}}$, the numerical valued function of t

$$(\xi(t), h) = \boldsymbol{E}\xi(t)\bar{h} \qquad (2.19)$$

is Lebesgue measurable.

We will call a random process $\boldsymbol{\xi}$ *simple*, if there is a finite or countable disjoint family of measurable sets Δ_k, $k = 1, 2, \ldots$ whose union is the line $(-\infty, \infty)$, and corresponding random variables ξ_k such that

$$\xi(t) = \xi_k, \qquad t \in \Delta_k, \qquad k = 1, 2, \ldots .$$

Theorem 2.2. *Suppose that the correlation function $B(t, s)$ of a wide-sense separable process $\boldsymbol{\xi}$ is measurable. Then $\boldsymbol{\xi}$ is measurable in the wide sense and, moreover, there exists a sequence of simple random processes $\boldsymbol{\xi}_n$, $n = 1, 2, \ldots$, which converges uniformly to $\boldsymbol{\xi}$; i.e.,*

$$(\boldsymbol{E} \mid \xi(t) - \xi_n(t) \mid^2)^{1/2} \equiv \| \xi(t) - \xi_n(t) \| \to 0 \qquad (2.20)$$

as $n \to \infty$, uniformly in t.

Proof. The linear combinations $\sum_k c_k\xi(t_k)$ of the values of $\boldsymbol{\xi}$ are everywhere dense in $H_{\boldsymbol{\xi}}$, and, therefore, for any $h \in H_{\boldsymbol{\xi}}$ the numerical function $(\xi(t), h)$ is the limit of functions of the form

$$\sum_k \bar{c}_k B(t, t_k) = (\xi(t), \sum_k c_k\xi(t_k)) ,$$

which are measurable as a consequence of the measurability of the correlation function $B(t, s)$. Hence $(\xi(t), h)$ is a measurable function of t for every $h \in H_\xi$.

Let $\{\xi_m\}$ be a countable everywhere dense set of elements in $H_{\boldsymbol{\xi}}$. For fixed n, the set T_{mn} of values of t for which

$$\| \xi(t) - \xi_m \| < \frac{1}{n}$$

is measurable (as was just proved, the function $\| \xi(t) - \xi_m \|^2 = B(t, t) + \| \xi_m \|^2 - 2 \operatorname{Re} (\xi(t), \xi_m)$ is measurable), and the union $\bigcup_m T_{mn}$ is the entire real line because the ξ_m are everywhere dense in H_ξ. We take $T'_{1n} = T_{1n}$, $T'_{mn} = T_{mn} - \bigcup_{k=1}^{m-1} T'_{kn}$, $m = 2, 3, \ldots$, and set

$$\xi_n(t) = \xi_m \quad \text{for} \quad t \in T'_{mn} .$$

The random processes $\boldsymbol{\xi}_n = \{\xi_n(t)\}$ are simple, and

$$\| \xi(t) - \xi_n(t) \| < \frac{1}{n}$$

for any t; thus, the process $\boldsymbol{\xi}$ is the uniform limit of the simple processes $\boldsymbol{\xi}_n$.

Suppose that $\boldsymbol{\xi}$ is a simple random process on the interval $[c, d]$:

$$\xi(t) = \xi_k \quad \text{for} \quad t \in \Delta_k , \qquad k = 1, 2, \ldots . \tag{2.21}$$

Let us assume that

$$\sum_{k=1}^{\infty} \| \xi_k \| \, | \Delta_k | < \infty , \tag{2.22}$$

where $| \Delta_k |$ denotes the Lebesgue measure of Δ_k. In this case we say that the random process $\boldsymbol{\xi}$ is *integrable in the wide sense*, and put

$$\int_c^d \xi(t) \, dt = \sum_{k=1}^{\infty} \xi_k \, | \Delta_k | \tag{2.23}$$

(it is clear, from (2.22), that the series on the right side of (2.23) converges in mean square). Thus, a random process $\boldsymbol{\xi}$ of the form (2.21) is integrable (in the wide sense) on the interval $[c, d]$ if

$$\int_c^d \| \xi(t) \| \, dt < \infty . \tag{2.24}$$

We remark that

$$\left\| \int_c^d \xi(t) \, dt \right\| \le \int_c^d \| \xi(t) \| \, dt . \tag{2.25}$$

We will say that an arbitrary random process $\boldsymbol{\xi}$ is *integrable* (in the wide sense), if there exists a sequence $\boldsymbol{\xi}_n$, $n = 1, 2, \ldots$ of simple integrable processes which converges uniformly to $\boldsymbol{\xi}$, i.e.,

$$\| \xi(t) - \xi_n(t) \| \to 0 \tag{2.26}$$

as $n \to \infty$, uniformly in t. In this case

$$\| \xi_m(t) - \xi_n(t) \| \to 0$$

as $n, m \to \infty$, uniformly in t, and, consequently,

$$\left\|\int_c^d [\xi_m(t) - \xi_n(t)]\,dt\right\|$$

$$\leq \int_c^d \|\xi_m(t) - \xi_n(t)\|\,dt \leq \sup_t \|\xi_m(t) - \xi_n(t)\| \cdot (d - c) \to 0$$

as $n, m \to \infty$. Therefore $\lim_{n\to\infty} \int_c^d \xi_n(t)\,dt$ exists and depends only upon the process ξ, and not the choice of sequence ξ_n, $n = 1, 2, \ldots$. We put

$$\int_c^d \xi(t)\,dt = \lim_{n\to\infty} \int_c^d \xi_n(t)\,dt\,. \tag{2.27}$$

An integrable process ξ obviously satisfies condition (2.24). Under rather wide restrictions, this condition is sufficient for integrability. Namely, we have:

Theorem 2.3. *If the correlation function of a wide-sense separable random process ξ is measurable, and, moreover, condition* (2.24) *is fulfilled, then ξ is integrable.*

Proof. By Theorem 2.2 there exists a sequence ξ_n, $n = 1, 2, \ldots$ of simple processes which converges uniformly to ξ. In particular, for sufficiently large n,

$$\|\xi_n(t)\| \leq \|\xi(t)\| + 1\,,$$

from which it follows that together with ξ, the processes ξ_n also satisfy (2.24) (for sufficiently large n). Consequently, the ξ_n are integrable.

The definition of the integral can be extended to an infinite interval $[c, d]$ in the following way:

$$\int_c^d \xi(t)\,dt = \lim_{\substack{c'\to c\\ d'\to d}} \int_{c'}^{d'} \xi(t)\,dt\,, \tag{2.28}$$

where $c < c' < d' < d$; the limit (in mean square) of the right side of (2.28) obviously exists if ξ satisfies the requirement (2.24).

The integral of a random process which we have introduced has all the usual properties.

Let us again consider a σ-additive random measure Φ. Suppose that $\varphi(t, \lambda)$ is a measurable function of two variables t, λ ($a \leq \lambda \leq b$, $c \leq t \leq d$), such that

$$\int_a^b |\varphi(t, \lambda)|^2 F(d\lambda) < \infty \tag{2.29}$$

for almost all t (here, as before, $F(d\lambda) = \boldsymbol{E}\,|\Phi(d\lambda)|^2$). Then for these t the integral

$$\xi(t) = \int_a^b \varphi(t, \lambda)\Phi(d\lambda) \tag{2.30}$$

exists. This integral defines a wide-sense measurable random process $\boldsymbol{\xi} = \{\xi(t)\}$ because, for any random variable h with $\boldsymbol{E}|h|^2 < \infty$, the numerical function

$$\boldsymbol{E}\xi(t)\bar{h} = \int_a^b \varphi(t, \lambda)F_h(d\lambda) , \tag{2.31}$$

where $F_h(d\lambda) = \boldsymbol{E}\Phi(d\lambda)\bar{h}$, is measurable. (The verification of (2.31) is a simple exercise in measure theory which we leave to the reader.)

If $\varphi(t, \lambda)$ satisfies the condition

$$\int_c^d \left[\int_a^b |\varphi(t, \lambda)|^2 F(d\lambda)\right]^{1/2} dt < \infty , \tag{2.32}$$

and the random measure Φ is *separable*, i.e., the space H_Φ generated by its values is separable, then the random process $\boldsymbol{\xi} = \{\xi(t)\}$ is also separable, and moreover integrable on $[c, d]$:

$$\int_c^d \xi(t)\,dt = \int_c^d \left[\int_a^b \varphi(t, \lambda)\Phi(d\lambda)\right] dt . \tag{2.33}$$

Further, if $\varphi(t, \lambda)$ is Lebesgue integrable on the interval $[c, d]$ for almost all λ (with respect to F) and

$$\int_a^b \left[\int_c^d |\varphi(t, \lambda)|\,dt\right]^2 F(d\lambda) < \infty , \tag{2.34}$$

then the integral

$$\int_a^b \left[\int_c^d \varphi(t, \lambda)\,dt\right] \Phi(d\lambda) \tag{2.35}$$

exists.

Theorem 2.4. *If the function* $\varphi(t, \lambda)$ *satisfies conditions* (2.32) *and* (2.34), *and the random measure* Φ *is separable, then the integrals in* (2.33) *and* (2.35) *coincide*:

$$\int_a^b \int_c^d \varphi(t, \lambda)\,dt\,\Phi(d\lambda) = \int_c^d \int_a^b \varphi(t, \lambda)\Phi(d\lambda)\,dt . \tag{2.36}$$

Proof. Let h be an arbitrary random variable such that $\boldsymbol{E}|h|^2 < \infty$. Then

$$\boldsymbol{E}\int_a^b \left[\int_c^d \varphi(t, \lambda)\,dt\right] \Phi(d\lambda)\bar{h} = \int_a^b \int_c^d \varphi(t, \lambda)\,dt F_h(d\lambda)$$

$$= \int_c^d \int_a^b \varphi(t, \lambda)F_h(d\lambda)\,dt = \boldsymbol{E}\int_c^d \left[\int_a^b \varphi(t, \lambda)\Phi(d\lambda)\right] dt\,\bar{h} .$$

The arbitrariness of h immediately implies (2.36).

3. Fourier transformation of a random measure

Let $\Lambda(d\lambda)$ be a random measure, defined on all subsets of the real line $-\infty < \lambda < \infty$ with finite Lebesgue measure, such that

$$\boldsymbol{E}\,|\,\Lambda(d\lambda)\,|^2 = \frac{1}{2\pi}d\lambda\,. \tag{3.1}$$

Then, for any interval $\Delta = (t_1, t_2)$, the integral

$$\zeta(\Delta) = \int_{-\infty}^{\infty} \frac{e^{i\lambda t_2} - e^{i\lambda t_1}}{i\lambda}\Lambda(d\lambda) \tag{3.2}$$

exists. Now the function

$$\varphi_\Delta(\lambda) = \frac{e^{i\lambda t_2} - e^{i\lambda t_1}}{i\lambda}$$

is the Fourier transform of the function

$$\tilde{\varphi}_\Delta(t) = \begin{cases} 1, & \text{for } t \in \Delta\,, \\ 0, & \text{for } t \notin \Delta\,; \end{cases}$$

i.e.,

$$\varphi_\Delta(\lambda) = \int_{-\infty}^{\infty} e^{i\lambda t}\tilde{\varphi}_\Delta(t)\,dt\,.$$

Suppose that the interval $\Delta' = (t_1', t_2')$ does not intersect Δ. Using (2.14) and Parseval's equality, we obtain

$$\begin{aligned} \boldsymbol{E}\zeta(\Delta)\overline{\zeta(\Delta')} &= \frac{1}{2\pi}\int_{-\infty}^{\infty} \varphi_\Delta(\lambda)\varphi_{\Delta'}(\lambda)\,d\lambda = \int_{-\infty}^{\infty} \tilde{\varphi}_\Delta(t)\overline{\tilde{\varphi}_{\Delta'}(t)\,dt} = 0\,, \\ \boldsymbol{E}\,|\,\zeta(\Delta)\,|^2 &= \frac{1}{2\pi}\int_{-\infty}^{\infty} |\,\varphi_\Delta(\lambda)\,|^2\,d\lambda = \int_{-\infty}^{\infty} |\,\tilde{\varphi}_\Delta(t)\,|^2\,dt = t_2 - t_1\,, \end{aligned} \tag{3.3}$$

which shows that the integral in (3.2) defines a random measure $\boldsymbol{\zeta} = \zeta(dt)$ on intervals $\Delta = (t_1, t_2)$ such that

$$\boldsymbol{E}\,|\,\zeta(dt)\,|^2 = dt\,. \tag{3.4}$$

By Theorem 2.1, the random measure $\boldsymbol{\zeta}$ can be extended to all Borel sets of the line $-\infty < t < \infty$ (the measure $\zeta(\Delta)$ of the interval $\Delta = (t_1, t_2)$ will coincide with that of the interval $[t_1, t_2))$.

Equality (3.2) can now be rewritten in the form

$$\int_{-\infty}^{\infty} \tilde{\varphi}_\Delta(t)\zeta(dt) = \int_{-\infty}^{\infty} \varphi_\Delta(\lambda)\Lambda(d\lambda)\,. \tag{3.5}$$

Now any function $\tilde{\varphi}(t)$ such that

$$\int_{-\infty}^{\infty} |\tilde{\varphi}(t)|^2 dt < \infty$$

can be approximated as closely as desired in mean square by linear combinations of functions of the form $\tilde{\varphi}_\Delta(t)$, and its Fourier transform

$$\varphi(\lambda) = \int_{-\infty}^{\infty} e^{i\lambda t}\tilde{\varphi}(t)\,dt$$

can be approximated in the same way by the corresponding linear combinations of the Fourier transforms $\varphi_\Delta(\lambda)$. From this, by virtue of (2.14), we conclude that (3.5) is valid not only for the functions $\tilde{\varphi}_\Delta(t)$ and $\varphi_\Delta(\lambda)$, but also for arbitrary square integrable functions $\tilde{\varphi}(t)$ and $\varphi(\lambda)$:

$$\int_{-\infty}^{\infty} \tilde{\varphi}(t)\zeta(dt) = \int_{-\infty}^{\infty} \varphi(\lambda)\Lambda(d\lambda)\,. \tag{3.6}$$

Taking, in particular, the interval $\Delta = (\lambda_1, \lambda_2)$ and

$$\varphi(\lambda) = \begin{cases} 1, & \text{for } \lambda \in \Delta \\ 0, & \text{for } \lambda \notin \Delta\,, \end{cases}$$

we obtain

$$\Lambda(\Delta) = \frac{1}{2\pi}\int_{-\infty}^{\infty} \frac{e^{-i\lambda_2 t} - e^{-i\lambda_1 t}}{-it}\zeta(dt)\,, \tag{3.7}$$

i.e., the random measure $\Lambda(d\lambda)$ can be obtained from the measure $\zeta(dt)$, defined by (3.1), by means of the inverse Fourier transformation.

4. The spectral representation of stationary processes

Let $\boldsymbol{\xi} = \{\xi_k(t)\}_{k=\overline{1,n}}$ be an n-dimensional wide-sense stationary random process, and H_ξ the space of its values.

Theorem 4.1. *There exists a family of unitary operators U_t, $-\infty < t < \infty$, on H_ξ such that*

$$U_t\xi_k(s) = \xi_k(t+s)\,, \qquad k = \overline{1, n}\,, \tag{4.1}$$

for any t, s.

The proof of this theorem rests upon a general lemma.

Lemma 4.1. *Let M be some set in a Hilbert space on which there is defined an isometric operator[†] U. Then U can be extended to an isometric operator on the closed linear manifold H_M generated by M.*

† An operator U on M is said to be isometric, if $(Uh', Uh'') = (h', h'')$ for any $h', h'' \in M$.

Proof. First we show that an isometric operator U is linear. Suppose that the elements $h_1, \ldots, h_m$, as well as the element h,

$$h = \sum_{k=1}^{m} c_k h_k , \tag{4.2}$$

belong to M. Then

$$(Uh, Uh') = (h, h') = \sum_{k=1}^{m} c_k(h_k, h') = \sum_{k=1}^{m} c_k(Uh_k, Uh') = \left(\sum_{k=1}^{m} c_k Uh_k, Uh'\right),$$

and so

$$\left(Uh - \sum_{k=1}^{m} c_k Uh_k, Uh'\right) = 0$$

for any element $h' \in M$, in particular, for $h' = h, h_1, \ldots, h_m$; therefore

$$\begin{gathered}\left(Uh - \sum_{k=1}^{m} c_k Uh_k, \quad Uh - \sum_{k=1}^{m} c_k Uh_k\right) = 0 , \\ Uh = \sum_{k=1}^{m} c_k Uh_k .\end{gathered} \tag{4.3}$$

We define U on every element h of the form (4.2), where $h_k \in M$, by the second equation in (4.3).

Now every element $h \in H_M$ is the limit of elements $h_n, n = 1, 2, \ldots$ of the form (4.2). We have

$$\lim_{n\to\infty} \| h_n - h \| = 0 , \qquad \lim_{m,n\to\infty} \| h_m - h_n \| = \lim_{m,n\to\infty} \| Uh_m - Uh_n \| = 0 ,$$

and therefore $\lim_{n\to\infty} Uh_n$ exists. Set

$$Uh = \lim_{n\to\infty} Uh_n . \tag{4.4}$$

It is easy to verify that the operator U, defined on all of H_M by (4.3) and (4.4), is isometric.

Proof of Theorem 4.1. Equality (4.1) defines, for each t, an isometric operator U_t on the set of all elements $\xi_k(s)$, since by stationarity we have

$$(U_t\xi_k(s), U_t\xi_l(s')) = (\xi_k(t+s), \xi_l(t+s')) = (\xi_k(s), \xi_l(s')) .$$

By Lemma 4.1 the operator U_t can be extended to an isometric operator on all of H_ξ. To prove that this extension is unitary, we have to establish that it maps H_ξ onto itself, i.e., for any element $h \in H_\xi$ there is an $h' \in H_\xi$ such that $h = U_t h'$ (we use the same symbol U_t for the extended operator). But this follows at once from the definition of H_ξ and U_t, since every element $h \in H_\xi$ is the limit of elements $h_n, n = 1, 2, \ldots,$ of the form

$$h_n = \sum_{m,k} c_{m,k}\xi_k(t_{m,k}) ,$$

and for the element h' we can take, for example,

$$h' = \lim_{n\to\infty} h'_n ,$$

where

$$h'_n = \sum_{m,k} c_{m,k}\xi_k(t_{m,k} - t) . \blacksquare$$

The family of unitary operators U_t, depending upon the parameter t, obviously satisfies the relation

$$U_tU_s = U_{t+s} \tag{4.5}$$

and is thus a group.

We will call the collection of operators U_t the *unitary family* of the process $\boldsymbol{\xi}$.

In the case where the parameter t assumes only integer values, the operators U_t can be represented as powers of the unitary operator $U = U_1$:

$$U_t = U^t . \tag{4.6}$$

The operator U, being unitary, has a spectral representation

$$U = \int_{-\pi}^{\pi} e^{i\lambda} E(d\lambda) , \tag{4.7}$$

where $E(d\lambda)$ is a spectral family of projection operators in H_ξ, which depend additively upon Borel sets Δ in the interval $[-\pi, \pi]$ (an *operator measure*), such that

$$E(\Delta)E(\Delta') = 0 , \qquad E(\Delta \cup \Delta') = E(\Delta) + E(\Delta') , \tag{4.8}$$

if the sets Δ and Δ' do not intersect (see, for example, Riesz and Nagy[*], Section 109). We have

$$U^t = \int_{-\pi}^{\pi} e^{i\lambda t} E(d\lambda) , \tag{4.9}$$

from which one obtains the spectral representation of the processes $\boldsymbol{\xi}_k = \{\xi_k(t)\}$;

$$\xi_k(t) = U^t\xi_k(0) , \qquad k = \overline{1, n} . \tag{4.10}$$

Namely,

$$\xi_k(t) = \int_{-\pi}^{\pi} e^{i\lambda t}\Phi_k(d\lambda) , \qquad k = \overline{1, n} , \tag{4.11}$$

where

$$\Phi_k(d\lambda) = E(d\lambda)\xi_k(0) \tag{4.12}$$

is a σ-additive random measure of the same type considered in the previous sections; from property (4.8) of a spectral family $E(d\lambda)$ it follows that

$$\boldsymbol{E}\,|\,\Phi_k(\Delta)\,|^2 \leq \boldsymbol{E}\,|\,\xi_k(0)\,|^2\,, \qquad k = \overline{1, n}\,, \tag{4.13}$$

for any Borel set Δ, and

$$\boldsymbol{E}\Phi_k(\Delta)\overline{\Phi_l(\Delta')} = 0 \tag{4.14}$$

for any k, l, if the sets Δ and Δ' do not intersect.

A similar representation is valid in the case of continuous time. Suppose that the correlation functions

$$B_{kl}(t) = \boldsymbol{E}\xi_k(t+s)\overline{\xi_l(s)}\,, \qquad k, l = \overline{1, n} \tag{4.15}$$

are measurable, and the process $\boldsymbol{\xi} = \{\xi_k(t)\}_{k=\overline{1,n}}$ is itself separable in the wide sense (i.e., its space of values H_ξ is separable).†

Then, by Theorem 2.2 the random processes ξ_k, $k = 1, n$, are measurable in the wide sense, from which follows the measurability of the numerical functions $(U_t h', h'')$ of t for any $h', h'' \in H_\xi$. By Stone's theorem (see, for example, Riesz and Nagy[*], Section 137), the family of unitary operators U_t, which forms a group, admits a spectral representation

$$U_t = \int_{-\infty}^{\infty} e^{i\lambda t} E(d\lambda)\,, \tag{4.16}$$

where $E(d\lambda)$ is a family of projection operators, defined on all Borel sets Δ of the line $-\infty < \lambda < \infty$ and having the properties described by (4.8).

The stationary processes $\boldsymbol{\xi}_k$,

$$\xi_k(t) = U_t \xi_k(0)\,, \qquad k = \overline{1, n}\,, \tag{4.17}$$

can be represented in the form

$$\xi_k(t) = \int_{-\infty}^{\infty} e^{i\lambda t} \Phi_k(d\lambda)\,, \tag{4.18}$$

where the σ-additive random measures $\Phi_k(d\lambda)$,

$$\Phi_k(d\lambda) = E(d\lambda)\xi_k(0)\,, \tag{4.19}$$

satisfy relations (4.13) and (4.14).

We will call the representations (4.11) and (4.18) of the stationary processes $\boldsymbol{\xi}_k$ *spectral representations*, the measures Φ_k appearing in these representations *random spectral measures*, and the column vector

$$\Phi = \{\Phi_k\}_{k=\overline{1,n}} \tag{4.20}$$

the *random spectral measure of the n-dimensional process* $\boldsymbol{\xi}$. Summarizing, we formulate the following theorem.

† This will be the case, for example, if the correlation functions $B_{kl}(t)$, $k, l = \overline{1, n}$, are all continuous.

Theorem 4.2. *Every multi-dimensional stationary process* $\boldsymbol{\xi} = \{\xi_k(t)\}_{k=\overline{1,n}}$ *admits a spectral representation*

$$\xi(t) = \int e^{i\lambda t}\Phi(d\lambda) \tag{4.21}$$

in the form of an integral with respect to a random spectral measure $\Phi = \{\Phi_k\}_{k=\overline{1,n}}$. (The limits of the integral are $-\pi, \pi$ in the discrete-parameter case and $-\infty, \infty$ in the continuous-parameter case.)

Example 4.1. Let $\boldsymbol{\xi}$ be a discrete-parameter stationary process such that

$$\xi(t+N) = \xi(t)$$

for all t and some integer N.

We set

$$\mu_j = \frac{2\pi}{N}j\,, \qquad \Psi_j = \sum_{k=1}^{N} e^{-ik\mu_j}\xi(k)\,, \qquad j = \overline{1,N}.$$

If U is the unitary operator corresponding to the process $\boldsymbol{\xi}$, then

$$U\Psi_j = \sum_{k=1}^{N} e^{-ik\mu_j}\xi(k+1) = e^{i\mu_j}\sum_{k=1}^{N} e^{-i(k+1)\mu_j}\xi(k+1) = e^{i\mu_j}\Psi_j\,.$$

Moreover,

$$\frac{1}{N}\sum_{j=1}^{N} e^{i\mu_j t}\Psi_j = \frac{1}{N}\sum_{k=1}^{N}\xi(k)\sum_{j=1}^{N} e^{i\mu_j(t-k)} = \frac{1}{N}\sum_{k=1}^{N}\xi(k)\sum_{j=1}^{N} e^{2\pi i j(t-k)/N} = \xi(t)\,,$$

since

$$\frac{1}{N}\sum_{j=1}^{N} e^{2\pi i j(t-k)/N} = \begin{cases} 1, & \text{if } \ t \equiv k \pmod N\,, \\ 0, & \text{if } \ t \not\equiv k \pmod N\,. \end{cases}$$

Setting

$$\lambda_j = \begin{cases} \mu_j\,, & \mu_j \le \pi\,, \\ \mu_j - 2\pi\,, & \mu_j > \pi\,, \end{cases}$$

$$\Phi(\lambda_j) = \frac{1}{N}\Psi_j\,, \qquad j = \overline{1,N}\,,$$

we see that

$$\xi(t) = \sum_{j=1}^{N} e^{i\lambda_j t}\Phi(\lambda_j)\,,$$

where the $\Phi(\lambda_j)$ are mutually uncorrelated random variables. We thus have the spectral representation of the process $\boldsymbol{\xi}$.

5. Correlation functions and spectral measures of stationary processes

Let

$$\boldsymbol{\xi} = \{\xi_k(t)\}_{k=\overline{1,n}} \tag{5.1}$$

be an n-dimensional stationary process, and

$$\xi(t) = \int e^{i\lambda t}\Phi(d\lambda) \tag{5.2}$$

its spectral representation,† where

$$\Phi = \{\Phi_k\}_{k=\overline{1\ n}} \tag{5.3}$$

(here Φ_k is the random spectral measure associated with the kth component ξ_k of the multi-dimensional process ξ). Let

$$B_{kl}(t) = \boldsymbol{E}\xi_k(t+s)\overline{\xi_l(s)}\ , \qquad k, l = \overline{1, n}\ . \tag{5.4}$$

We will call the matrix

$$B(t) = \{B_{kl}(t)\}_{k=\overline{1,n}}^{l=\overline{1,n}} \tag{5.5}$$

the *correlation matrix* of the process ξ.

Set

$$F_{kl}(\Delta) = \boldsymbol{E}\Phi_k(\Delta)\overline{\Phi_l(\Delta)}\ , \qquad k, l = \overline{1, n}\ . \tag{5.6}$$

By the properties (4.13) and (4.14) of random spectral measures, the complex-valued set functions F_{kl} are σ-additive and have bounded variation:

$$|F_{kl}(\Delta)| \leq [F_{kk}(\Delta)]^{1/2}[F_{ll}(\Delta)]^{1/2} \leq [B_{kk}(0)]^{1/2}[B_{ll}(0)]^{1/2} \tag{5.7}$$

for any Borel set Δ. Obviously

$$B_{kl}(t) = \int e^{i\lambda t}F_{kl}(d\lambda)\ , \qquad k, l = \overline{1, n}\ . \tag{5.8}$$

The functions F_{kl} are, in turn, determined from the $B_{kl}(t)$ by means of the inverse Fourier transformation; i.e., for any interval $\Delta = (\lambda_1, \lambda_2)$ with endpoints λ_1 and λ_2 such that $F_{kl}(\{\lambda_1\}) = F_{kl}(\{\lambda_2\}) = 0$ (where k, l are fixed), the following relation holds:

$$F_{kl}(\Delta) = \frac{1}{2\pi}B_{kl}(0)\cdot[\lambda_2 - \lambda_1] + \lim_{T\to\infty}\frac{1}{2\pi}\sum_{0<|t|\leq T}B_{kl}(t)\frac{e^{-i\lambda_2 t} - e^{-i\lambda_1 t}}{-it} \tag{5.9}$$

in the discrete-parameter case, and

$$F_{kl}(\Delta) = \lim_{T\to\infty}\frac{1}{2\pi}\int_{-T}^{T}\frac{e^{-i\lambda_2 t} - e^{-i\lambda_1 t}}{-it}B_{kl}(t)\,dt \tag{5.10}$$

in the continuous-parameter case.

We will call the matrix

† From now on, for convenience we will omit the limits of integration, which are $-\pi, \pi$ in the case of discrete time, and $-\infty, \infty$ in the case of continuous time.

$$F = \{F_{kl}\}_{k=\overline{1,n}}^{l=\overline{1,n}} \tag{5.11}$$

the *spectral measure* of the process ξ.

In the case where all the elements F_{kl} of the spectral measure F are absolutely continuous, so that the derivatives

$$f_{kl}(\lambda) = \frac{F_{kl}(d\lambda)}{d\lambda}, \qquad k, l = \overline{1, n}, \tag{5.12}$$

exist, we will say that the multi-dimensional stationary process ξ has a *spectral density*

$$f(\lambda) = \{f_{kl}(\lambda)\}_{k=\overline{1,n}}^{l=\overline{1,n}}. \tag{5.13}$$

The spectral measure F is a σ-additive family of matrices; i.e.,

$$F\left(\bigcup_{k=1}^{\infty} \Delta_k\right) = \sum_{n=1}^{\infty} F(\Delta_k) \tag{5.14}$$

if the Δ_k are disjoint sets, and, moreover, the matrix $F(\Delta)$ is *positive definite* for any set Δ, since

$$\sum_{k,l=1}^{n} c_k \bar{c}_l F_{kl}(\Delta) = \boldsymbol{E}\left|\sum_{k=1}^{n} c_k \Phi_k(\Delta)\right|^2 \geq 0 \tag{5.15}$$

for any complex numbers $c_1, \ldots, c_n$. The correlation function $B(t)$ has the characteristic property of positive definiteness:

$$\sum_{p,q=1}^{N} c_p \bar{c}_q B_{k_p k_q}(t_p - t_q) \geq 0 \tag{5.16}$$

for any number N of arbitrary numbers $c_1, \ldots, c_N$ and indices $k_1, \ldots, k_N$ (and any parameter values $t_1, \ldots, t_N$). Indeed, the sum in (5.16) is simply the mathematical expectation

$$\boldsymbol{E}\left|\sum_{p=1}^{N} c_p \xi_{k_p}(t_p)\right|^2,$$

which is nonnegative.

Theorem 5.1. *A matrix function*

$$B(t) = \{B_{kl}(t)\}_{k=\overline{1,n}}^{l=\overline{1,n}}$$

is the correlation function of some multi-dimensional wide-sense stationary process, if and only if it satisfies condition (5.16).

In proving this result, for simplicity we shall restrict ourselves to the case where the elements $B_{kl}(t)$ of the matrix B are continuous functions of t; it is then sufficient to define the values of ξ only for some countable everywhere dense set of values of the parameter t, for example, the rational numbers, and then extend the definition of $\xi(t)$ to all t by continuity.

Theorem 5.1 is an obvious consequence of the following general lemma.

Lemma 5.1. *In order that there exist, in some Hilbert space H, a sequence of elements*

$$h_1, h_2, \ldots \tag{5.16}$$

such that

$$(h_i, h_j) = B_{ij}, \tag{5.18}$$

where $B_{ij}(i, j = 1, 2, \ldots)$ is some given collection of complex numbers, it is necessary and sufficient that for any $N, k_1, \ldots, k_N$ the inequality

$$S = \sum_{p,q=1}^{N} c_p \bar{c}_q B_{k_p k_q} \geq 0 \tag{5.19}$$

hold for any complex numbers $c_1, \ldots, c_N$.

Proof. The necessity of (5.19) is clear, since

$$S = \left| \sum_{p=1}^{N} c_p h_{k_p} \right|^2 \geq 0 .$$

Suppose, conversely, that (5.19) holds. Then the matrix $B^{(m)} = \{B_{kj}\}$, $k, j = \overline{1, m}$, is positive definite. Let $b^{(m)} = \{b_{kj}\}$, $k, j = \overline{1, m}$, be the positive square root of $B^{(m)}$. We choose an orthonormal system of elements

$$e_1^{(m)}, \ldots, e_m^{(m)}$$

in H and set

$$h_k^{(m)} = \sum_{j=1}^{m} b_{kj}^{(m)} e_j^{(m)}, \qquad k = \overline{1, m} . \tag{5.20}$$

We have

$$(h_k^{(m)}, h_j^{(m)}) = \sum_{l=1}^{m} b_{kl}^{(m)} b_{lj}^{(m)} = B_{kj} .$$

Carrying out this construction for all m, we find the desired sequence (5.17) by the following inductive process. Set

$$h_1 = h_1^{(1)} .$$

Assuming that the elements

$$h_1, \ldots, h_m$$

have already been found, we define an operator T_m on the elements $h_1^{(m+1)}, \ldots, h_m^{(m+1)}$ according to

$$T_m h_k^{(m+1)} = h_k , \qquad k = \overline{1, m} .$$

It is easy to see that T_m is an isometric operator, and it can be extended to an isometric operator on all of H.†

We define the next element h_{m+1} as

$$h_{m+1} = T_m h_{m+1}^{(m+1)} .$$

The elements $h_1, \ldots, h_m, h_{m+1}$ obviously satisfy (5.18), as was to be proved. ∎

Remark. In the general case where i and j range over an arbitrary index set $\mathscr{A}$, the preceding lemma can be proved by considering the linear space $\mathscr{H}$ of all complex-valued functions on $\mathscr{A}$ which are different from zero at only finitely many points, and defining a Hermitean bilinear form

$$(f, g) = \sum_{i, j \in \mathscr{A}} B_{ij} f(i) \bar{g}(j) \qquad (f, g \in \mathscr{H})$$

on $\mathscr{H}$. If we write $f \sim g$ when $(f - g, f - g) = 0$, then $\sim$ is an equivalence relation in $\mathscr{H}$. The set of all equivalence classes of elements of $\mathscr{H}$ is a pre-Hilbert space; we take for H its completion. Then the element $h_i (i \in \mathscr{A})$ may be defined as the element of H consisting of the equivalence class of elements of $\mathscr{H}$ which contains the function on $\mathscr{A}$ which equals 1 at the point i and zero everywhere else.

Suppose we are given a matrix set function

$$F = \{F_{kl}\}_{k=\overline{1,n}}^{l=\overline{1,n}}$$

whose elements F_{kl} are σ-additive complex-valued set functions of bounded variation.

Theorem 5.2. *In order that the matrix function F be the spectral measure of some wide-sense stationary n-dimensional random process, it is necessary and sufficient that the matrix $F(\Delta)$ be positive definite for every Borel set Δ.*

Proof. We have already seen that the spectral measure of a stationary process is always positive definite (cf. (5.15)).

Let us now consider the positive definite matrix set function $F = \{F_{kl}\}_{k=\overline{1,n}}^{l=\overline{1,n}}$. Suppose that $B_{kl}(t)$ are the functions related to the components F_{kl} by relation (5.8). For any $N, t_1, \ldots, t_N$ we have

† Setting, in addition, $T_m f_k = f'_k$, $k = 1, 2, \ldots$, where f_k and f'_k are orthonormal bases in the orthogonal complements of the linear spans of $h_1^{(m+1)}, \ldots, h_m^{(m+1)}$ and $h_1, \ldots, h_m$, respectively, we obtain an isometric operator T_m which, by Lemma 4.1, can be extended to all of H.

$$\sum_{p,q=1}^{N} c_p\bar{c}_q B_{k_pk_q}(t_p - t_q) = \int \sum_{p,q=1}^{N} c_p\bar{c}_q e^{i\lambda(t_p-t_q)} F_{k_pk_q}(d\lambda)$$

$$= \int \sum_{k,l=1}^{n} \varphi_k(\lambda)\overline{\varphi_l(\lambda)} F_{kl}(d\lambda) \geq 0 ,$$

where

$$\varphi_k(\lambda) = \sum_{k_p=k} c_p e^{i\lambda t_p} ,$$

and the complex numbers $c_1, \ldots, c_N$ are arbitrary. Thus, the matrix $B(t) = \{B_{kl}(t)\}_{k=\overline{1,n}}^{l=\overline{1,n}}$ satisfies the conditions of Theorem 5.1 and is therefore the correlation function of some n-dimensional stationary random process $\boldsymbol{\xi}$. In view of the uniqueness of the representation (5.8), we conclude that F is the spectral measure of $\boldsymbol{\xi}$.

Let $\boldsymbol{\xi} = \{\xi_k(t)\}_{k=\overline{1,n}}$ and $\boldsymbol{\eta} = \{\eta_j(t)\}_{j=\overline{1,m}}$ be stationary processes which are stationarily correlated (i.e., the components $\xi_k(t)$, $\eta_j(t)$, $k = \overline{1, n}$, $j = \overline{1, m}$, are all stationarily correlated with one another). We will call the matrix

$$B^{\xi\eta}(t) = \{B_{kj}^{\xi\eta}(t)\}_{k=\overline{1,n}}^{j=\overline{1,m}} \tag{5.21}$$

with elements

$$B_{kj}^{\xi\eta}(t) = \boldsymbol{E}\xi_k(t + s)\overline{\eta_j(s)} \tag{5.22}$$

the *joint correlation function* of $\boldsymbol{\xi}$ and $\boldsymbol{\eta}$.

Let

$$\Phi^{\xi} = \{\Phi_k^{\xi}\}_{k=\overline{1,n}} \quad \text{and} \quad \Phi^{\eta} = \{\Phi_j^{\eta}\}_{j=\overline{1,m}}$$

be the random spectral measures of these processes. We set

$$F_{kj}^{\xi\eta}(d\lambda) = \boldsymbol{E}\Phi_k^{\xi}(d\lambda)\overline{\Phi_j^{\eta}(d\lambda)} \tag{5.23}$$

and call the matrix set function

$$F^{\xi\eta} = \{F_{kj}^{\xi\eta}\}_{k=\overline{1,n}}^{j=\overline{1,m}} , \tag{5.24}$$

whose elements are the σ-additive complex-valued set functions (5.23), the *joint spectral measure* of $\boldsymbol{\xi}$ and $\boldsymbol{\eta}$. In the case where all of the measures $F_{kj}^{\xi\eta}$ are absolutely continuous, we will call the matrix function

$$f^{\xi\eta}(\lambda) = \{f_{kj}^{\xi\eta}(\lambda)\}_{k=\overline{1,n}}^{j=\overline{1,m}} , \tag{5.25}$$

where

$$f_{kj}^{\xi\eta}(\lambda) = \frac{F_{kj}^{\xi\eta}(d\lambda)}{d\lambda} ,$$

the *joint spectral density* of $\boldsymbol{\xi}$ and $\boldsymbol{\eta}$.

Of course, the elements $B_{kj}^{\xi\eta}$ and $F_{kj}^{\xi\eta}$ are connected by relations analogous to (5.8)-(5.10).

6. The ergodic theorem and the law of large numbers

Suppose that the wide-sense stationary process ξ has a continuous correlation function $B(t)$ (in the discrete-parameter case we will always consider the correlation function to be formally continuous), and that

$$\xi(t) = \int e^{i\lambda t}\Phi(d\lambda) \tag{6.1}$$

is its spectral representation. It follows from Theorems 2.2 and 2.3 that ξ is measurable and integrable on any finite interval.

Let us consider the time average of ξ:

$$\frac{1}{T}\sum_{0}^{T-1}\xi(t) = \int_{-\pi}^{\pi}\left[\frac{1}{T}\sum_{0}^{T-1}e^{i\lambda t}\right]\Phi(d\lambda) = \int_{-\pi}^{\pi}\frac{1-e^{i\lambda T}}{T(1-e^{i\lambda})}\Phi(d\lambda) \tag{6.2}$$

in the case of discrete time, and

$$\frac{1}{T}\int_{0}^{T}\xi(t)\,dt = \int_{-\infty}^{\infty}\left[\frac{1}{T}\int_{0}^{T}e^{i\lambda t}dt\right]\Phi(d\lambda) = \int_{-\infty}^{\infty}\frac{e^{i\lambda T}-1}{i\lambda T}\Phi(d\lambda) \tag{6.3}$$

in the case of continuous time. For definiteness, we will consider the continuous-parameter case. Then

$$\begin{aligned}\boldsymbol{E}\left|\frac{1}{T}\int_{0}^{T}\xi(t)\,dt - \Phi(0)\right|^{2} \\ = \int_{\lambda\neq 0}\left|\frac{e^{i\lambda T}-1}{i\lambda T}\right|^{2}F(d\lambda) = \int_{\lambda\neq 0}\frac{4\sin^{2}(\lambda T/2)}{\lambda^{2}T^{2}}F(d\lambda)\,,\end{aligned} \tag{6.4}$$

where $F(d\lambda) = \boldsymbol{E}\,|\,\Phi(d\lambda)\,|^{2}$ is the spectral measure of ξ. We split the integral on the right side of (6.4) into two parts:

$$\begin{aligned}\int_{\lambda\neq 0}\frac{4\sin^{2}(\lambda T/2)}{\lambda^{2}T^{2}}F(d\lambda) = \int_{0<|\lambda|\leq\varepsilon}\frac{4\sin^{2}(\lambda T/2)}{\lambda^{2}T^{2}}F(d\lambda) \\ + \int_{|\lambda|>\varepsilon}\frac{4\sin^{2}(\lambda T/2)}{\lambda^{2}T^{2}}F(d\lambda)\,.\end{aligned}$$

Since

$$\int_{|\lambda|>\varepsilon}\frac{4\sin^{2}(\lambda T/2)}{\lambda^{2}T^{2}}F(d\lambda) \leq C\frac{1}{\varepsilon^{2}T^{2}} \to 0\,,$$

as $T\to\infty$, for any $\varepsilon>0$, and

$$\int_{0<|\lambda|\leq\varepsilon}\frac{4\sin^{2}(\lambda T/2)}{\lambda^{2}T^{2}}F(d\lambda) \leq \int_{0<|\lambda|\leq\varepsilon}F(d\lambda) \to 0$$

as $\varepsilon\to 0$, then

$$E\left|\frac{1}{T}\int_0^T \xi(t)\,dt - \Phi(0)\right|^2 \to 0 \tag{6.5}$$

as $T \to \infty$.

Similarly, in the discrete-parameter case

$$E\left|\frac{1}{T}\sum_0^{T-1} \xi(t) - \Phi(0)\right|^2 \to 0 \tag{6.6}$$

as $T \to \infty$.

We have thus proven the following theorem.

Theorem 6.1. *The time average* (6.2) (*or* (6.3)) *of a stationary process* ξ *converges in mean square, as* $T \to \infty$, *to the value* $\Phi(0)$ *of the spectral measure of* ξ.

We shall say that a process ξ is *ergodic*, if its "time average" converges to the mathematical expectation $E\xi(t)(E\xi(t) = m)$.

It follows from Theorem 6.1 that a process ξ is ergodic if and only if

$$\Phi(0) = m \tag{6.7}$$

with probability 1. This fact can be characterized in terms of the spectral measure F of ξ. Namely, it follows from (6.7) that

$$F(0) = E\,|\,\Phi(0)\,|^2 = |\,m\,|^2\,. \tag{6.8}$$

As was remarked on p. 6, the set function $F_1(d\lambda)$, defined for sets Δ by

$$F_1(\Delta) = E\Phi(\Delta) = E\Phi(\Delta)\cdot 1\,, \tag{6.9}$$

is a complex-valued measure which, in view of the stationarity of ξ, is concentrated at the point $\lambda = 0$. This is because

$$m = E\xi(t) = \int e^{i\lambda t} F_1(d\lambda) \tag{6.10}$$

is a constant, not depending upon t. Thus, we always have

$$E\Phi(0) = m\,. \tag{6.11}$$

Now suppose that condition (6.8) is fulfilled. Then

$$E\,|\,\Phi(0) - m\,|^2 = E\,|\,\Phi(0)\,|^2 - |\,m\,|^2 = 0\,, \tag{6.12}$$

from which follows (6.7).

We have thus proven the following theorem.

Theorem 6.2. *In order that a wide-sense stationary process* ξ, *with* $E\xi(t) = m$, *be ergodic, it is necessary and sufficient that its spectral measure* F *satisfy* (6.8).

We remark that for an ergodic process ξ, Theorem 6.1 implies the *law of large numbers*: for any $\varepsilon > 0$

$$P\left\{\left|\frac{1}{T}\sum_{0}^{T-1}\xi(t) - m\right| > \varepsilon\right\} \to 0 \tag{6.13}$$

as $T \to \infty$ (discrete-parameter case), or

$$P\left\{\left|\frac{1}{T}\int_{0}^{T}\xi(t)\,dt - m\right| > \varepsilon\right\} \to 0 \tag{6.14}$$

as $T \to \infty$ (continuous-parameter case).

Further, the following relations can be obtained by a proof entirely analogous to that of Theorem 6.1:

$$\lim_{T\to\infty}\frac{1}{T}\sum_{0}^{T-1}e^{-i\lambda_0 t}\xi(t) = \Phi(\lambda_0) \qquad \text{(discrete case)}\,; \tag{6.15}$$

$$\lim_{T\to\infty}\frac{1}{T}\int_{0}^{T}e^{-i\lambda_0 t}\xi(t)\,dt = \Phi(\lambda_0) \qquad \text{(continuous case)}\,. \tag{6.16}$$

Suppose now that $\Delta = (\lambda_1, \lambda_2)$ is an interval such that $\Phi(\lambda_1) = \Phi(\lambda_2) = 0$, and

$$\varphi_\Delta(\lambda) = \begin{cases} 1\,, & \text{for } \lambda_1 < \lambda < \lambda_2\,, \\ \dfrac{1}{2}, & \text{for } \lambda = \lambda_1\,,\ \lambda = \lambda_2\,, \\ 0\,, & \text{for } \lambda < \lambda_1\,,\ \lambda > \lambda_2\,. \end{cases}$$

For definiteness, we will consider the case of discrete time ($-\pi \le \lambda_1 < \lambda_2 \le \pi$).

The Fourier series of the function $\varphi_\Delta(\lambda)$,

$$\varphi_\Delta(\lambda) = \frac{1}{2\pi}(\lambda_2 - \lambda_1) + \frac{1}{2\pi}\sum_{t\neq 0}\frac{e^{-i\lambda_2 t} - e^{-i\lambda_1 t}}{-it}e^{i\lambda t}\,, \tag{6.17}$$

converges at every point λ of the interval $[-\pi, \pi]$, and since $\varphi_\Delta(\lambda)$ is a function of bounded variation, the partial sums

$$S_T(\lambda) = \frac{1}{2\pi}(\lambda_2 - \lambda_1) + \frac{1}{2\pi}\sum_{0<|t|\le T}\frac{e^{-i\lambda_2 t} - e^{-i\lambda_1 t}}{-it}e^{i\lambda t}$$

are uniformly bounded, and therefore

$$\lim_{T\to\infty}\int_{-\pi}^{\pi}|\varphi_\Delta(\lambda) - S_T(\lambda)|^2 F(d\lambda) = 0\,. \tag{6.18}$$

It follows at once that

$$\begin{aligned}\Phi(\Delta) &= \int_{-\pi}^{\pi}\varphi_\Delta(\lambda)\Phi(d\lambda) = \lim_{T\to\infty}\int_{-\pi}^{\pi}S_T(\lambda)\Phi(d\lambda) \\ &= \lim_{T\to\infty}\left[\frac{1}{2\pi}(\lambda_2 - \lambda_1)\xi(0) + \frac{1}{2\pi}\sum_{0<|t|\le T}\frac{e^{-i\lambda_2 t} - e^{-i\lambda_1 t}}{-it}\xi(t)\right],\end{aligned} \tag{6.19}$$

where the limit must be understood in the sense of convergence in mean square.

One can show, similarly, that in the continuous-parameter case

$$\Phi(\Delta) = \lim_{T\to\infty} \frac{1}{2\pi} \int_{-T}^{T} \frac{e^{-i\lambda_2 t} - e^{-i\lambda_1 t}}{-it} \xi(t)\, dt \tag{6.20}$$

for any interval $\Delta = (\lambda_1, \lambda_2)$ such that $\Phi(\lambda_1) = \Phi(\lambda_2) = 0$.

Summarizing, we obtain the following theorem:

Theorem 6.3. *The values of the random spectral measure Φ can be expressed in terms of the values of the process ξ according to the relations* (6.19) and (6.20).

To conclude this section, we mention a useful property of a stationary process ξ (with continuous time) *having a bounded spectrum*:

$$\xi(t) = \int_{-w}^{w} e^{i\lambda t} \Phi(d\lambda) , \tag{6.21}$$

where the spectral measure $\Phi(d\lambda)$ is concentrated on the open interval $(-w, w)$.

Theorem 6.4. *Every stationary process with a bounded spectrum, concentrated on the interval $(-w, w)$, can be represented in the form*

$$\xi(t) = \sum_{-\infty}^{\infty} \frac{1}{w} \frac{\sin w\left(t - \frac{\pi}{w}k\right)}{t - \frac{\pi}{w}k} \xi\left(\frac{\pi}{w}k\right) , \tag{6.22}$$

where the series converges in mean square.

Proof. The function $e^{i\lambda t}$ of λ, considered on the interval $[-w, w]$, has a Fourier series

$$e^{i\lambda t} = \sum_{-\infty}^{\infty} \frac{1}{w} \frac{\sin w\left(t - \frac{\pi}{w}k\right)}{t - \frac{\pi}{w}k} e^{i(\pi/w)k\lambda}$$

which converges in mean square with respect to the measure $F(d\lambda) = \boldsymbol{E}\,|\,\Phi(d\lambda)\,|^2$. Consequently,

$$\int_{-w}^{w} e^{i\lambda t} \Phi(d\lambda) = \sum_{-\infty}^{\infty} \frac{1}{w} \frac{\sin\left(t - \frac{\pi}{w}k\right)}{t - \frac{\pi}{w}k} \int_{-w}^{w} e^{i(\pi/w)k\lambda} \Phi(d\lambda) ,$$

which implies the representation (6.22) for ξ.

7. The spectral representation of elements in the space of values of a stationary process

We begin by introducing some notation.

A matrix a, consisting of elements $a_{kj}(k = \overline{1, n};\ j = \overline{1, m})$ and having n rows and m columns, will be denoted by $\{a_{kj}\}_{k=\overline{1, n}}^{j=\overline{1, m}}$. A matrix a, consisting of a single row of elements $a_1, \ldots, a_m$, will be called a row vector and denoted by $\{a_j\}^{j=\overline{1, m}}$. Analogously, a matrix a, consisting of a single column of elements $a_1, \ldots, a_n$, will be called a column vector and denoted by $\{a_k\}_{k=\overline{1, n}}$. By the product of the matrices $a = \{a_{kj}\}_{k=\overline{1, n}}^{j=\overline{1, m}}$ and $b = \{b_{jl}\}_{j=\overline{1, m}}^{l=\overline{1, n'}}$ we will understand, as usual, the matrix $c = ab = \{c_{kl}\}_{k=\overline{1, m}}^{l=\overline{1, n'}}$, where $c_{kl} = \sum_{j=1}^{m} a_{kj} b_{jl}$. Further, by the adjoint of the matrix $a = \{a_{kj}\}_{k=\overline{1, n}}^{j=\overline{1, m}}$ we mean the matrix $a^* = \{\bar{a}_{jk}\}_{j=\overline{1, m}}^{k=\overline{1, n}}$; by the norm $\| a \|$ of a matrix $a = \{a_{kj}\}_{k=\overline{1, n}}^{j=\overline{1, m}}$ we will mean the quantity $\| a \| = [\sum_{k=1}^{n} \sum_{j=1}^{m} | a_{kj} |^2]^{1/2}$, and finally, by the trace $\operatorname{Tr} a$ of a square matrix $a = \{a_{kj}\}_{k=\overline{1, n}}^{j=\overline{1, n}}$ we will understand the sum of its diagonal elements:

$$\operatorname{Tr} a = \sum_{k=1}^{n} a_{kk} .$$

Let H_ξ be the space of values of the n-dimensional stationary process $\boldsymbol{\xi} = \{\xi_k(t)\}_{k=\overline{1, n}}$, whose spectral representation is

$$\xi(t) = \int e^{i\lambda t} \Phi(d\lambda) , \qquad \Phi = \{\Phi_k\}_{k=\overline{1, n}} . \tag{7.1}$$

We shall show that for any element $h \in H_\xi$ there exists a vector function $\varphi(\lambda) = \{\varphi_k(\lambda)\}^{k=\overline{1, n}}$ such that h is representable in the form of an integral with respect to the random measure Φ:

$$h = \int \varphi(\lambda) \Phi(d\lambda) = \int \sum_{1}^{n} \varphi_k(\lambda) \Phi_k(d\lambda) . \tag{7.2}$$

Let $F = \{F_{kl}\}_{k=\overline{1, n}}^{l=\overline{1, n}}$ be the spectral measure of $\boldsymbol{\xi}$, and let μ be some positive measure with respect to which all of the elements F_{kl} of F are absolutely continuous.† We denote the densities of the complex measures F_{kl} with respect to the measure μ by $f_{kl}^{(\mu)}(\lambda)$:

† For the measure μ we can take, for example, the set function defined by

$$\mu = \sum_{k=1}^{n} F_{kk}$$

since, in view of the positive definiteness of the matrix $F(\Delta)$ for any Borel set Δ, the vanishing of all the diagonal elements $F_{kk}(\Delta)$ for some Δ implies that $F_{kl}(\Delta) = 0$ for all k, l.

$$f_{kl}^{(\mu)}(\lambda) = \frac{F_{kl}(d\lambda)}{\mu(d\lambda)}, \qquad k, l = \overline{1, n} . \tag{7.3}$$

Since the matrix $F(\Delta) = \{F_{kl}(\Delta)\}_{k=\overline{1,n}}^{l=\overline{1,n}}$ is positive definite for any Borel set Δ (cf. Theorem 5.2), the matrix function

$$f^{(\mu)}(\lambda) = \{f_{kl}^{(\mu)}(\lambda)\}_{k=\overline{1,n}}^{l=\overline{1,n}} \tag{7.4}$$

will be positive definite for almost all λ (with respect to μ).

Let us consider a vector function $\varphi(\lambda) = \{\varphi_k(\lambda)\}^{k=\overline{1,n}}$. We will say that $\varphi(\lambda)$ belongs to the space $L^2(F)$, if the function

$$[\varphi(\lambda)f^{(\mu)}(\lambda)\overset{*}{\varphi}(\lambda)] = \sum_{k,l=1}^{n} \varphi_k(\lambda)\overline{\varphi_l(\lambda)}f_{kl}^{(\mu)}(\lambda)$$

is integrable with respect to μ, i.e., if

$$\int [\varphi(\lambda)f^{(\mu)}(\lambda)\overset{*}{\varphi}(\lambda)]\mu(d\lambda) < \infty , \tag{7.5}$$

where the limits of integration are $-\pi, \pi$ in the case of discrete time, and $-\infty, \infty$ in the case of continuous time. Note that for a simple function φ, assuming at most countably many different values, say $\varphi(\lambda) = \varphi^{(p)}$ for $\lambda \in \Delta_p$,

$$\int [\varphi(\lambda)f^{(\mu)}(\lambda)\overset{*}{\varphi}(\lambda)]\mu(d\lambda) = \sum_p \varphi^{(p)}F(\Delta_p)\overset{*}{\varphi}{}^{(p)} . \tag{7.6}$$

If the vector functions φ and ψ both belong to $L^2(F)$, then the function $[\varphi f^{(\mu)}\overset{*}{\psi}]$ is integrable with respect to μ, since, in view of the positive definiteness of the matrix $f^{(\mu)}$, we have

$$| \varphi f^{(\mu)}\overset{*}{\psi} | \leq [\varphi f^{(\mu)}\overset{*}{\varphi}]^{1/2}[\psi f^{(\mu)}\overset{*}{\psi}]^{1/2}$$

for almost all λ with respect to μ, and, by the Cauchy-Bunyakovskii inequality, we have

$$\int [\varphi f^{(\mu)}\overset{*}{\psi}]\mu(d\lambda) \leq \left\{\int [\varphi f^{(\mu)}\overset{*}{\varphi}]\mu(d\lambda)\right\}^{1/2}\left\{\int [\psi f^{(\mu)}\overset{*}{\psi}]\mu(d\lambda)\right\}^{1/2} . \tag{7.7}$$

Neither the integral in (7.5) nor the space $L^2(F)$ depends upon the choice of the measure μ. If ν is another measure with respect to which the F_{kl} are all absolutely continuous, then

$$\int_\Delta [\varphi f^{(\mu)}\overset{*}{\psi}]\mu(d\lambda) = \int_\Delta [\varphi f^{(\nu)}\overset{*}{\psi}]\nu(d\lambda) \tag{7.8}$$

for any vector functions $\varphi, \psi \in L^2(F)$ and any Borel set Δ. Indeed, if we denote by $\tilde{\mu}$ and $\tilde{\nu}$ the absolutely continuous parts of μ and ν relative to ν and μ, respectively, and set $\alpha(\lambda) = \tilde{\mu}(d\lambda)/\tilde{\nu}(d\lambda)$, then, as is easily seen,

$$f_{kl}^{(\mu)}(\lambda) = f_{kl}^{(\tilde{\mu})}(\lambda) = \alpha(\lambda) f_{kl}^{(\tilde{\nu})}(\lambda) = \alpha(\lambda) f_{kl}^{(\nu)}(\lambda) \tag{7.9}$$

for almost all λ with respect to $\tilde{\mu}$ and $\tilde{\nu}$, from which follows (7.8).

We denote the common value of the integrals in (7.8) by $\int_\Delta \varphi F(d\lambda)\overset{*}{\psi}$; that is,

$$\int_\Delta \varphi F(d\lambda)\overset{*}{\psi} = \int_\Delta [\varphi f^{(\mu)}\overset{*}{\psi}]\mu(d\lambda) . \tag{7.10}$$

Furthermore, we will say, in speaking about some given property, that it is fulfilled almost everywhere with respect to the spectral measure F if it is fulfilled for all λ, with the exception of some set Δ_0 for which $F(\Delta_0) = 0$.

Let us note some simple properties of the integral defined above:

$$\left| \int_\Delta \varphi F(d\lambda)\overset{*}{\psi} \right| \le \left[\int_\Delta \varphi F(d\lambda)\overset{*}{\varphi}\right]^{1/2} \left[\int_\Delta \psi F(d\lambda)\overset{*}{\psi}\right]^{1/2} , \tag{7.11}$$

$$\left| \int_\Delta \varphi F(d\lambda)\overset{*}{\psi} \right| \le n^{1/2} \sup_\lambda || \varphi(\lambda) || \sup_\lambda || \psi(\lambda) || \, || F(\Delta) || , \tag{7.12}$$

and, finally,

$$\int_\Delta \varphi F(d\lambda)\overset{*}{\varphi} = 0 \tag{7.13}$$

if and only if $|| \varphi(\lambda) || = 0$ almost everywhere with respect to F on the set Δ.

The proof of these properties is left to the reader.

By virtue of (7.11)-(7.13), if two vector functions φ and ψ belong to $L^2(F)$, then the vector function $a\varphi + b\psi$, where a and b are arbitrary complex numbers, also belongs to $L^2(F)$, so that $L^2(F)$ is a linear space. If we do not distinguish between two vector functions φ and ψ whose difference satisfies the condition

$$\int [\varphi - \psi] F(d\lambda) [\overset{*}{\varphi} - \overset{*}{\psi}] = 0 , \tag{7.14}$$

and if we introduce a scalar product according to

$$(\varphi, \psi) = \int \varphi F(d\lambda)\overset{*}{\psi} , \tag{7.15}$$

then $L^2(F)$ becomes a Hilbert space with norm $\|\varphi\| = (\varphi, \varphi)^{1/2}$.

Lemma 7.1. *The space $L^2(F)$ is complete; i.e., for any sequence $\varphi^{(p)}$, $p = 1, 2, \ldots$, of elements of $L^2(F)$ such that*

$$\lim_{p, q \to \infty} || \varphi^{(p)} - \varphi^{(q)} || = 0 , \tag{7.16}$$

there exists a vector function $\varphi \in L^2(F)$ *such that*

$$\lim_{p \to \infty} || \varphi - \varphi^{(p)} || = 0 . \tag{7.17}$$

Proof. We choose the auxiliary measure μ so that the matrix $f^{(\mu)} = \{f_{kl}^{(\mu)}\}_{k=\overline{1, n}}^{l=\overline{1, n}}$, with components $f_{kl}^{(\mu)}(\lambda) = F_{kl}(d\lambda)/\mu(d\lambda)$, is different from zero almost everywhere with respect to μ (for instance, we can define μ as in the footnote on p. 28).

Let $m(\lambda)$ denote the smallest nonzero eigenvalue of the matrix $f^{(\mu)}(\lambda)$, θ_λ—the subspace of all n-dimensional vectors $\varphi = \{\varphi_k\}^{k=\overline{1, n}}$ satisfying the condition $\varphi f^{(\mu)}(\lambda) = 0$, and R_λ—the orthogonal complement of θ_λ in the n-dimensional space on which we consider $f^{(\mu)}(\lambda)$ (for fixed λ) to act. Obviously, $||\varphi|| = 0$ if and only if $\varphi(\lambda) \in \theta_\lambda$ for almost all λ with respect to μ. It is easily seen that for any vector function $\varphi \in L^2(F)$ one can find another vector function $\tilde{\varphi} \in L^2(F)$ such that $||\varphi - \tilde{\varphi}|| = 0$ and $\tilde{\varphi}(\lambda) \in R_\lambda$ for almost all λ with respect to μ, and for these λ

$$\varphi(\lambda) f^{(\mu)}(\lambda) \overset{*}{\varphi}(\lambda) \geq m(\lambda) \sum_1^n | \tilde{\varphi}_k(\lambda) |^2 .$$

In view of this, we may assume without loss of generality that $\varphi^{(p)} = \tilde{\varphi}^{(p)}$, $p = 1, 2, \ldots$, and then

$$|| \varphi^{(p)} - \varphi^{(q)} || \geq \int m(\lambda) \sum_1^n | \varphi_k^{(p)}(\lambda) - \varphi_k^{(q)}(\lambda) |^2 \mu(d\lambda) \to 0$$

as $p, q \to \infty$. It follows that one can find a subsequence, which we again denote by $\{\varphi^{(p)}\}$, $p = 1, 2, \ldots$, such that

$$\sum_1^n | \varphi_k^{(p)}(\lambda) - \varphi_k^{(q)}(\lambda) |^2 \to 0 ,$$

as $p, q \to \infty$, almost everywhere with respect to μ, and so there exists a vector function $\varphi = \{\varphi_k\}^{k=\overline{1, n}}$ to which the subsequence $\{\varphi^{(p)}\}$ converges:

$$\lim_{p \to \infty} \sum_{k=1}^n | \varphi_k^{(p)}(\lambda) - \varphi_k(\lambda) |^2 = 0$$

for almost all λ with respect to μ.

Therefore, for such λ we have

$$\lim_{p \to \infty} \varphi^{(p)} f^{(\mu)} \overset{*}{\varphi}{}^{(p)} = \varphi f^{(\mu)} \overset{*}{\varphi} .$$

As the sequence $\{\varphi^{(p)}\}$ is fundamental (i.e., satisfies (7.16)) there exists a constant C such that

$$\|\varphi^{(p)}\|^2 = \int [\varphi^{(p)} f^{(\mu)} \overset{*}{\varphi}{}^{(p)}] \mu(d\lambda) \leq C$$

for all $p = 1, 2, \ldots$, and, by Fatou's lemma, the integral of the function $[\varphi f^{(\mu)} \overset{*}{\varphi}]$ is bounded by C:

$$\int [\varphi f^{(\mu)} \overset{*}{\varphi}] \mu(d\lambda) \leq C .$$

This relation shows that the vector function φ belongs to $L^2(F)$. Further, we have, for any $\varepsilon > 0$,

$$\|\varphi^{(p)} - \varphi^{(q)}\| \leq \varepsilon$$

for p and q sufficiently large. Letting $p \to \infty$ along those values of p, for which $\varphi^{(p)}(\lambda) \to \varphi(\lambda)$ almost everywhere with respect to μ, and using Fatou's lemma, we obtain

$$\|\varphi - \varphi^{(q)}\| \leq \varepsilon$$

for q sufficiently large.

Let us return now to the n-dimensional stationary process $\xi = \{\xi_k(t)\}_{k=\overline{1,n}}$. We establish a correspondence between random variables $h \in H_\xi$ of the form

$$h = \sum_{k=1}^{n} \int \varphi_k(\lambda) \Phi_k(d\lambda) = \int \sum_{k=1}^{n} \varphi_k(\lambda) \Phi_k(d\lambda) = \int \varphi(\lambda) \Phi(d\lambda) , \tag{7.18}$$

where

$$\int |\varphi_k(\lambda)|^2 F_{kk}(d\lambda) < \infty , \qquad k = \overline{1, n} , \tag{7.19}$$

and the vector functions $\varphi = \{\varphi_k\}^{k=\overline{1,n}}$ which occur in the representation (7.18). This correspondence is an isometric mapping into the space $L^2(F)$ since, if

$$h' = \int \sum_{k=1}^{n} \varphi'_k(\lambda) \Phi_k(d\lambda) = \int \varphi'(\lambda) \Phi(d\lambda)$$

is a random variable of the form (7.18), then

$$(h, h') = \int \varphi F(d\lambda) \overset{*}{\varphi}{}' = (\varphi, \varphi') . \tag{7.20}$$

By Lemma 4.1 this correspondence can be extended to an isometric mapping of H_ξ onto $L^2(F)$, because the vector functions $\varphi = \{\varphi_k\}$ which satisfy (7.19) are everywhere dense in $L^2(F)$ (indeed, the set of all φ with bounded components has this property).

This result shows that to every element $h \in H_\xi$ there corresponds some vector function $\varphi \in L^2(F)$, and if $\varphi \in L^2(F)$ is the limit of a sequence $\{\varphi^{(p)}\}$, $p = 1, 2, \ldots$, satisfying (7.19), then

$$h = \lim_{p\to\infty} \sum_{k=1}^{n} \int \varphi_k^{(p)}(\lambda)\Phi_k(d\lambda) = \lim_{p\to\infty} \int \varphi^{(p)}(\lambda)\Phi(d\lambda) .$$

The limit does not depend upon the choice of sequence $\{\varphi^{(p)}\}$ converging to φ because the correspondence which we established is an isometry; we will denote this limit† by

$$h = \int \sum_{k=1}^{n} \varphi_k(\lambda)\Phi_k(d\lambda) = \int \varphi(\lambda)\Phi(d\lambda) . \tag{7.21}$$

Formula (7.21) gives us a *spectral representation* for the elements h in the space H_ξ of values of the stationary process ξ.

We will call the vector function $\varphi = \{\varphi_k\}^{k=\overline{1,n}}$ in (7.21) the *spectral characteristic* of the random variable h. We emphasize that the integral in (7.21) is defined for any $\varphi \in L^2(F)$, and relation (7.20) holds for arbitrary $h, h' \in H_\xi$.

It should be emphasized that the vector function φ in the representation (7.21) of an element $h \in H_\xi$ is not (generally speaking) uniquely defined. Namely, if $\tilde{\varphi} \in L^2(F)$ is such that

$$\int [\varphi - \tilde{\varphi}]F(d\lambda)[\overset{*}{\varphi} - \overset{*}{\tilde{\varphi}}] = 0 , \tag{7.22}$$

then φ can be replaced in (7.21) by $\tilde{\varphi}$.

Further, if T is a linear operator on H_ξ, then the equation

$$h' = Th = T\left[\int \varphi(\lambda)\Phi(d\lambda)\right] = \int \varphi'(\lambda)\Phi(d\lambda) = \int [T'\varphi](\lambda)\Phi(d\lambda) \tag{7.23}$$

defines a linear operator T' in $L^2(F)$, $T'\varphi = \varphi'$, and conversely, to every linear operator T' in $L^2(F)$ there corresponds a linear operator T in H_ξ.

It is easy to see that to the unitary operator U_t of the unitary family of ξ there corresponds the operator of multiplication by $e^{i\lambda t}$ in $L^2(F)$. This follows from the fact that to the values $\xi_k(t)$ of the process ξ there correspond the vector functions $e^{i\lambda t}\delta_k$ in $L^2(F)$ (where $\delta_k = \{\delta_{kl}\}^{l=\overline{1,n}}$ is a constant vector, with components $\delta_{kk} = 1$, $\delta_{kl} = 0$ for $k \neq 1$), and that (7.23), applied to the operator $T = U_t$, yields

$$U_t\xi_k(s) = U_t\left[\int e^{i\lambda s}\delta_k\Phi(d\lambda)\right] = \xi_k(t+s) = \int e^{i\lambda(t+s)}\delta_k\Phi(d\lambda) . \tag{7.24}$$

Similarly, to the values $\Phi_k(\Delta)$ of the spectral measure of ξ there correspond the vector functions $\chi_\Delta(\lambda)\delta_k$, where $\chi_\Delta(\lambda)$ is the characteristic function of the set Δ ($\chi_\Delta(\lambda) = 1$ if $\lambda \in \Delta$, and zero otherwise), and to the

† We remark that φ_k may not satisfy condition (7.19), i.e., the individual integrals $\int\varphi_k(\lambda)\Phi_k(d\lambda)$ may not exist in the sense of Section 2.

projection operators $E(\Delta)$ there correspond the operators of multiplication by the functions $\chi_\Delta(\lambda)$.

8. Linear transformations of stationary processes

Let $\boldsymbol{\xi} = \{\xi_k(t)\}_{k=\overline{1,n}}$ be some n-dimensional stationary process whose spectral representation is

$$\xi(t) = \int e^{i\lambda t}\Phi^\xi(d\lambda)\,, \qquad \Phi^\xi = \{\Phi_k^\xi\}_{k=\overline{1,n}}\,. \tag{8.1}$$

We will say that the m-dimensional stationary process $\boldsymbol{\eta} = \{\eta_j(t)\}_{j=\overline{1,m}}$ is obtained from $\boldsymbol{\xi}$ by a *linear transformation*, if each of its components admits a spectral representation of the form

$$\eta_j(t) = \int e^{i\lambda t}\varphi_j(\lambda)\Phi^\xi(d\lambda)\,, \qquad j = \overline{1,m}\,, \tag{8.2}$$

with certain vector functions $\varphi_j = \{\varphi_{jk}\}^{k=\overline{1,n}}$ from $L^2(F)$.

Relation (8.2) can be written in matrix form:

$$\eta(t) = \int e^{i\lambda t}\varphi_{\eta\xi}(\lambda)\Phi^\xi(d\lambda)\,. \tag{8.3}$$

(Here, the matrix $\varphi_{\eta\xi}(\lambda) = \{\varphi_{jk}(\lambda)\}^{k=\overline{1,n}}_{j=\overline{1,m}}$ symbolically acts on the column vector $\Phi^\xi(d\lambda) = \{\Phi_k^\xi(d\lambda)\}_{k=\overline{1,n}}$). Formulae (8.2) and (8.3) show that the random variables $\eta_j(t)$—the values of the stationary process $\boldsymbol{\eta}$—belong to the space H_ξ.

Being a stationary process, $\boldsymbol{\eta}$ has its own spectral representation:

$$\eta(t) = \int e^{i\lambda t}\Phi^\eta(d\lambda)\,; \qquad \Phi^\eta = \{\Phi_j^\eta\}_{j=\overline{1,m}}\,. \tag{8.4}$$

It follows from (8.2) that the random spectral measure $\Phi^\eta = \{\Phi_j^\eta\}_{j=\overline{1,m}}$ of the process $\boldsymbol{\eta}$ is such that

$$\Phi_j^\eta(\Delta) = \int_\Delta \varphi_j(\lambda)\Phi^\xi(d\lambda)\,, \qquad j = \overline{1,m}\,. \tag{8.5}$$

In matrix form, (8.5) can be written as

$$\Phi^\eta(\Delta) = \int_\Delta \varphi_{\eta\xi}(\lambda)\Phi^\xi(d\lambda)\,. \tag{8.6}$$

The components $F_{ij}^{\eta\eta}$ of the spectral measure $F^{\eta\eta} = \{F_{ij}^{\eta\eta}\}^{j=\overline{1,m}}_{i=\overline{1,m}}$ of $\boldsymbol{\eta}$ are expressable in terms of the spectral measure $F^{\xi\xi} = \{F_{kl}^{\xi\xi}\}^{l=\overline{1,n}}_{k=\overline{1,n}}$ of $\boldsymbol{\xi}$ by means of the relations

$$F_{ij}^{\eta\eta}(\Delta) = \int_\Delta \varphi_i F^{\xi\xi}(d\lambda)\overset{*}{\varphi}_j\,, \qquad i, j = \overline{1, m}\,, \tag{8.7}$$

or, in matrix form,

$$F^{\eta\eta}(\Delta) = \int_\Delta \varphi_{\eta\xi} F^{\xi\xi}(d\lambda)\overset{*}{\varphi}_{\eta\xi}\,. \tag{8.8}$$

We will call the matrix function

$$\varphi_{\eta\xi} = \{\varphi_{jk}\}_{j=\overline{1, m}}^{k=\overline{1, n}}$$

the *spectral characteristic* of the linear transformation being considered.

The stationary processes ξ and η are obviously stationarily correlated. Let their joint spectral measure be

$$F^{\eta\xi} = \{F_{jk}^{\eta\xi}\}_{j=\overline{1, m}}^{k=\overline{1, n}}.$$

We have

$$\begin{aligned} F^{\eta\eta}(d\lambda) &= \varphi_{\eta\xi}(\lambda)F^{\xi\xi}(d\lambda)\overset{*}{\varphi}_{\eta\xi}(\lambda)\,, \\ F^{\eta\xi}(d\lambda) &= \varphi_{\eta\xi}(\lambda)F^{\xi\xi}(d\lambda)\,. \end{aligned} \tag{8.9}$$

It turns out that relations (8.9) are not only necessary, but also sufficient for the multi-dimensional stationary process η to be obtainable from the multi-dimensional stationary process ξ by a linear transformation with spectral characteristic $\varphi_{\eta\xi}$.

Lemma 8.1. *Suppose that the stationary process* $\eta = \{\eta_j(t)\}_{j=\overline{1,m}}$ *is stationarily correlated with the stationary process* $\xi = \{\xi_k(t)\}_{k=\overline{1,n}}$, *and that the stationary process* ζ *is obtainable from* ξ *by means of a linear transformation, and its spectral measures satisfy the conditions*

$$F^{\eta\eta}(d\lambda) = F^{\zeta\zeta}(d\lambda)\,, \qquad F^{\eta\xi}(d\lambda) = F^{\zeta\xi}(d\lambda)\,. \tag{8.10}$$

Then the processes η *and* ζ *are identical.*

Proof. The relations

$$\begin{aligned} T\zeta_j(t) &= \eta_j(t)\,, \qquad j = \overline{1, m}\,, \\ T\xi_k(t) &= \xi_k(t)\,, \qquad k = \overline{1, n}\,, \quad -\infty < t < \infty\,, \end{aligned} \tag{8.11}$$

define an isometric operator T on the elements $\zeta_i(t)$ and $\xi_k(t)$ in H_ξ; indeed,

$$\boldsymbol{E}\zeta_j(t)\overline{\zeta_{j'}(t')} = \int e^{i\lambda(t-t')}F_{jj'}^{\zeta\zeta}(d\lambda) = \int e^{i\lambda(t-t')}F_{jj'}^{\eta\eta}(d\lambda) = \boldsymbol{E}\eta_j(t)\overline{\eta_{j'}(t')}$$

and similarly

$$\boldsymbol{E}\zeta_j(t)\overline{\xi_k(t')} = \boldsymbol{E}\eta_j(t)\overline{\xi_k(t')}\,.$$

By Lemma 4.1, T can be extended to an isometric operator on all of H_ξ. But the lower of relations (8.11) shows that T is the identity operator (it carries the $\xi_k(t)$ into themselves), and therefore

$$\zeta_j(t) = \eta_j(t)\,, \qquad j = \overline{1, m}\,,$$

for all t, as was to be proved.

Theorem 8.1. *Let the multi-dimensional stationary processes* η *and* ξ *be stationarily correlated. In order that* η *be obtainable from* ξ *by a linear transformation with spectral characteristic* $\varphi_{\eta\xi}$, *it is necessary and sufficient that the spectral measures* $F^{\eta\eta}$, $F^{\eta\xi}$, *and* $F^{\xi\xi}$ *of these processes satisfy conditions* (8.9).

Proof. Let

$$\xi(t) = \int e^{i\lambda t}\Phi(d\lambda)\,.$$

Let us define a stationary process ξ by

$$\zeta(t) = \int e^{i\lambda t}\varphi_{\eta\xi}(\lambda)\Phi(d\lambda)\,. \tag{8.12}$$

The integral in (8.12) exists because the integral

$$\int \varphi_{\eta\xi}F^{\xi\xi}(d\lambda)\overset{*}{\varphi}_{\eta\xi} = \int F^{\eta\eta}(d\lambda)$$

is finite. The spectral measures of ζ, η, and ξ obviously satisfy conditions (8.10), from which it follows by Lemma 8.1 that ζ in fact coincides with η.

Remark 1. A stationary m-dimensional process η which is stationarily correlated with an n-dimensional process ξ is obtainable from ξ by a linear transformation if and only if there is a value t_0 for which the random variables $\eta_j(t_0)$, $j = \overline{1, m}$, belong to the space H_ξ of values of ξ. In this case $\eta_j(t) = U_{t-t_0}\eta_j(t_0)$, $j = \overline{1, m}$, where $\{U_t\}$ is the unitary family of ξ. Obviously, in this case all the values $\eta_j(t)$ belong to the space H_ξ; the spectral characteristics $\varphi_j(\lambda) = \{\varphi_{jk}(\lambda)\}^{k=\overline{1,n}}$ of the random variables $\eta_j(0)$, $j = \overline{1, n}$, are the rows of the matrix $\varphi(\lambda) = \{\varphi_{jk}(\lambda)\}^{k=\overline{1,n}}_{j=\overline{1,m}}$ defining the linear transformation by means of which the process η can be obtained from ξ.

Remark 2. If the stationary process ξ has a spectral density $f^{\xi\xi}$, then a process η which is obtainable from ξ by a linear transformation with spectral characteristic $\varphi_{\eta\xi}$ also has a spectral density, which (as follows from (8.9)) is given by

$$f^{\eta\eta} = \varphi_{\eta\xi} f^{\xi\xi} \varphi_{\eta\xi}^* , \qquad f^{\eta\xi} = \varphi_{\eta\xi} f^{\xi\xi} , \tag{8.13}$$

where $f^{\eta\xi}$ is the joint spectral density.

Remark 3. If η is obtainable from ξ by a linear transformation with a spectral characteristic which is, for almost every λ with respect to $F^{\xi\xi}$, a nonsingular matrix, then ξ, in turn, can be obtained from η by a linear transformation, and

$$\varphi_{\xi\eta} = \varphi_{\eta\xi}^{-1} . \tag{8.14}$$

The proofs of these results are left to the reader. Let us consider some examples.

Example 8.1. Let ξ be a continuous-parameter stationary process,

$$\xi(t) = \int_{-\infty}^{\infty} e^{i\lambda t} \Phi(d\lambda) ,$$

whose spectral measure F satisfies the condition

$$\int_{-\infty}^{\infty} \lambda^2 F(d\lambda) < \infty .$$

Consider the stationary process η which is obtained from ξ by a linear transformation with spectral characteristic $\varphi(\lambda) = i\lambda$,

$$\eta(t) = \int_{-\infty}^{\infty} e^{i\lambda t}(i\lambda) \Phi(d\lambda) .$$

It is easily seen that η can be obtained by formally differentiating ξ with respect to time:

$$\eta(t) = \frac{d}{dt} \xi(t) .$$

This relation can be given a rigorous meaning. Namely, for every fixed t the function $i\lambda e^{i\lambda t}$ is the limit in mean square of the function $\varphi_\varepsilon(\lambda) = (1/\varepsilon)[e^{i\lambda(t+\varepsilon)} - e^{i\lambda t}]$ as $\varepsilon \to 0$;

$$\lim_{\varepsilon\to 0} \int_{-\infty}^{\infty} | i\lambda e^{i\lambda t} - \varphi_\varepsilon(\lambda) |^2 F(d\lambda) = 0 .$$

Therefore $\eta(t)$ is the limit in mean square of the random variables $(1/\varepsilon)[\xi(t+\varepsilon) - \xi(t)]$:

$$\lim_{\varepsilon\to 0} \boldsymbol{E} \left| \eta(t) - \frac{\xi(t+\varepsilon) - \xi(t)}{\varepsilon} \right|^2 = 0 .$$

The process η is called the derivative (in mean square) of the stationary process ξ.

Example 8.2 Let ξ be a discrete-parameter stationary process;

$$\xi(t) = \int_{-\pi}^{\pi} e^{i\lambda t}\Phi(d\lambda),$$

and suppose that the stationary process η is obtained from ξ by a linear transformation with a spectral characteristic $\varphi(\lambda)$ which has an absolutely convergent Fourier series:

$$\varphi(\lambda) = \sum_{-\infty}^{\infty} c(s)e^{-i\lambda s}, \qquad \sum_{-\infty}^{\infty} | c(s) | < \infty .$$

In this case

$$\eta(t) = \int_{-\pi}^{\pi} e^{i\lambda t}\varphi(\lambda)\Phi(d\lambda) = \sum_{-\infty}^{\infty} c(t-s)\xi(s) .$$

Example 8.3. Suppose that ξ is a continuous-parameter stationary process,

$$\xi(t) = \int_{-\infty}^{\infty} e^{i\lambda t}\Phi(d\lambda),$$

and the stationary process η is obtained from ξ by a linear transformation with a spectral characteristic $\varphi(\lambda)$ which is the Fourier transform of some integrable function:

$$\varphi(\lambda) = \int_{-\infty}^{\infty} e^{-i\lambda t}c(t)\,dt, \qquad \int_{-\infty}^{\infty} | c(t) |\,dt < \infty .$$

Then

$$\eta(t) = \int_{-\infty}^{\infty} e^{i\lambda t}\varphi(\lambda)\Phi(d\lambda) = \int_{-\infty}^{\infty} c(t-s)\xi(s)\,ds .$$

Example 8.4. Let ξ be a continuous-parameter stationary process,

$$\xi(t) = \int_{-\infty}^{\infty} e^{i\lambda t}\Phi(d\lambda),$$

and suppose that the stationary process η satisfies the constant coefficient differential equation

$$a_0\eta^{(n)}(t) + a_1\eta^{(n-1)}(t) + \cdots + a_n\eta(t) = \xi(t) ,$$

where the derivatives $\eta^{(k)}(t)$, $k = \overline{1, n}$, are understood as derivatives in mean square. It is clear from Example 8.1 that ξ is obtainable from η by means of a linear transformation with spectral characteristic

$$\psi(\lambda) = a_0(i\lambda)^n + a_1(i\lambda)^{n-1} + \cdots + a_n ,$$

and, consequently, η can be obtained from ξ by a linear transformation with spectral characteristic $\varphi(\lambda) = \psi^{-1}(\lambda)$:

$$\eta(t) = \int_{-\infty}^{\infty} e^{i\lambda t}\frac{1}{a_0(i\lambda)^n + a_1(i\lambda)^{n-1} + \cdots + a_n}\Phi(d\lambda),$$

assuming that

$$\int_{-\infty}^{\infty} \frac{1}{|a_0(i\lambda)^n + a_1(i\lambda)^{n-1} + \cdots + a_n|^2} F(d\lambda) < \infty .$$

This condition is in fact equivalent to the existence of a stationary solution η of the preceding differential equation.

9. Stationary processes of constant rank

We will say that a multi-dimensional stationary process $\boldsymbol{\xi} = \{\xi_k(t)\}_{k=\overline{1,n}}$ *has rank m*, if it possesses a spectral density $f(\lambda) = \{f_{kl}(\lambda)\}_{k=\overline{1,n}}^{l=\overline{1,n}}$ which has rank m for almost all λ.

Lemma 9.1. *A positive definite matrix $f = \{f_{kl}\}_{k=\overline{1,n}}^{l=\overline{1,n}}$ of rank m can be represented in the form*

$$f = \frac{1}{2\pi}\varphi\overset{*}{\varphi}, \tag{9.1}$$

where φ is a rectangular matrix of the form $\varphi = \{\varphi_{kj}\}_{k=\overline{1,n}}^{j=\overline{1,m}}$.

Proof. Let $g = \{g_{kl}\}_{k=\overline{1,n}}^{l=\overline{1,n}}$ be the positive square root of the matrix $2\pi f$, and let V be a unitary matrix which reduces g to diagonal form:

$$d = Vg\overset{*}{V} = \{d_{kl}\}_{k=\overline{1,n}}^{l=\overline{1,n}}, \qquad \begin{array}{ll} d_{kk} > 0 & \text{for} \quad k = 1, m , \\ d_{kk} = 0 & \text{for} \quad k = m+1, n . \end{array}$$

Let $\hat{d}$ be the rectangular matrix obtained from d by omitting the last $n-m$ columns. It is easy to see that the matrix $\varphi = \overset{*}{V}\hat{d}$ satisfies (9.1).

Lemma 9.2. *Let $\varphi = \{\varphi_{kj}\}_{k=\overline{1,n}}^{j=\overline{1,m}}$ be a rectangular matrix of rank m. Then there exists a matrix ψ of the form $\psi = \{\psi_{ik}\}_{i=\overline{1,m}}^{k=\overline{1,n}}$ which satisfies the equation*

$$\psi\varphi = I_m , \tag{9.2}$$

where I_m is the unit matrix of order m.

Proof. The system of m equations

$$\sum_{k=1}^{n} \psi_{ik}\varphi_{kj} = \delta_{ij} , \qquad j = \overline{1, m} ,$$

has a solution for each $i = \overline{1, m}$, since the rank of its coefficient matrix φ is equal to m. If $\psi_{i1}, \ldots, \psi_{in}$ satisfy this system, then the matrix $\psi = \{\psi_{ik}\}_{i=\overline{1,m}}^{k=\overline{1,n}}$ will obviously satisfy (9.2).

Let us consider a multi-dimensional stationary process $\boldsymbol{\xi} = \{\xi_k(t)\}_{k=\overline{1,n}}$

of rank m with spectral density $f(\lambda) = \{f_{kl}(\lambda)\}_{k=\overline{1,n}}^{l=\overline{1,n}}$. Since the rank of the matrix $f(\lambda)$ equals m for almost all λ, there exist matrix functions $\varphi(\lambda) = \{\varphi_{kj}(\lambda)\}_{k=\overline{1,n}}^{j=\overline{1,m}}$ and $\psi(\lambda) = \{\psi_{ik}(\lambda)\}_{i=\overline{1,m}}^{k=\overline{1,n}}$ which satisfy (9.1) and (9.2) for almost all λ. From these relations we conclude that

$$\psi f \overset{*}{\psi} = \frac{1}{2\pi} I_m \tag{9.3}$$

almost everywhere.

Let

$$\xi(t) = \int e^{i\lambda t} \Phi(d\lambda) \tag{9.4}$$

be the spectral representation of $\boldsymbol{\xi}$. By virtue of (9.3), the integral

$$\Lambda_j(\Delta) = \int_\Delta \psi_j(\lambda) \Phi(d\lambda) \tag{9.5}$$

exists for any bounded Borel set Δ, where the vector function ψ_j is the jth row of the matrix $\psi : \psi_j(\lambda) = \{\psi_{jk}(\lambda)\}^{k=\overline{1,n}}$. Now (9.5) defines random measures Λ_j, $j = \overline{1, m}$, which by the choice of ψ are mutually uncorrelated, i.e.,

$$\boldsymbol{E} \Lambda_j(\Delta) \overline{\Lambda_{j'}(\Delta')} = 0 \tag{9.6}$$

if $j \neq j'$, for any Borel sets Δ and Δ', and, moreover,

$$\boldsymbol{E} \,|\, \Lambda_j(d\lambda) \,|^2 = \frac{1}{2\pi} d\lambda \tag{9.7}$$

for all $j = \overline{1, m}$.

Let us discuss the discrete-parameter case. We consider the stationary process

$$\zeta(t) = \int_{-\pi}^{\pi} e^{i\lambda t} \Lambda(d\lambda), \qquad \Lambda = \{\Lambda_j\}_{j=\overline{1,m}}. \tag{9.8}$$

Properties (9.6) and (9.7) of the random measure $\Lambda = \{\Lambda_j\}_{j=\overline{1,m}}$ imply that the stationary process $\boldsymbol{\zeta} = \{\zeta_j(t)\}_{j=\overline{1,m}}$ is an uncorrelated process; i.e., its values are mutually uncorrelated:

$$\boldsymbol{E} \,|\, \zeta_j(t) \,|^2 = 1, \qquad j = \overline{1, m}, \qquad \boldsymbol{E} \zeta_i(t) \overline{\zeta_j(s)} = 0 \tag{9.9}$$

for $t \neq s$ and all $i, j = \overline{1, m}$ as well as for $i \neq j$ and all t, s. It follows from (9.1)-(9.3) that

$$(\varphi\psi - I_n) f (\overset{*}{\psi}\overset{*}{\varphi} - I_n) = 0 \tag{9.10}$$

for almost all λ, and, therefore, that

$$\xi(t) = \int_{-\pi}^{\pi} e^{i\lambda t}\Phi(d\lambda) = \int_{-\pi}^{\pi} e^{i\lambda t}\varphi(\lambda)\psi(\lambda)\Phi(d\lambda) = \int_{-\pi}^{\pi} e^{i\lambda t}\varphi(\lambda)\Lambda(d\lambda)\,. \tag{9.11}$$

Obviously, the elements $\varphi_{kj}(\lambda)$ of the matrix function φ are square integrable. Let

$$\varphi_{kj}(\lambda) = \sum_{-\infty}^{\infty} c_{kj}(s)e^{-i\lambda s}\,, \qquad k = \overline{1, n}\,, \qquad j = \overline{1, m}\,, \tag{9.12}$$

be their Fourier series expansions. From (9.11) and (9.12) we obtain a representation of ξ in the form of a moving average:

$$\xi(t) = \sum_{-\infty}^{\infty} c(t-s)\zeta(s)\,, \qquad c(t) = \{c_{kj}(t)\}_{k=\overline{1, n}}^{j=\overline{1, m}}\,. \tag{9.13}$$

A similar representation can also be obtained in the case of continuous time. Namely, let the random measures $\zeta_j(dt)$, $j = \overline{1, m}$, be the Fourier transforms of the random measures $\Lambda_j(d\lambda)$, defined by (9.5):

$$\zeta_j(\Delta) = \int_{-\infty}^{\infty} \frac{e^{i\lambda t_2} - e^{i\lambda t_1}}{i\lambda}\Lambda_j(d\lambda)\,, \qquad j = \overline{1, m}\,, \tag{9.14}$$

for any interval $\Delta = (t_1, t_2)$. Obviously, the measures $\zeta_j(dt)$ are mutually uncorrelated, and $\boldsymbol{E}\,|\,\zeta_j(dt)\,|^2 = dt$, $j = \overline{1, m}$.

Analogously to (9.11),

$$\xi(t) = \int_{-\infty}^{\infty} e^{i\lambda t}\varphi(\lambda)\Lambda(d\lambda)\,, \tag{9.15}$$

where the elements $\varphi_{kj}(\lambda)$ of the matrix φ are square integrable, and, consequently, can be represented in the form of Fourier integrals:

$$\varphi_{kj}(\lambda) = \int_{-\infty}^{\infty} e^{i\lambda t}c_{kj}(t)\,dt\,, \qquad k = \overline{1, n}\,, \qquad j = \overline{1, m}\,. \tag{9.16}$$

Applying formula (3.6) of this chapter to the right side of (9.15), we obtain a representation of ξ in the form of a "moving average":

$$\xi_k(t) = \sum_{j=1}^{m} \int_{-\infty}^{\infty} c_{kj}(t-s)\zeta_j(ds)\,, \qquad k = \overline{1, n}\,, \tag{9.17}$$

or, in matrix form,

$$\xi(t) = \int_{-\infty}^{\infty} c(t-s)\zeta(ds)\,, \qquad c(t) = \{c_{kj}(t)\}_{k=\overline{1, n}}^{j=\overline{1, m}}\,. \tag{9.18}$$

We have, in fact, proven the following theorem.

Theorem 9.1. *Every representation of the type* (9.1) *of the spectral density* $f(\lambda)$ *of a stationary process* ξ (*of rank* m) *gives rise to a represen-*

tation (9.13) *or* (9.18) *of* ξ *in the form of a moving average, and the values of the mutually uncorrelated measures* ζ_j, $j = \overline{1, m}$, *appearing in these representations belong to the space* H_ξ of values of ξ.

It is not hard to prove that the representations (9.13) or (9.18), having the properties mentioned in Theorem 9.1, are possible only for processes having constant rank m.

Indeed, let $\varphi = \{\varphi_{kj}\}_{k=\overline{1, n}}^{j=\overline{1, m}}$ and $\Lambda = \{\Lambda_j\}_{j=\overline{1, m}}$ be the Fourier transforms of $c = \{c_{kj}\}_{k=\overline{1, n}}^{j=\overline{1, m}}$ and $\zeta = \{\zeta_j\}_{j=\overline{1, m}}$. The closed linear manifold generated by the values of the uncorrelated measures ζ_j coincides with the space H_Λ of elements of the form $h = \int \psi(\lambda)\Lambda(d\lambda)$, $\int \| \psi(\lambda) \|^2 d\lambda < \infty$. Obviously, $H_\xi \subseteq H_\Lambda$. We have to prove that if $H_\xi = H_\Lambda$, then the stationary process ξ has rank m, i.e., its spectral density $f = (1/2\pi)\varphi \cdot \overset{*}{\varphi}$ has rank m almost everywhere. Let $H_\xi = H_\Lambda$ and assume that on some set of positive Lebesgue measure the rank of the matrix $f(\lambda)$ is less than m; then there exists a vector function $\psi(\lambda) = \{\psi_j(\lambda)\}^{j=\overline{1, m}}$ such that $\int \| \psi(\lambda) \|^2 d\lambda \neq 0$ and $\varphi\overset{*}{\psi} \equiv 0$. This would mean that the element $h = \int \psi(\lambda)\Lambda(d\lambda)$ is orthogonal to H_ξ, since

$$(\xi_k(t), h) = \int e^{i\lambda t} \sum_{j=1}^{m} \varphi_{kj}(\lambda)\overline{\psi_j(\lambda)}\, d\lambda = 0$$

for all k and t. Thus, for $H_\xi = H_\Lambda$ the stationary process ξ of the form (9.13) or (9.18) has constant rank m.

If we are already given a representation of the process ξ in the form of a moving average, then the uncorrelated measures ζ_j appearing in this representation can be determined from formulae (9.8) or (9.14). Starting with the given coefficients $c(t)$ of this representation (which have the property that

$$\sum_{-\infty}^{\infty} | c(t) |^2 < \infty \tag{9.19}$$

in the case of discrete time, and

$$\int_{-\infty}^{\infty} \| c(t) \|^2 dt < \infty \tag{9.20}$$

in the case of continuous time) and working back, we arrive at all the properties already deduced, and, in particular, to a decomposition of the type (9.1) for the spectral density $f(\lambda)$.

It should be noted that in the case where the spectral density f of the stationary process ξ is degenerate, the equation (9.2) does not uniquely determine the matrix ψ. In spite of this, the value $\Lambda_j(\Delta)$ in formula (9.5) is the same for any matrix ψ satisfying relation (9.2). This is explained by the fact that different solutions ψ and $\tilde{\psi}$ of (9.2) satisfy a relation similar to (7.22). The same is true concerning the values of the uncorrelated measures

$$\zeta(t) = \int_{-\pi}^{\pi} e^{i\lambda t}\varphi(\lambda)\Phi(d\lambda) \tag{9.21}$$

in the case of discrete time, and

$$\zeta(\Delta) = \int_{-\infty}^{\infty} \frac{e^{i\lambda t_2} - e^{i\lambda t_1}}{i\lambda}\varphi(\lambda)\Phi(d\lambda)\,, \qquad \Delta = (t_1, t_2) \tag{9.22}$$

in the case of continuous time.

10. Stationary processes with rational spectral densities

An important class of wide-sense stationary random processes consists of processes with spectral densities $f(\lambda) = \{f_{kl}(\lambda)\}_{k=\overline{1,n}}^{l=\overline{1,n}}$ whose components $f_{kl}(\lambda)$ are rational functions of $e^{-i\lambda}$ in the discrete-parameter case, and of λ in the continuous-parameter case.

Since every minor of such a spectral density is a rational function (of $e^{-i\lambda}$ or of λ), each minor is either identically equal to zero, or vanishes at only a finite number of points. Therefore, the rank of the matrix $f(\lambda)$ is the same at all points λ, with the possible exception of a finite number. From this we conclude (cf. Theorem 9.1) that a stationary process $\boldsymbol{\xi} = \{\xi_k(t)\}_{k=\overline{1,n}}$ with rational spectral density can be represented in the form of a moving average.

We shall show that the matrix function φ giving rise to this representation (φ satisfies relation (9.1)) can be chosen so that its components will be rational functions (of $e^{-i\lambda}$ or λ). This fact helps us in solving the important problem of the prediction of a stationary process.

Lemma 10.1. *Every nonnegative rational function $f(\lambda)$ of $e^{-i\lambda}$ can be represented in the form*

$$f(\lambda) = \frac{|P(e^{-i\lambda})|^2}{|Q(e^{-i\lambda})|^2}\,, \tag{10.1}$$

where the polynomials

$$P(z) = \sum_0^m p_k z^k\,, \qquad Q(z) = \sum_0^n q_k z^k$$

have no zeros in the (open) unit disc. If, moreover,

$$f(\lambda) = f(-\lambda)\,, \tag{10.2}$$

then the coefficients p_k, $k = \overline{0, m}$, and q_k, $k = \overline{0, n}$, can be chosen real.

Proof. Let us assume, for simplicity, that $f > 0$. Then

$$f(\lambda) = ce^{-i\nu\lambda}\frac{\prod_{k=1}^{m'}(e^{-i\lambda} - v_k)}{\prod_{k=1}^{n'}(e^{-i\lambda} - w_k)},$$

where the complex numbers v_k, w_k are different from 0 and 1, and the sets $\{v_k\}$, $\{w_k\}$ are disjoint. Inasmuch as $f(\lambda)$ is real,

$$f(\lambda) = \bar{c}e^{i\nu\lambda}\frac{\prod_{k=1}^{m'}(e^{i\lambda} - \bar{v}_k)}{\prod_{k=1}^{n'}(e^{i\lambda} - \bar{w}_k)} = c'e^{i\lambda(\nu+m'-n')}\frac{\prod_{k=1}^{m'}(\bar{v}_k^{-1} - e^{-i\lambda})}{\prod_{k=1}^{n'}(\bar{w}_k^{-1} - e^{-i\lambda})},$$

and, consequently, for any v_k and w_k one can find $v_{k'}$ and $w_{k'}$, respectively, such that $v_k = \overline{v_{k'}^{-1}}$ and $w_k = \overline{w_{k'}^{-1}}$.

Since $f(\lambda)$ coincides with the absolute values of all the above expressions written for it, and

$$|e^{-i\lambda} - \overline{z^{-1}}| = |z|^{-1}|\bar{z}e^{-i\lambda} - 1| = |z^{-1}||e^{-i\lambda} - z|,$$

it is easy to see that $f(\lambda)$ can be represented in the form (10.1).

If $f(\lambda)$ satisfies (10.2), then to every root v_k there corresponds a root $v_{k'} = \bar{v}_k$, and to every root w_k there corresponds a root $w_{k'} = \bar{w}_k$, so that the coefficients of the polynomials P and Q can be chosen real. ▮

In a similar way one has the following result.

Lemma 10.2. *Every nonnegative, rational function $f(\lambda)$ of λ can be represented in the form*

$$f(\lambda) = \frac{|P(\lambda)|^2}{|Q(\lambda)|^2}, \tag{10.3}$$

where the polynomials

$$P(z) = \sum_0^m p_k z^k, \qquad Q(z) = \sum_0^n q_k z^k$$

have no zeros in the lower (open) half-plane.

If $f(\lambda)$ is an even function, then

$$f(\lambda) = \frac{|P'(i\lambda)|^2}{|Q'(i\lambda)|^2}, \tag{10.4}$$

where the polynomials $P'(z)$ and $Q'(z)$, defined by $P'(iz) = P(z)$, $Q'(iz) = Q(z)$, have real coefficients.

Now let $f(\lambda) = \{f_{kl}(\lambda)\}_{k=\overline{1,n}}^{l=\overline{1,n}}$ be some positive definite matrix of rank m, with rational elements. Then there exists a principal minor $M(\lambda)$ of order m of $f(\lambda)$ which is not identically zero and, consequently, vanishes at only a finite number (at most) of points. For definiteness let $M(\lambda)$ be the minor of order m standing in the upper left corner of the matrix $f(\lambda)$. Let us denote by $M_j(\lambda)$ the principal minor of order j, standing in the upper left corner of $f(\lambda)$; by virtue of the positive definiteness of the matrix function $f(\lambda)$, $M_j(\lambda) > 0$ for $j = \overline{1, m}$ at those points λ where $M(\lambda) = M_m(\lambda) > 0$ (for $j > m$, obviously, $M_j(\lambda) \equiv 0$). In particular, $f_{11}(\lambda) = M_1(\lambda) > 0$ at those points.

Adding to the kth row of the matrix $f(\lambda)$ $(k = \overline{2, n})$ the first row, multiplied by $-f_{k1}/f_{11}$, and then adding to the lth column $(l = \overline{2, n})$ the first column, multiplied by $-f_{1l}/f_{11}$, we obtain the matrix

$$f^{(2)}(\lambda) = \begin{pmatrix} f_{11} & 0 \\ 0 & g^{(2)} \end{pmatrix},$$

where the elements of the matrix $g^{(2)} = \{g_{kl}^{(2)}\}_{k=\overline{2, n}}^{l=\overline{2, n}}$ have the form

$$g_{kl}^{(2)} = f_{kl} - \frac{f_{k1} f_{1l}}{f_{11}}.$$

The element $g_{22}^{(2)}(\lambda) = M_2(\lambda)/M_1(\lambda)$ is not identically zero, and one can apply to $g^{(2)}$ the same process as was just applied to the matrix $g^{(1)} = f$. Continuing this process, we arrive at the mth step at a diagonal matrix $f^{(m)}(\lambda)$ of the form

$$f^{(m)} = \{d_{kl}\}_{k=\overline{1, n}}^{l=\overline{1, n}}, \tag{10.5}$$

$$d_{11}(\lambda) = M_1(\lambda), \quad d_{kk}(\lambda) = M_k(\lambda)/M_{k-1}(\lambda) \quad \text{for} \quad k = \overline{2, m},$$
$$d_{kk}(\lambda) \equiv 0 \quad \text{for} \quad k = \overline{m+1, n}.$$

It is not hard to verify that the matrix $f(\lambda)$ can be represented in the form

$$f = g d g^*,$$

where $d = \{d_{ij}\}_{i=\overline{1, m}}^{j=\overline{1, m}}$ is the diagonal matrix whose elements are given by (10.5), and the components $g_{kj}(\lambda)$ of the matrix $g = \{g_{kj}\}_{k=\overline{1, n}}^{j=\overline{1, m}}$,

$$\begin{aligned} g_{kj}(\lambda) &= 0 \quad \text{for} \quad j > k, \\ g_{kj}(\lambda) &= \frac{g_{kj}^{(j)}}{d_{jj}}, \qquad j < k \\ g_{jj}(\lambda) &\equiv 1, \end{aligned} \tag{10.6}$$

can be obtained by means of the following recursion relations:

$$\begin{aligned} g_{kl}^{(1)} &= f_{kl}, \\ g_{kl}^{(i)} &= g_{kl}^{(i-1)} - \frac{g_{k, i-1}^{(i-1)} - g_{i-1, l}^{(i-1)}}{g_{i-1, i-1}^{(i-1)}}. \end{aligned} \tag{10.7}$$

We note that all the elements of the matrices $g = g(\lambda)$ and $d = d(\lambda)$ are rational functions.

Let

$$g_{kj}(\lambda) = \frac{P_{kj}(z)}{Q_{kj}(z)}, \tag{10.8}$$

where $z = e^{-i\lambda}$ in the case of discrete time and $z = \lambda$ in the case of continuous time. Let $\alpha_p^{(j)}$, $p = 1, 2, \ldots$, be the zeros of the set of polynomials Q_{kj}, $k = \overline{1, m}$, lying in the unit disc (the lower half-plane), taken as many times as their maximum multiplicity. We set

$$c_j(z) = \prod_p (z - \alpha_p^{(j)}) ,$$
$$D_j(z) = \frac{d_{jj}(\lambda)}{| c_j(z) |^2} . \tag{10.9}$$

The nonnegative functions $D_j(z)$, being rational with respect to z, can be represented, according to formula (10.2) ((10.4)), in the form

$$D_j(z) = \left| \frac{P_j(z)}{Q_j(z)} \right|^2 , \tag{10.10}$$

where the polynomials P_j and Q_j do not have zeros in the unit disc (the lower half-plane). We set

$$\Gamma_{kj}(z) = \sqrt{2\pi}\, g_{kj}(\lambda) c_j(z) \frac{P_j(z)}{Q_j(z)} , \qquad k = \overline{1, n} , \quad j = \overline{1, m} , \tag{10.11}$$

where $z = e^{-i\lambda}$ in the case of discrete time, and $z = \lambda$ in the case of continuous time. The functions $\Gamma_{kj}(z)$ are rational with respect to z and analytic in the unit disc (the lower half-plane). It is not hard to verify that

$$f(\lambda) = \frac{1}{2\pi} \Gamma(z) \overset{*}{\Gamma}(z) , \qquad \Gamma(z) = \{\Gamma_{kj}(z)\}_{k=\overline{1, n}}^{j=\overline{1, m}} . \tag{10.12}$$

Furthermore whereas in the one-dimensional case the function $\Gamma(z) = P(z)/Q(z)$ in the appropriate representation of the spectral density is not only analytic, but in addition has no zeros in the relevant domain, in the multi-dimensional case the matrix function $\Gamma(z) = \{\Gamma_{kj}(z)\}_{k=\overline{1, n}}^{j=\overline{1, m}}$, which is rational in z, can be so chosen that its rank, for all z in the appropriate domain (the unit disc or the lower half-plane), is equal to m. Indeed, if the matrix $\Gamma(z)$, obtained above with elements of the form (10.11), does not have this property, then, starting from $\Gamma(z)$, it is easy to arrive at an analytic matrix function which has rank m everywhere in the appropriate domain. In fact, the minors of order m of the matrix $\Gamma(z)$ with elements of the form (10.11), being rational functions of $e^{-i\lambda}$ or of λ, are either identically zero or have only a finite number of zeros. If (starting with the discrete-parameter case) the rank of $\Gamma(z)$ at some point $z = \alpha$ in the unit disc is less than m, then all of its minors of order m vanish at this point. We choose some m rows of $\Gamma(z)$ having the property that all the remaining rows are linear combinations of them, both at $z = \alpha$ and in some neighborhood of $z = \alpha$.

Obviously, $\Gamma(\alpha)$ can be represented as $\Gamma(\alpha) = \mu \cdot \hat{\Gamma}(\alpha)$, where $\hat{\Gamma}(z)$ is the square matrix consisting of the m rows chosen, and $\mu = \{\mu_{kj}\}_{k=\overline{1,n}}^{j=\overline{1,m}}$ is the matrix of the coefficients used in expressing the rows of $\Gamma(\alpha)$ as linear combinations of the m rows chosen. The square matrix $\hat{\Gamma}(\alpha)$ can, in turn, be represented as $\hat{\Gamma}(\alpha) = UDV$, where

$$D = \begin{pmatrix} \lambda_1 & & & & & & 0 \\ & \cdot & & & & & \\ & & \cdot & & & & \\ & & & \lambda_p & & & \\ & & & & 0 & & \\ & & & & & \cdot & \\ 0 & & & & & & 0 \end{pmatrix},$$

V is the unitary matrix which reduces the product $\hat{\Gamma}(\alpha)\hat{\Gamma}(\alpha)^*$ to diagonal form, and $U = V_1 V$, where V_1 is the unitary matrix appearing in the polar decomposition of $\hat{\Gamma}(\alpha)$ ($\hat{\Gamma}(\alpha) = V_1 H$, $H = \sqrt{\hat{\Gamma}(\alpha)\hat{\Gamma}(\alpha)^*}$; see, e.g., Gantmakher[*] or Riesz-Nagy[*]). If we now multiply the matrix function $\hat{\Gamma}(z)$, which is degenerate at the point $z = \alpha$ (its rank at this point is $p < m$) by the matrix function $B(z)$ of the form

$$B(z) = V^{-1}\begin{pmatrix} I_p & 0 \\ 0 & b(z)I_{m-p} \end{pmatrix}, \quad \text{where} \quad b(z) = \begin{cases} \dfrac{1-\bar{\alpha}z}{z-\alpha}\dfrac{\alpha}{|\alpha|}, & \alpha \neq 0, \\ \dfrac{1}{z}, & \alpha = 0, \end{cases}$$

which is a unitary matrix almost everywhere on the boundary of the unit disc, we obtain an analytic matrix function $\hat{\Gamma}(z)B(z)$ which is "less" degenerate in the neighborhood of $z = \alpha$ and has elements which are rational in z. The matrix function $\Gamma(z)B(z)$ will have similar properties, and, moreover, will satisfy, as does $\Gamma(z)$ itself, the boundary condition (10.12). This method, applied successively to all the zeros of the initial matrix $\Gamma(z)$, leads us to an analytic matrix function with rational elements and rank m. The same is true in the case of matrix functions in the lower half-plane; here, for example, it is sufficient to use a fractional linear transformation of the unit disc into the lower half-plane.

We have thus established the following result.

Theorem 10.1. *A positive definite matrix function* $f = \{f_{kl}(\lambda)\}_{k=\overline{1,n}}^{l=\overline{1,n}}$ *of rank m, with elements which are rational functions of* $e^{-i\lambda}$ *(of* λ*), can be represented in the form*

$$f(\lambda) = \frac{1}{2\pi}\Gamma(e^{-i\lambda})\overset{*}{\Gamma}(e^{-i\lambda}), \tag{10.13}$$

[or

$$f(\lambda) = \frac{1}{2\pi}\Gamma(\lambda)\overset{*}{\Gamma}(\lambda)] , \tag{10.14}$$

where the elements of the matrix function $\Gamma(z)$ are rational in z, and $\Gamma(z)$ is analytic in the unit disc (the lower half-plane) and has rank m for all z in this domain.

Let us consider a stationary process $\boldsymbol{\xi} = \{\xi_k(t)\}_{k=\overline{1,n}}$ having a rational spectral density $f(\lambda) = \{f_{kl}(\lambda)\}_{k=\overline{1,n}}^{l=\overline{1,n}}$ of rank m.

Let us start with the discrete-parameter case. We represent the matrix $f(\lambda)$ in the form (10.12). By virtue of the analyticity of the matrix Γ, its Fourier coefficients $c(t) = \{c_{kj}(t)\}_{k=\overline{1,n}}^{j=\overline{1,m}}$,

$$c(t) = \frac{1}{2\pi}\int_{-\pi}^{\pi} e^{i\lambda t}\Gamma(e^{-i\lambda})\,d\lambda ,$$

vanish for negative t, and thus

$$\Gamma(e^{-i\lambda}) = \sum_0^\infty c(t)e^{-i\lambda t} . \tag{10.15}$$

If $\boldsymbol{\zeta} = \{\zeta_j(t)\}_{j=\overline{1,m}}$ is the uncorrelated process corresponding, by Theorem 9.1, to the matrix $\varphi(\lambda) = \Gamma(e^{-i\lambda})$, then

$$\xi(t) = \sum_{-\infty}^{t} c(t-s)\zeta(s) . \tag{10.16}$$

We have obtained a representation of $\boldsymbol{\xi}$ as a moving average.

Let $\boldsymbol{\xi}$ be a one-dimensional process with spectral density $f(\lambda)$:

$$f(\lambda) = \frac{1}{2\pi}|\,\Gamma(e^{-i\lambda})\,|^2 , \qquad \Gamma(z) = \frac{\sum_0^m p_k z^k}{\sum_0^n q_k z^k} . \tag{10.17}$$

In this case, if Φ is the spectral measure of $\boldsymbol{\xi}$,

$$\begin{aligned}\sum_{k=0}^{n} q_k\xi(t-k) &= \int_{-\pi}^{\pi} e^{i\lambda t}\left[\sum_{k=1}^{n} q_k e^{-i\lambda k}\right]\Phi(d\lambda)\\ &= \int_{-\pi}^{\pi} e^{i\lambda t}\left[\sum_{k=0}^{m} p_k e^{-i\lambda k}\right]\frac{\Phi(d\lambda)}{\Gamma(e^{-i\lambda})} = \sum_{k=0}^{m} p_k\zeta(t-k) ,\end{aligned} \tag{10.18}$$

where $\boldsymbol{\zeta} = \{\zeta(t)\}$ is the sequence of uncorrelated random variables

$$\zeta(t) = \int_{-\pi}^{\pi} e^{i\lambda t}\frac{\Phi(d\lambda)}{\Gamma(e^{-i\lambda})} \tag{10.19}$$

appearing in the moving average representation (10.16) of $\boldsymbol{\xi}$.

Analogously, a continuous-parameter stationary process $\boldsymbol{\xi} = \{\xi_k(t)\}_{k=\overline{1,n}}$ with rational spectral density $f(\lambda) = \{f_{kl}(\lambda)\}_{k=\overline{1,n}}^{l=\overline{1,n}}$ of rank m can be represented in the form

$$\xi(t) = \int_{\infty}^{t} c(t-s)\zeta(ds) , \tag{10.20}$$

where $\boldsymbol{\zeta} = \{\zeta_j\}_{j=\overline{1,m}}$ is the uncorrelated measure corresponding to the matrix $\varphi(\lambda) = \Gamma(\lambda)$ in (10.13) (cf. formula (9.22)), and the matrix $c(t) = \{c_{kj}(t)\}_{k=\overline{1,n}}^{j=\overline{1,m}}$,

$$c(t) = \frac{1}{2\pi}\int_{-\infty}^{\infty} e^{i\lambda t}\Gamma(\lambda)\,d\lambda , \tag{10.21}$$

vanishes for negative t.

Suppose that $\boldsymbol{\xi} = \{\xi(t)\}$ is a one-dimensional stationary process with spectral density $f(\lambda) = (1/2\pi) \mid \Gamma(\lambda) \mid^2$, where

$$\Gamma(\lambda) = \frac{P'(i\lambda)}{Q'(i\lambda)} . \tag{10.22}$$

Let $a(t)$ be any infinitely differentiable function which vanishes outside some finite interval (i.e., a so-called "finite" function), and let

$$\tilde{a}(\lambda) = \int_{-\infty}^{\infty} e^{-i\lambda t}a(t)\,dt \tag{10.23}$$

be its Fourier transform. The function $\tilde{a}(\lambda)$ tends to zero, at infinity, faster than any power of λ, and therefore

$$\int_{-\infty}^{\infty} \mid \tilde{a}(\lambda) \mid^2 f(\lambda)\,d\lambda < \infty .$$

Let

$$\xi(t) = \int_{-\infty}^{\infty} e^{i\lambda t}\Phi(d\lambda) \tag{10.24}$$

be the spectral representation of $\boldsymbol{\xi}$, and consider the stationary process $\boldsymbol{\eta}$,

$$\eta(t) = \int_{-\infty}^{\infty} e^{i\lambda t}\tilde{a}(\lambda)\Phi(d\lambda) = \int_{-\infty}^{\infty} a(t-s)\xi(s)\,ds .$$

Since

$$\int_{-\infty}^{\infty} \lambda^{2k} \mid \tilde{a}(\lambda) \mid^2 f(\lambda)\,d\lambda < \infty$$

for any k, the process $\boldsymbol{\eta}$ is infinitely differentiable in mean square. We have

$$\begin{aligned} Q'\left(\frac{d}{dt}\right)\eta(t) &= \int_{-\infty}^{\infty} e^{i\lambda t}Q'(i\lambda)\tilde{a}(\lambda)\Phi(d\lambda) \\ &= \int_{-\infty}^{\infty} e^{i\lambda t}Q'(i\lambda)\tilde{a}(\lambda)\Gamma(\lambda)\Lambda(d\lambda) \\ &= \int_{-\infty}^{\infty} e^{i\lambda t}P'(i\lambda)\tilde{a}(\lambda)\Lambda(d\lambda) , \end{aligned}$$

where the random measure $\Lambda(d\lambda)$ is such that

$$\Lambda(d\lambda) = \frac{\Phi(d\lambda)}{\Gamma(\lambda)}; \qquad \boldsymbol{E}\,|\,\Lambda(d\lambda)\,|^2 = \frac{d\lambda}{2\pi}.$$

Let $\zeta(dt)$ be the Fourier transform of $\Lambda(d\lambda)$. Then, using relation (3.6), we have

$$Q'\Big(\frac{d}{dt}\Big)\eta(t) = \int_{-\infty}^{\infty} e^{i\lambda t} P'(i\lambda)\tilde{a}(\lambda)\Lambda(d\lambda) = \int_{-\infty}^{\infty}\Big[P'\Big(\frac{d}{dt}\Big)a(t-s)\Big]\zeta(ds)\,.$$

Obviously,

$$Q'\Big(\frac{d}{dt}\Big)\eta(t) = Q'\Big(\frac{d}{dt}\Big)\Big[\int_{-\infty}^{\infty} a(t-s)\xi(s)\,ds\Big] = \int_{-\infty}^{\infty}\Big[Q'\Big(\frac{d}{dt}\Big)a(t-s)\Big]\xi(s)\,ds\,,$$

and, therefore,

$$\int_{-\infty}^{\infty}\Big[Q'\Big(\frac{d}{dt}\Big)a(t-s)\Big]\xi(s)\,ds = \int_{-\infty}^{\infty}\Big[P'\Big(\frac{d}{dt}\Big)a(t-s)\Big]\zeta(ds) \qquad (10.25)$$

for any "finite" (i.e., infinitely differentiable with compact support) function $a(t)$.

II

LINEAR FORECASTING OF STATIONARY DISCRETE PARAMETER PROCESSES

1. Linear prediction. Statement of the problem

Suppose that we have a multi-dimensional stationary process $\boldsymbol{\xi} = \{\xi_k(t)\}_{k=\overline{1,n}}$. We assume that this process has been observed up to time t, i.e., its values $\xi_k(s)$, $k=\overline{1,n}$, $s \leq t$ are known, and that from a knowledge of these values it is required to predict its values at some other moment of time $t+\tau$, $\tau > 0$, where the method of prediction is to be linear. The last statement means the following: the random variables $\hat{\xi}_k(t,\tau)$, which are the forecasts of the unknown values $\xi_k(t+\tau)$, $k=\overline{1,n}$, must belong to the subspace $H_\xi^-(t)$—the linear manifold, closed in the sense of mean square convergence, generated by the $\xi_k(s)$, $k=\overline{1,n}$, $s \leq t$, whose values are known. A linear forecast is considered best possible, if its errors $\sigma_k(\tau)$, $k=\overline{1,n}$,

$$\sigma_k^2(\tau) = \boldsymbol{E}|\xi_k(t+\tau) - \hat{\xi}_k(t,\tau)|^2 , \tag{1.1}$$

are the smallest possible, i.e.,

$$\rho_k^2(\tau) = \min_{h \in \boldsymbol{H}_\xi^-(t)} \boldsymbol{E}|\xi_k(t+\tau) - h|^2 . \tag{1.2}$$

The *problem of linear extrapolation* consists in finding the random variables $\hat{\xi}_k(t,\tau)$ which yield the best linear forecast.

This problem has a simple geometric meaning. Namely, it is required to construct the perpendicular from the point $\xi_k(t+\tau)$ in H_ξ onto the subspace $H_\xi^-(t)$. The projections $\hat{\xi}_k(t,\tau)$ of the elements $\xi_k(t+\tau)$

onto $H_\xi^-(t)$ furnish the best linear approximations to them, and the lengths of the corresponding perpendiculars are the errors $\sigma_k(\tau)$ of these approximations.

Let $\{U_t\}$ be the unitary family of the process $\xi = \{\xi_k(t)\}_{k=\overline{1,n}}$:

$$U_t \xi_k(s) = \xi_k(t+s) \tag{1.3}$$

for any s, t and $k = \overline{1, n}$. Obviously,

$$U_t H_\xi^-(s) = H_\xi^-(t+s) , \tag{1.4}$$

and, by virtue of the unitarity of U_t,

$$U_t \hat{\xi}_k(s, \tau) = \hat{\xi}_k(t+s, \tau) , \qquad k = \overline{1, n} . \tag{1.5}$$

Thus, the random process $\hat{\boldsymbol{\xi}}(\cdot, \tau) = \{\hat{\xi}_k(t, \tau)\}_{k=\overline{1,n}}$ (here, τ is fixed) is stationary, and can be obtained from $\boldsymbol{\xi}$ by a linear transformation:

$$\hat{\xi}(t, \tau) = \int e^{i\lambda t} \hat{\varphi}(\lambda, \tau) \Phi(d\lambda) , \tag{1.6}$$

where $\Phi = \{\Phi_k\}_{k=\overline{1,n}}$ is the random spectral measure of the stationary process $\boldsymbol{\xi}$. We will consider the quantities $\hat{\xi}_k(t, \tau)$ as found if we have found the spectral characteristic $\hat{\varphi}(\lambda, \tau) = \{\hat{\varphi}_{kl}(\lambda)\}_{k=\overline{1,n}}^{l=\overline{1,n}}$ in the representation (1.6).

The solution of the problem of linear extrapolation will be given first for the discrete-parameter case.

2. Regularity and singularity of stationary processes

From the point of view of linear extrapolation, it is natural to distinguish the class of stationary processes $\boldsymbol{\xi} = \{\xi_k(t)\}_{k=\overline{1,n}}$ for which linear forecasting enables one to define the unknown quantities without error; i.e.,

$$\hat{\xi}_k(t, \tau) = \xi_k(t+\tau) , \qquad k = \overline{1, n} , \tag{2.1}$$

for all t and τ. (It is easily seen that if (2.1) holds for some $t = t_0$ and $\tau = \tau_0$, then it automatically holds for all t and τ.) We say that such a process $\boldsymbol{\xi}$ is *linearly singular*. From the physical point of view, such singular processes are exceptional.

We will be interested principally in processes for which the best linear forecast of the infinitely removed future consists only of a knowledge of its mean:

$$\lim_{\tau \to \infty} \hat{\xi}_k(t, \tau) = \boldsymbol{E}\xi_k , \qquad k = \overline{1, n} \tag{2.2}$$

where the limit is in mean square (recall that the expectation of an ergodic process can always be defined from a one-sided infinite sequence of the values $\xi(s)$, $s \le t$). Such a process is said to be *linearly regular*.[†]

One can assume, without loss of generality, that $\boldsymbol{E}\xi_k = 0$, as will henceforth be done throughout this chapter.

Singularity and regularity have simple geometric meanings. Let us define S_ξ as the intersection of the subspaces $H_\xi^-(t)$:

$$S_\xi = \bigcap_t H_\xi^-(t) . \tag{2.3}$$

Theorem 2.1. *A stationary process*

$$\boldsymbol{\xi} = \{\xi_k(t)\}_{k=\overline{1, n}}$$

is linearly regular if and only if

$$S_\xi = 0 , \tag{2.4}$$

and is linearly singular if and only if

$$S_\xi = H_\xi . \tag{2.5}$$

Proof. The equivalence of (2.1) and (2.5) is obvious, since in the case of a singular process $\boldsymbol{\xi}$,

$$H_\xi^-(t) = H_\xi = S_\xi$$

for all t.

Further, the regularity of $\boldsymbol{\xi}$ shows (using (1.5)) that for any t the projection $\hat{\xi}_k(s, t-s)$ of the variable $\xi_k(t)$ onto the subspace $H_\xi^-(s)$ tends to zero as $s \to -\infty$, and, therefore, the projection of $\xi_k(t)$ onto the subspace S_ξ is the zero element, since S_ξ is contained in $H_\xi^-(s)$ for all s. Since H_ξ is, by definition, the closed linear manifold generated by the $\xi_k(t)$, the projection of any element of H_ξ onto S_ξ vanishes, which is equivalent to $S_\xi = 0$. The reader can easily complete the proof by using the following simple lemma.

Lemma 2.1. *If a family of subspaces $H(t)$ of a Hilbert space H has the property that $H(s) \subseteq H(t)$ for $s < t$ and $\bigcap_t H(t) = 0$, then for any element $h \in H$ its projection $h(t)$ onto $H(t)$ tends to zero as $t \to -\infty$.*

Proof. Using the elementary properties of projection operators, it is easily seen that for any sequence $t_1 > t_2 > \cdots$ of real numbers tending to $-\infty$, the elements $h(t_1) - h(t_2)$, $h(t_2) - h(t_3)$, $\cdots$ are mutually orthogonal, and

$$\left\| \sum_{i=1}^{n} [h(t_i) - h(t_{i+1})] \right\| \le \| h(t_1) \| .$$

† For brevity we shall at times omit the word "linearly" in the terms "linearly regular" and "linearly singular."

It follows that the series $\sum_{i=1}^{\infty} [h(t_i) - h(t_{i+1})]$ converges, and its sum is $h(t_1) - \lim_{i\to\infty} h(t_i)$. Thus $\lim_{i\to\infty} h(t_i)$ exists, and since it is evidently contained in each subspace $H(t_i)$, hence in $\bigcap_t H(t)$, it equals 0.

We will say that a stationary process $\boldsymbol{\eta} = \{\eta_j(t)\}_{j=\overline{1,m}}$ is *subordinate* to the stationary process $\boldsymbol{\xi} = \{\xi_k(t)_{k=\overline{1,n}}$, if $\boldsymbol{\eta}$ is obtained from $\boldsymbol{\xi}$ by means of a linear transformation and, moreover,

$$H_\eta^-(t) \subseteq H_\xi^-(t) \tag{2.6}$$

for all t. Relation (2.6) is fulfilled for all t, if it is fulfilled for some one $t = t_0$, as $\eta_j(t) = U_t\eta_j(0)$, $j = \overline{1, m}$, where U_t is the unitary family of the stationary process $\boldsymbol{\xi}$, from which it follows that

$$H_\eta^-(t) = U_{t-t_0}H_\eta^-(t_0) \subseteq U_{t-t_0}H_\xi^-(t_0) = H_\xi^-(t) .$$

Theorem 2.2. *Every stationary process*

$$\boldsymbol{\xi} = \{\xi_k(t)\}_{k=\overline{1,n}}$$

can be represented in a unique way in the form

$$\xi(t) = \eta(t) + \zeta(t), \tag{2.7}$$

where the stationary processes $\boldsymbol{\eta} = \{\eta_k(t)\}_{k=\overline{1,n}}$ *and* $\boldsymbol{\xi} = \{\eta_k(t)\}_{k=\overline{1,n}}$ *are subordinate to* $\boldsymbol{\xi}$, *mutually uncorrelated,* i.e.,

$$\boldsymbol{E}\eta_k(t)\overline{\zeta_1(s)} = 0 , \qquad k = \overline{1, n} , \tag{2.8}$$

for any s and t, and $\boldsymbol{\eta}$ is linearly regular, while $\boldsymbol{\zeta}$ is linearly singular.

Proof. If $\boldsymbol{\eta}$ and $\boldsymbol{\zeta}$ satisfy all the conditions of the theorem, then it is easily seen that the subspaces $H_\eta^-(t)$ and $H_\zeta^-(t)$ are mutually orthogonal, and their direct sum is just $H_\xi^-(t)$. Moreover, the subspace S_ξ is the direct sum of the orthogonal subspaces S_η and S_ζ.

Since $\boldsymbol{\eta}$ is assumed regular, then $S_\eta = 0$, and, therefore,

$$S_\xi = S_\zeta = H_\zeta .$$

Condition (2.8) now implies that the $\eta_k(t)$, $k = \overline{1, n}$, are the perpendiculars from the $\xi_k(t)$ onto the subspace S_ξ, and the $\zeta_k(t)$ are the corresponding projections. Thus, if $\boldsymbol{\eta}$ and $\boldsymbol{\zeta}$ exist, they have the forms just described; i.e., they are unique.

Now let $\boldsymbol{\xi}$ be an arbitrary stationary process. We denote by $\eta_k(t)$ the perpendicular from $\xi_k(t)$ onto S_ξ, and by $\zeta_k(t)$ the corresponding projection. Let U_t be the unitary family of $\boldsymbol{\xi}$. Since $U_tH_\xi^-(s) = H_\xi^-(t + s)$, the subspace S_ξ is invariant under U_t:

$$U_tS_\xi = S_\xi . \tag{2.9}$$

Since U_t is a unitary operator in H_ξ, the orthogonal complement of S_ξ in H_ξ will be invariant under U_t. But it is clear that this orthogonal complement is just H_η, and so

$$U_t H_\eta = H_\eta . \tag{2.10}$$

Consequently,

$$\xi_k(t+s) = \eta_k(t+s) + \zeta_k(t+s) = U_s\eta_k(t) + U_s\zeta_k(t), \qquad k = \overline{1, n},$$

from which, taking (2.9) and (2.10) into consideration, we conclude that

$$\eta_k(t+s) = U_s\eta_k(t),$$
$$\zeta_k(t+s) = U_s\zeta_k(t), \qquad k = \overline{1, n},$$

i.e,, the random processes $\boldsymbol{\eta} = \{\eta_k(t)\}_{k=\overline{1,n}}$ and $\boldsymbol{\zeta} = \{\zeta_k(t)\}_{k=\overline{1,n}}$ are stationary and subordinate to $\boldsymbol{\xi}$. Further, as is easily seen, $H_\xi^-(t)$ is the orthogonal direct sum of $H_\eta^-(t)$ and $H_\zeta^-(t)$:

$$H_\xi^-(t) = H_\eta^-(t) \oplus H_\zeta^-(t),$$

and, on the other hand,

$$H_\xi^-(t) = H_\eta^- \oplus S_\xi .$$

Therefore,

$$H_\zeta^-(t) = S_\xi = S_\zeta ,$$

and, consequently, the process $\boldsymbol{\zeta}$ is singular. The regularity of $\boldsymbol{\eta}$ results from the fact that the subspaces $H_\eta^-(t)$ are orthogonal to S_ξ, and, therefore, the subspace S_η, belonging to all $H_\eta^-(t)$ and, a fortiori, to all $H_\xi^-(t)$, is simultaneously in S_ξ and orthogonal to S_ξ; i.e., $S_\eta = 0$. ▮

We remark that if the stationary process $\boldsymbol{\xi}$ is represented as a sum (2.7) of mutually uncorrelated processes $\boldsymbol{\eta}$ and $\boldsymbol{\zeta}$ which are subordinate to it, then linear extrapolation on $\boldsymbol{\xi}$ can be carried out by first extrapolating on $\boldsymbol{\eta}$ and $\boldsymbol{\zeta}$ separately, and then adding the quantities $\hat{\eta}(t, \tau)$ and $\hat{\zeta}(t, \tau)$ thus obtained:

$$\hat{\xi}(t, \tau) = \hat{\eta}(t, \tau) + \hat{\zeta}(t, \tau) . \tag{2.11}$$

This follows at once from the fact that

$$H_\xi^-(t) = H_\eta^-(t) \oplus H_\zeta^-(t) \tag{2.12}$$

for any t.

Relation (2.11) makes it evident that the problem of the linear extrapolation of any stationary process $\boldsymbol{\xi}$ reduces to that of the extrapolation of a regular process, since any process $\boldsymbol{\xi}$ can be represented in the form (2.7); since the singular process $\boldsymbol{\zeta}$ can always be extrapolated without error, to find the $\hat{\xi}(t, \tau)$ it is sufficient to find the quantities $\hat{\eta}(t, \tau)$ which give the best linear extrapolation of the regular stationary process $\boldsymbol{\eta}$.

3. Wold's decomposition

Let $\boldsymbol{\xi} = \{\xi_k(t)\}_{k=\overline{1,n}}$ be a linearly regular stationary process, and $\{U_t\}$ its unitary family.

We denote by $D_\xi(t)$ the orthogonal complement of $H_\xi^-(t-1)$ in the subspace $H_\xi^-(t)$:

$$D_\xi(t) = H_\xi^-(t) \ominus H_\xi^-(t-1) . \tag{3.1}$$

Since $U_s H_\xi^-(t) = H_\xi^-(t+s)$ for any t and s, then

$$U_s D_\xi(t) = D_\xi(t+S) .$$

From its definition, one sees that the subspace $D_\xi(t)$ is generated by the perpendiculars from the $\xi_k(t)$, $k = \overline{1, n}$, onto the subspace $H_\xi^-(t-1)$, and hence that its dimension m does not exceed the dimension n of the process $\boldsymbol{\xi}$.

By virtue of the regularity of $\boldsymbol{\xi}$,

$$S_\xi = \bigcap_t H_\xi^-(t) = 0 ,$$

and consequently (see the proof of Lemma 2.1) each of the $H_\xi^-(t)$ can be represented as the orthogonal direct sum of the subspaces $D_\xi(s)$, $s \leq t$:

$$H_\xi^-(t) = \sum_{-\infty}^{t} \oplus D_\xi(s) . \tag{3.3}$$

In particular, for the entire space H_ξ we obtain

$$H_\xi = \sum_{-\infty}^{\infty} \oplus D_\xi(s) . \tag{3.4}$$

If we choose an orthonormal basis ζ_j, $j = \overline{1, m}$, in one of the $D_\xi(s)$, say in $D_\xi(0)$, and set

$$\zeta_j(t) = U_t \zeta_j , \qquad j = \overline{1, m} , \tag{3.5}$$

then the family $\boldsymbol{\zeta} = \{\zeta_j(t)\}_{j=\overline{1,m}}$ will be an uncorrelated process, subordinate to $\boldsymbol{\xi}$. From (3.4) and (3.5) it follows that the $\zeta_j(t)$, $j = \overline{1, m}$, $-\infty < t < \infty$, form a basis in H_ξ, and, therefore,

$$\xi_k(t) = \sum_{-\infty}^{t} \sum_{j=1}^{m} c_{kj}(t-s)\zeta_j(s) , \qquad c_{kj}(t) = \boldsymbol{E}\xi(t)\overline{\zeta_j(0)} , \qquad k = \overline{1, n} ; \tag{3.6}$$

i.e., $\boldsymbol{\xi}$ is obtained as a moving average of the uncorrelated process $\boldsymbol{\zeta}$:

$$\xi(t) = \sum_{-\infty}^{t} c(t-s)\zeta(s) , \qquad c(t) = \{c_{kj}(t)\}_{k=\overline{1,n}}^{j=\overline{1,m}} . \tag{3.7}$$

We will call (3.7) *Wold's decomposition*, and $\boldsymbol{\zeta} = \{\zeta_j(t)\}_{j=\overline{1,m}}$, a *fundamental process*.

An uncorrelated process $\boldsymbol{\zeta} = \{\zeta_j(t)\}_{j=\overline{1,m}}$, stationarily correlated with $\boldsymbol{\xi}$, is by definition fundamental if its values $\zeta_j(t)$, $j = \overline{1, m}$, at a given

t form an orthonormal basis in the subspace $D_\xi(t)$. Obviously, this requirement is equivalent to the following:

$$H_\zeta^-(t) = H_\xi^-(t) \tag{3.8}$$

(for at least one t, and hence for all t).

It is easy to see that a fundamental process is defined up to multiplication by an arbitrary unitary matrix $C = \{c_{ij}\}_{i=\overline{1,m}}^{j=\overline{1,m}}$. Namely, if $\tilde{\zeta} = \{\tilde{\zeta}_j(t)\}_{j=\overline{1,m}}$, as well as ζ, is a fundamental process (for ξ), then there exists some unitary matrix C such that

$$\tilde{\zeta}(t) = C\zeta(t) , \tag{3.9}$$

and, conversely, for any unitary matrix C and any fundamental process ζ, (3.9) defines a fundamental process $\tilde{\zeta}$.

It is evident from Wold's decomposition (3.7), and (3.8), that the projection $\hat{\xi}_k(t, \tau)$ of $\xi_k(t + \tau)$ onto the subspace $H_\xi^-(t)$ can be represented in the form

$$\hat{\xi}_k(t, \tau) = \sum_{-\infty}^{t} \sum_{j=1}^{m} c_{kj}(t + \tau - s)\zeta_j(s) , \qquad k = \overline{1, n} , \tag{3.10}$$

and thus the problem of extrapolating the stationary process ξ reduces to finding a fundamental process ξ and the corresponding coefficients in Wold's decomposition; i.e., the matrices $c(t) = \{c_{kj}(t)\}_{k=\overline{1,m}}^{j=\overline{1,m}}$.

4. The general formula of linear extrapolation

Let $\xi = \{\xi_k(t)\}_{k=\overline{1,n}}$ be a linearly regular stationary process, and $c(t) = \{c_{kj}(t)\}_{k=\overline{1,m}}^{j=\overline{1,m}}$ the coefficients of some version of Wold's decomposition of ξ.

From the results of Section 9 of Chapter I it follows that ξ has a spectral density $f(\lambda) = \{f_{kl}(\lambda)\}_{k=\overline{1,n}}^{l=\overline{1,n}}$ which has rank m for almost all λ, and is representable in the form

$$f(\lambda) = \frac{1}{2\pi}\varphi(\lambda)\overset{*}{\varphi}(\lambda) , \tag{4.1}$$

where

$$\varphi(\lambda) = \{\varphi_{kj}(\lambda)\}_{k=\overline{1,n}}^{j=\overline{1,m}} = \sum_{0}^{\infty} c(t)\, e^{-i\lambda t} . \tag{4.2}$$

Let us consider the separate components $\varphi_{kj}(\lambda)$ of the matrix function $\varphi(\lambda)$,

$$\varphi_{kj}(\lambda) = \sum_{0}^{\infty} c_{kj}(t)\, e^{-i\lambda t} , \qquad k = \overline{1, n} ; \quad j = \overline{1, m} . \tag{4.3}$$

Since

$$\sum_{0}^{\infty} \sum_{k=1}^{n} \sum_{j=1}^{m} |c_{kj}(t)|^2 = \sum_{k=1}^{n} \boldsymbol{E}|\xi_k(0)|^2 < \infty , \tag{4.4}$$

the functions $\Gamma_{kj}(z)$ of the complex variable z,

$$\Gamma_{kj}(z) = \sum_{0}^{\infty} c_{kj}(t) z^t , \qquad k = \overline{1, n} ; \quad j = \overline{1, m} , \tag{4.5}$$

are analytic in the unit disc, and the functions $\varphi_{kj}(\lambda)$ represent their boundary values:

$$\lim_{\rho\to1} \int_{-\pi}^{\pi} |\varphi_{kj}(\lambda) - \Gamma_{kj}(\rho e^{-i\lambda})|^2 \, d\lambda = \lim_{\rho\to1} \sum_{0}^{\infty} |c_{kj}(t)|^2 (1-\rho^t)^2 = 0 .^{\dagger} \tag{4.6}$$

One says that the matrix function $f(\lambda) = \{f_{kl}(\lambda)\}_{k=\overline{1,n}}^{l=\overline{1,n}}$ of rank m *admits a factorization,* if it can be represented in the form (4.1) with a matrix $\varphi(\lambda)$ having the above-mentioned properties, i.e., (4.2)-(4.4).

Suppose that it is known that the stationary process $\boldsymbol{\xi}$ has a spectral density $f(\lambda)$ of rank m which admits a factorization. Then, by Theorem 9.1 of Chapter I, $\boldsymbol{\xi}$ can be represented as a moving average:

$$\xi(t) = \sum_{-\infty}^{t} c(t-s)\zeta(s) ,$$

where $\boldsymbol{\zeta} = \{\zeta_j(t)\}_{j=\overline{1,m}}$ is some uncorrelated process, from which it follows that

$$H_\xi^-(t) \subseteq H_\zeta^-(t) ,$$

and, consequently,

$$S_\xi \subseteq S_\zeta = 0 ,$$

since it is evident that any uncorrelated process is regular.

Thus, we have the following result.

Theorem 4.1. *A stationary process $\boldsymbol{\xi} = \{\xi_k(t)\}_{k=\overline{1,n}}$ is linearly regular if and only if it has rank m and its spectral density $f(\lambda)$ admits a factorization.*

Definition. We will say that a function $\gamma(z)$, analytic in the unit disc, belongs to the class H_δ if

$$H_\delta(\gamma) = \sup_{0\le\rho<1} \int_{-\pi}^{\pi} |\gamma(\rho e^{-i\lambda})|^\delta \, d\lambda < \infty . \tag{4.7}$$

As is evident from (4.4), the functions $\Gamma_{kj}(z)$, defined by (4.5), belong to the class H_2:

† For further details on boundary values, see Privalov[*] and Hoffman[*].

$$\int_{-\pi}^{\pi} |\Gamma_{kj}(\rho e^{-i\lambda})|^2 d\lambda = \sum_0^\infty |c_{kj}(t)|^2 \rho^{2t} \le \sum_0^\infty |c_{kj}(t)|^2 , \tag{4.8}$$

We set $\Gamma(z) = \{\Gamma_{kj}(z)\}_{k=\overline{1,n}}^{j=\overline{1,m}}$. Obviously, the matrix function $\Gamma(z)$ is analytic in the unit disc; i.e.,

$$\Gamma(z) = \sum_0^\infty c(t) z^t , \tag{4.9}$$

and the coefficients $c(t) = \{c_{kj}(t)\}_{k=\overline{1,n}}^{j=\overline{1,m}}$ of its power-series expansion are also the coefficients in Wold's decomposition of $\boldsymbol{\xi}$. We note that, by virtue of the representation (3.10), the problem of extrapolating the process $\boldsymbol{\xi}$ reduces to finding the matrix $\Gamma(z)$, since, if $\Gamma(z)$ is known, one can find the coefficients $c(t)$ of its power-series expansion, and the fundamental process $\boldsymbol{\zeta} = \{\zeta_j(t)\}_{j=\overline{1,m}}$ can be obtained from $\boldsymbol{\xi}$ by a linear transformation with spectral characteristic $\psi(\lambda) = \{\psi_{jk}(\lambda)\}_{j=\overline{1,m}}^{k=\overline{1,n}}$ satisfying the equation

$$\psi(\lambda)\varphi(\lambda) = I_m , \tag{4.10}$$

where $\varphi(\lambda)$ is the boundary value of the matrix $\Gamma(z)$, and I_m is the m-dimensional unit matrix (cf. Section 9 of Chapter I). Concerning the matrix function $\Gamma(z)$, we know at present only that it satisfies the boundary condition (4.1).

Let $\tilde{\Gamma}(z) = \{\tilde{\Gamma}_{kj}(z)\}_{k=\overline{1,n}}^{j=\overline{1,m}}$ be an arbitrary analytic (in the unit disc) matrix function whose power series expansion is

$$\tilde{\Gamma}(z) = \sum_0^\infty \tilde{c}(t) z^t , \tag{4.11}$$

and whose components $\tilde{\Gamma}_{kj}(z)$ are functions in the class H_2. Let us assume that the boundary values $\tilde{\varphi}(\lambda) = \{\tilde{\varphi}_{kj}(\lambda)\}_{k=\overline{1,n}}^{j=\overline{1,m}}$ of $\tilde{\Gamma}(z)$,

$$\tilde{\varphi}(\lambda) = \sum_0^\infty \tilde{c}(t) e^{-i\lambda t} , \tag{4.12}$$

satisfy condition (4.1). By Theorem 9.1 of Chapter I, there is associated with the matrix function $\tilde{\varphi}(\lambda)$ a certain uncorrelated process $\tilde{\boldsymbol{\zeta}} = \{\tilde{\zeta}_j(t)\}_{j=\overline{1,m}}$ such that

$$\xi(t) = \sum_{-\infty}^{t} \tilde{c}(t-s)\tilde{\zeta}(s) . \tag{4.13}$$

It is evident from (4.13) that the stationary process $\boldsymbol{\xi}$ is subordinate to the uncorrelated process $\tilde{\boldsymbol{\zeta}}$, i.e.,

$$H_\xi^-(t) \subseteq H_{\tilde{\zeta}}^-(t) . \tag{4.14}$$

Now, if $\boldsymbol{\zeta}$ is a fundamental process for $\boldsymbol{\xi}$, the subspaces $H_\xi^-(t)$ and

$H_\zeta^-(t)$ coincide, and, therefore,

$$H_\zeta^-(t) \subseteq H_\xi^-(t) . \tag{4.15}$$

This relation enables us to establish the following analytic fact.

Theorem 4.2. *The analytic matrix* $\Gamma(z) = \{\Gamma_{kj}(z)\}_{k=\overline{1,n}}^{j=\overline{1,m}}$ *corresponding to a fundamental process* ζ *(for* ξ*) is maximal among analytic matrices* $\tilde{\Gamma}(z) = \{\tilde{\Gamma}_{kj}(z)\}_{k=\overline{1,n}}^{j=\overline{1,m}}$ *with components from the class* H_2, *and satisfying the boundary condition* (4.1); *i.e.*,

$$\Gamma(0)\overset{*}{\Gamma}(0) \geq \tilde{\Gamma}(0)\overset{*}{\tilde{\Gamma}}(0) .\dagger \tag{4.16}$$

Proof. Let $\alpha_1, \ldots, \alpha_n$ be arbitrary complex numbers, and consider the perpendicular $\tilde{h}$ from the point $\eta = \sum_{k=1}^n \alpha_k \xi_k(1)$ onto the subspace $H_\xi^-(0)$. By virtue of the representation (4.13),

$$\tilde{h} = \sum_{k=1}^n \alpha_k \sum_{j=1}^m \tilde{c}_{kj}(0)\tilde{\zeta}_j(1) = \sum_{k=1}^n \alpha_k \sum_{j=1}^m \tilde{\Gamma}_{kj}(0)\tilde{\zeta}_j(1) , \tag{4.17}$$

and

$$||\tilde{h}||^2 = \sum_{k,l=1}^n \alpha_k \bar{\alpha}_l \sum_{j=1}^m \tilde{\Gamma}_{kj}(0)\overline{\tilde{\Gamma}_{lj}(0)} . \tag{4.18}$$

Let us consider the perpendicular from the same point η onto the subspace $H_\zeta^-(0)$.

From relation (4.15) we have

$$||h||^2 = \sum_{k,l=1}^n \alpha_k \bar{\alpha}_l \sum_{j=1}^m \Gamma_{kj}(0)\overline{\Gamma_{lj}(0)} \geq \sum_{k,l=1}^n \alpha_k \bar{\alpha}_l \sum_{j=1}^m \tilde{\Gamma}_{kj}(0)\overline{\tilde{\Gamma}_{kj}(0)} = ||\tilde{h}||^2 , \tag{4.19}$$

which is equivalent to (4.16).

Theorem 4.3. *Let* $\xi = \{\xi_k(t)\}_{k=\overline{1,n}}$ *be an n-dimensional linearly regular process with spectral density* $f(\lambda) = \{f_{kl}(\lambda)\}_{k=\overline{1,n}}^{l=\overline{1,n}}$, *and let* $\Gamma(z) = \{\Gamma_{kj}(z)\}_{k=\overline{1,n}}^{j=\overline{1,m}}$ *be some maximal analytic matrix, satisfying the boundary condition* (4.1). *Then the uncorrelated process* $\zeta = \{\zeta_j(t)\}_{j=\overline{1,m}}$, *associated with the matrix* $\varphi(\lambda) = \Gamma(e^{-i\lambda})$, *is fundamental for the process* ξ.

Proof. By virtue of the maximality of the matrix $\Gamma(z)$, the lengths $||h_k||$ of the perpendiculars h_k from the points $\xi_k(1)$ onto the subspace $H_\zeta^-(0)$ are maximal (cf. (4.19)); i.e., they coincide with the lengths $||\xi_k(1) - \hat{\xi}_k(0, 1)||$ of the perpendiculars $\xi_k(1) - \hat{\xi}_k(0, 1)$ from the same points $\xi_k(1)$ onto the subspace $H_\xi^-(0)$. But since $H_\xi^-(0) \subseteq H_\zeta^-(0)$, it is obvious that these perpendiculars must coincide:

$$h_k = \xi_k(1) - \hat{\xi}_k(0, 1), \qquad k = \overline{1, n} .$$

† That is, the difference $\Gamma(0)\overset{*}{\Gamma}(0) - \tilde{\Gamma}(0)\overset{*}{\tilde{\Gamma}}(0)$ is positive definite.

This means that the subspaces $D_\xi(1)$ and $D_\zeta(1)$ coincide, and, consequently, ζ is fundamental for ξ.

It is evident, from the results obtained above, that a maximal matrix is unique up to multiplication by a constant unitary matrix, and that the problem of the best linear extrapolation of a regular process $\xi = \{\xi_k(t)\}_{k=\overline{1,n}}$ with spectral density $f(\lambda) = \{f_{kl}(\lambda)\}_{k=\overline{1,n}}^{l=\overline{1,n}}$ reduces to the following analytic problem: *to find a maximal analytic matrix* $\Gamma(z)$ *whose boundary value* $\varphi(\lambda) = \Gamma(e^{-i\lambda})$ *satisfies condition* (4.1).

Indeed, if the matrix $\Gamma(z)$ is known, then the stationary process $\hat{\xi}(\cdot, \tau) = \{\hat{\xi}_k(t, \tau)\}_{k=\overline{1,n}}$, consisting of the best linear forecasts (τ units of time ahead) of the process ξ, is obtained from ξ by the linear transformation

$$\hat{\xi}(t, \tau) = \int_{-\pi}^{\pi} e^{i\lambda t}\hat{\varphi}(\lambda, \tau)\Phi(d\lambda) , \tag{4.20}$$

where $\Phi = \{\Phi_k\}_{k=\overline{1,n}}$ is the random spectral measure of ξ. The spectral characteristic $\hat{\varphi}(\lambda, \tau)$ has the form

$$\hat{\varphi}(\lambda, \tau) = \varphi_\tau(\lambda)\psi(\lambda) , \tag{4.21}$$

where the matrix function $\varphi_\tau(\lambda)$ is defined by a Fourier series,

$$\varphi_\tau(\lambda) = \sum_0^\infty c(s + \tau) e^{-i\lambda s} , \tag{4.22}$$

whose coefficients $c(s) = \{c_{kj}(s)\}_{k=\overline{1,n}}^{j=\overline{1,m}}$ coincide with the coefficients of the power series expansion of $\Gamma(z)$,

$$\Gamma(z) = \sum_{s=0}^\infty c(s)z^s ,$$

and the matrix $\psi(\lambda) = \{\psi_{jk}(\lambda)\}_{j=\overline{1,m}}^{k=\overline{1,n}}$ is defined by the equation

$$\psi(\lambda)\varphi(\lambda) = I_m , \qquad \varphi(\lambda) = \Gamma(e^{-i\lambda}) . \tag{4.23}$$

In a number of cases a maximal matrix $\Gamma(z)$ can be found from the spectral density $f(\lambda)$ by a rather effective method. For example, as we shall see below, in the case of a spectral density with rational elements, the matrix of rank m with rational elements which figures in Theorem 10.1 of the previous chapter is maximal. (A method for finding this matrix was described in detail in Section 10 of Chapter I.)

Let us make several remarks regarding some general properties of analytic matrices with elements in the class H_2 which satisfy the same boundary condition of type (4.1).

Remark 1. If the matrix $\Gamma(z) = \{\Gamma_{kj}(z)\}_{k=\overline{1,n}}^{j=\overline{1,m}}$ is maximal, then every analytic matrix $\tilde{\Gamma}(z)$, satisfying the same boundary condition as $\Gamma(z)$, can be represented in the form

$$\tilde{\Gamma}(z) = \Gamma(z)A(z) , \qquad (4.24)$$

where the analytic matrix $A(z) = \{A_{ij}(z)\}_{i=\overline{1,m}}^{j=\overline{1,m}}$, which is unitary almost everywhere on the unit circle, has the property that

$$I_m - A(0)\overset{*}{A}(0) \geq 0 . \qquad (4.25)$$

Indeed, if we turn to the uncorrelated process $\tilde{\zeta}$ corresponding to the matrix function $\tilde{\Gamma}(z)$ (see Theorem 9.1 of Chapter I), then relation (4.15) holds for it, where ζ is the fundamental process corresponding to the maximal matrix $\Gamma(z)$. This relation shows that the uncorrelated process ζ can be obtained from the uncorrelated process $\tilde{\zeta}$ by a moving average:

$$\zeta(t) = \sum_{s=-\infty}^{t} a(t-s)\tilde{\zeta}(s) , \qquad a(t) = \{a_{ij}(t)\}_{i=\overline{1,m}}^{j=\overline{1,m}} ,$$

which, together with the representations (3.7) and (4.13), leads us to (4.24), in which the matrix function

$$A(z) = \sum_{t=0}^{\infty} a(t)z^t$$

has the properties indicated above. (As an analytic martix with elements in the class H_2, $A(z)$ satisfies the boundary condition $I_m = A(e^{-i\lambda})\overset{*}{A}(e^{-i\lambda})$ —in fact, the spectral density of the uncorrelated process ζ, which is fundamental for itself, is $(1/2\pi)I_m$.)

Remark 2. A matrix function $\Gamma(z) = \{\Gamma_{kj}(z)\}_{k=\overline{1,n}}^{j=\overline{1,m}}$ which is analytic in the unit disc and satisfies the boundary condition (4.1) is maximal if and only if, for every minor $M_p(z)$ of order m of $\Gamma(z)$ which is not identically zero, the absolute value $|M_p(0)|$ is maximal among the set of values obtained by letting $\Gamma(z)$ range over all analytic matrices satisfying (4.1).

To prove this assertion, let us first consider the case in which the matrix $\Gamma(z)$ is square. The maximality condition (4.16) is equivalent to the requirement that each of the proper values $\mu_1 \geq \mu_2 \geq \cdots \geq \mu_n$ of the matrix $\Gamma(0)\overset{*}{\Gamma}(0)$ be not less than the corresponding proper values $\tilde{\mu}_1 \geq \tilde{\mu}_2 \geq \cdots \geq \tilde{\mu}_n$ of any matrix $\tilde{\Gamma}(0)\overset{*}{\tilde{\Gamma}}(0)$ (see, for example, Gelfand[*]). This, in turn, is equivalent to the maximality condition

$$|\det \Gamma(0)|^2 = \det \Gamma(0)\overset{*}{\Gamma}(0) = \prod_{k=1}^{n} \mu_k \geq \prod_{k=1}^{n} \tilde{\mu}_k = \det \tilde{\Gamma}(0)\overset{*}{\tilde{\Gamma}}(0) = |\det \tilde{\Gamma}(0)|^2 .$$

Further, $\det \Gamma(0)\overset{*}{\Gamma}(0)$ is nothing more than the Gramian of the perpendiculars from the points $\xi_1(t), \ldots, \xi_n(t)$, the values of the stationary process ξ with spectral density $f(\lambda) = (1/2\pi)\Gamma(e^{-i\lambda})\overset{*}{\Gamma}(e^{-i\lambda})$, onto the subspace $H_\zeta^-(t-1)$ (the uncorrelated process ζ corresponds in familiar fashion to the analytic matrix $\Gamma(z)$). Therefore, if the process ξ is itself uncorrelated, then obviously $\det \Gamma(0)\overset{*}{\Gamma}(0) \leq 1$, where the equality holds if and only if $\zeta(t)$ is obtained from $\xi(t)$ by multiplication by a constant unitary matrix: $\zeta(t) = V\xi(t)$. Applying these results to the matrix function $A(z) = \{A_{ij}(z)\}_{i=\overline{1,n}}^{j=\overline{1,n}}$, we conclude that $|\det A(0)| = 1$ if and only if $A(z)$ is itself a constant unitary matrix: $A(z) = V$.

Finally, if we consider a matrix function $\Gamma(z) = \{\Gamma_{kj}(z)\}_{k=\overline{1,n}}^{j=\overline{1,m}}$ of general type, then it is easily seen that each of its minors of order m is obtained from the corresponding minor of a maximal matrix by multiplication by the quantity $\det A(0)$, whose modulus never exceeds 1 and equals 1 if and only if $A(z)$ is a constant unitary matrix, or, what is the same, if and only if the matrix $\Gamma(z)$ is maximal. The validity of Remark 2 is now obvious.

Remark 3. For all z, $|z| < 1$, a maximal matrix $\Gamma(z) = \{\Gamma_{kj}(z)\}_{k=\overline{1,n}}^{j=\overline{1,m}}$ has the same rank m.

Indeed, if the matrix $\Gamma(z)$ is degenerate at some interior point $z = \alpha$ of the unit disc, then it can be brought into the form (see Section 10 of Chapter I)

$$\Gamma(\alpha) = MV\begin{pmatrix} \lambda_1 & & & & \\ & \ddots & & & \\ & & \lambda_p & & \\ & & & 0 & \\ & & & & \ddots \\ & & & & & 0 \end{pmatrix}V, \qquad p < m,$$

which shows that the matrix $\tilde{\Gamma}(z) = \Gamma(z)B(z)$, where

$$B(z) = V^{-1}\begin{pmatrix} I_p & 0 \\ 0 & b(z)I_{m-p} \end{pmatrix}, \qquad b(z) = \begin{cases} \dfrac{1-\bar{\alpha}z}{z-\alpha}\dfrac{\alpha}{|\alpha|}, & \alpha \neq 0, \\ \dfrac{1}{z}, & \alpha = 0 \end{cases}$$

is analytic with elements of class H_2 and satisfies the same boundary condition as does the matrix $\Gamma(z)$; but $|\det B(0)| > 1$, so that none of the minors of order m of $\Gamma(z)$ are maximal in absolute value. Consequently, if the matrix $\Gamma(z)$ is degenerate at some interior point $z = \alpha$ of the unit disc, it cannot be maximal.

5. Linear extrapolation of one-dimensional stationary processes

In this section we will consider one-dimensional stationary processes, for which we will give a complete characterization from the point of view of the problem of linear extrapolation.

Theorem 5.1. *In order that the stationary process ξ be linearly regular, it is necessary and sufficient that it have an almost everywhere positive spectral density $f(\lambda)$ such that*

$$\int_{-\pi}^{\pi} \log f(\lambda)\, d(\lambda) > -\infty . \tag{5.1}$$

Proof. Let the stationary process ξ be regular. Then, by Theorem 4.1, it has an almost everywhere positive spectral density $f(\lambda)$ which admits a factorization, i.e., there exists an analytic function $\Gamma(z)$ of the class H_2, such that

$$f(\lambda) = \frac{1}{2\pi}|\Gamma(e^{-i\lambda})|^2 . \tag{5.2}$$

Suppose $\Gamma(z)$ is maximal. Then (by Remark 3 of Section 4) it has no zeros inside the unit disc, and, therefore, the function $B(z) = \log(\Gamma(z)/\sqrt{2\pi})$ is analytic and the function $\operatorname{Re} B(z) = \log(|\Gamma(z)|/\sqrt{2\pi})$ is harmonic in the unit disc. We set

$$\log^+ \zeta = \begin{cases} \log \zeta , & \text{if } \log \zeta \geq 0 , \\ 0 , & \text{if } \log \zeta < 0 . \end{cases}$$

Then

$$\begin{aligned} \frac{1}{2\pi}\int_{-\pi}^{\pi}\left|\log\frac{|\Gamma(\rho e^{-i\lambda})|}{\sqrt{2\pi}}\right|d\lambda &= \frac{1}{2\pi}\int_{-\pi}^{\pi} 2\log^+\frac{|\Gamma(\rho e^{-i\lambda})|}{\sqrt{2\pi}}d\lambda - \frac{1}{2\pi}\int_{-\pi}^{\pi}\log\frac{|\Gamma(\rho e^{-i\lambda})|}{\sqrt{2\pi}}d\lambda \\ &= \frac{1}{2\pi}\int_{-\pi}^{\pi} 2\log^+\frac{|\Gamma(\rho e^{-i\lambda})|}{\sqrt{2\pi}}\,d\lambda - \log\frac{|\Gamma(0)|}{\sqrt{2\pi}} \\ &\leq \frac{1}{2\pi}\int_{-\pi}^{\pi}\frac{|\Gamma(\rho e^{-i\lambda})|^2}{2\pi}\,d\lambda - \log\frac{|\Gamma(0)|}{\sqrt{2\pi}} \\ &\leq \frac{1}{2\pi}\int_{-\pi}^{\pi} f(\lambda)\,d\lambda - \log\frac{|\Gamma(0)|}{\sqrt{2\pi}} . \end{aligned} \tag{5.3}$$

Since

$$\lim_{\rho\to 1}\frac{|\Gamma(\rho e^{-i\lambda})|^2}{2\pi} = f(\lambda) , \tag{5.4}$$

then from (5.3) we obtain

$$\frac{1}{4\pi}\int_{-\pi}^{\pi}|\log f(\lambda)|\,d\lambda \leq \frac{1}{2\pi}\int_{-\pi}^{\pi} f(\lambda)\,d\lambda - \log\frac{|\Gamma(0)|}{\sqrt{2\pi}} . \tag{5.5}$$

The function $f(\lambda)$ being integrable, inequality (5.5) implies (5.1).

Suppose now that the spectral density $f(\lambda)$ of the stationary process

ξ satisfies the conditions of the theorem. Let us consider the analytic (in the unit disc) function $\Gamma(z)$ of the form

$$\Gamma(z) = \sqrt{2\pi} \exp\left\{\frac{1}{4\pi}\int_{-\pi}^{\pi} \log f(\lambda)\frac{e^{-i\lambda}+z}{e^{-i\lambda}-z}d\lambda\right\}. \tag{5.6}$$

We have

$$\log\frac{|\Gamma(z)|^2}{2\pi} = \int_{-\pi}^{\pi} \log f(\lambda)P_\rho(\mu-\lambda)\,d\lambda\,,$$

$$\frac{1}{2\pi}|\Gamma(z)|^2 \leq \int_{-\pi}^{\pi} f(\lambda)P_\rho(\mu-\lambda)\,d\lambda\,, \tag{5.7}$$

$$\frac{1}{2\pi}\int_{-\pi}^{\pi}|\Gamma(z)|^2\,d\mu \leq \int_{-\pi}^{\pi} f(\lambda)\,d\lambda\,,$$

where $z=\rho e^{-i\mu}$, and $P_\rho(\mu-\lambda)$ is the Poisson kernel:

$$P_\rho(\mu-\lambda) = \frac{1}{2\pi}\frac{1-\rho^2}{1+\rho^2-2\rho\cos(\mu-\lambda)}\,.$$

As is known (see, for example, Privalov[*] or Hoffman[*]), this kernel has the property that

$$\lim_{\rho\to1}\int_{-\pi}^{\pi} \log f(\lambda)P_\rho(\mu-\lambda)\,d\lambda = \log f(\mu) \tag{5.8}$$

for almost all μ, from which it follows that

$$\lim_{\rho\to1}\frac{|\Gamma(\rho e^{-i\lambda})|^2}{2\pi} = f(\lambda) \tag{5.9}$$

for almost all λ. Relations (5.7) and (5.9) show that $\Gamma(z)$ belongs to the class H_2, and its boundary value $\Gamma(e^{-i\lambda})$ satisfies condition (5.2); therefore, $f(\lambda)$ admits a factorization. By Theorem 4.1, this implies that ξ is regular.

As was shown in the preceding section, the problem of the linear extrapolation of a regular stationary process ξ with spectral density $f(\lambda)$ reduces to finding a maximal analytic function $\Gamma(z)$ satisfying the boundary condition (5.2).

Theorem 5.2. *A maximal analytic function $\Gamma(z)$, satisfying the boundary condition* (5.2), *is given by*

$$\Gamma(z) = \sqrt{2\pi} \exp\left\{\frac{1}{4\pi}\int_{-\pi}^{\pi} \log f(\lambda)\frac{e^{-i\lambda}+z}{e^{-i\lambda}-z}d\lambda\right\}. \tag{5.10}$$

Proof. That the function $\Gamma(z)$, defined by (5.10), satisfies the boundary condition (5.2) has already been established in the proof of the preceding theorem. To establish its maximality, it is sufficient to verify that

$$|\Gamma(0)|^2 = 2\pi \exp\left\{\frac{1}{2\pi}\int_{-\pi}^{\pi} \log f(\lambda)\, d\lambda\right\} = \inf_P \int_{-\pi}^{\pi} |1 + P(e^{-i\lambda})|^2 f(\lambda)\, d\lambda\,, \quad (5.11)$$

where the infimum is taken over all polynomials $P(z)$ such that $P(0) = 0$. Indeed, the square σ^2 of the error of the best linear extrapolation of ξ, one step ahead, is, on the one hand,

$$\begin{aligned}\sigma^2 &= \inf_{c(s)} \boldsymbol{E}\left|\xi(0) - \sum_{s<0} c(s)\xi(s)\right|^2 \\ &= \inf_{c(s)} \int_{-\pi}^{\pi}\left|1 - \sum_{s<0} c(s)\, e^{-i\lambda s}\right|^2 f(\lambda)\, d\lambda = \inf_P \int_{-\pi}^{\pi} |1 + P(e^{-i\lambda})|^2 f(\lambda)\, d\lambda\,, \quad (5.12)\end{aligned}$$

and, on the other hand, σ^2 coincides with the modulus squared of the value of a maximal function at $z = 0$ (i.e., with the modulus squared of the first coefficient in Wold's decomposition). Therefore (5.11) shows that the value $|\Gamma(0)|^2$ is maximal.

To prove (5.11), we observe the following relation:

$$\exp\left\{\frac{1}{2\pi}\int_{-\pi}^{\pi} \log f(\lambda)\, d\lambda\right\} = \inf_{\psi} \frac{1}{2\pi}\int_{-\pi}^{\pi} e^{\psi(\lambda)} f(\lambda)\, d\lambda\,, \quad (5.13)$$

where the infimum is taken over all (real) functions $\psi(\lambda)$ for which

$$\int_{-\pi}^{\pi} \psi(\lambda)\, d\lambda = 0\,. \quad (5.14)$$

Indeed, using the inequality between the geometric and arithmetic means, we obtain

$$\exp\left\{\frac{1}{2\pi}\int_{-\pi}^{\pi} \log f(\lambda)\, d\lambda\right\} = \exp\left\{\frac{1}{2\pi}\int_{-\pi}^{\pi} \log\, [e^{\psi(\lambda)} f(\lambda)]\, d\lambda\right\} \le \frac{1}{2\pi}\int_{-\pi}^{\pi} e^{\psi(\lambda)} f(\lambda)\, d\lambda\,,$$

and equality holds for

$$\psi(\lambda) = \frac{1}{2\pi}\int_{-\pi}^{\pi} \log f(\lambda)\, d\lambda - \log f(\lambda)\,.$$

It is clear that (5.13) is not violated if the infimum is taken only over functions $\psi(\lambda)$ which are real trigonometric polynomials, since any function $\psi(\lambda)$ can be approximated by trigonometric polynomials in such a way that the integral on the right side of (5.13) is changed by an arbitrarily small amount.

Further, if $\psi(\lambda)$ is a real trigonometric polynomial, satisfying (5.14), it can be represented in the form $\psi(\lambda) = P(e^{-i\lambda}) + \overline{P(e^{-i\lambda})}$, where $P(z)$ is a polynomial in z with constant term zero, and then $e^{\psi(\lambda)} = |\exp P(e^{-i\lambda})|^2$. The function $Q(z) = e^{P(z)} - 1$ is analytic and vanishes at $z = 0$. From (5.13) we obtain

$$\exp\left\{\frac{1}{2\pi}\int_{-\pi}^{\pi}\log f(\lambda)\,d\lambda\right\} \geq \inf_{Q}\frac{1}{2\pi}\int_{-\pi}^{\pi}|1+Q(e^{-i\lambda})|^2 f(\lambda)\,d\lambda\,. \tag{5.16}$$

Obviously, any function $Q(e^{-i\lambda})$, where $Q(z)$ is of the form $Q(z)=e^{R(z)} - 1$, can be uniformly approximated by polynomials $P(e^{-i\lambda})$ in $e^{i\lambda}$, $P(0)$, $= 0$, and, therefore,

$$2\pi\exp\left\{\frac{1}{2\pi}\int_{-\pi}^{\pi}\log f(\lambda)\,d\lambda\right\} \geq \inf_{P}\int_{-\pi}^{\pi}|1+P(e^{-i\lambda})|^2 f(\lambda)\,d\lambda\,. \tag{5.17}$$

But the right side of (5.17), as was mentioned above, is precisely the modulus squared of the value of any maximal function at $z=0$, while the left side of (5.17) equals $|\Gamma(0)|^2$. It follows that $\Gamma(z)$ is itself a maximal function.

An important class of stationary processes are those having spectral densities which are rational functions of $e^{-i\lambda}$. By Lemma 10.1 of Chapter I, a non-negative function $f(\lambda)$ which is rational in $e^{-i\lambda}$ can be represented in the form

$$f(\lambda)=\frac{|P(e^{-i\lambda})|^2}{|Q(e^{-i\lambda})|^2}\,, \tag{5.18}$$

where the polynomials $P(z)$ and $Q(z)$ do not have zeros inside the unit disc.†

Let ξ be a stationary process with a rational (in $e^{-i\lambda}$) spectral density $f(\lambda)$ of the form (5.18). By the results of Section 10, Chapter I (in particular, (10.15)), it follows that ξ is a regular process. How do we find a maximal function for it?

Let us consider the function

$$\Gamma(z)=\sqrt{2\pi}\,\frac{P(z)}{Q(z)}\,. \tag{5.19}$$

This function is analytic and does not have zeros inside the unit disc. The function $B(z)=\log(\Gamma(z)/\sqrt{2\pi})$ is also analytic in the unit disc, and its real part $\operatorname{Re} B(z)=\log(|\Gamma(z)|/\sqrt{2\pi})$ is harmonic and continuous on the boundary $z=e^{-i\lambda}$, with the possible exception of a finite number of points w_p at which it equals $-\infty$. Therefore‡

$$\begin{aligned}\operatorname{Re} B(\rho\, e^{-i\mu}) &= \frac{1}{2\pi}\int_{-\pi}^{\pi}\operatorname{Re} B(e^{-i\lambda})\frac{1-\rho^2}{1+\rho^2-2\rho\cos(\mu-\lambda)}\,d\lambda\\ &= \frac{1}{4\pi}\int_{-\pi}^{\pi}\log f(\lambda)\frac{1-\rho^2}{1+\rho^2-2\rho\cos(\mu-\lambda)}\,d\lambda\,,\end{aligned} \tag{5.20}$$

† Expressions for P and Q are easily constructed, if one knows the zeros and poles of $f(\lambda)$ lying outside, or on the boundary of the unit disc.

‡ See Privalov[*] or Hoffman[*].

from which

$$\log \frac{|\Gamma(0)|}{\sqrt{2\pi}} = \frac{1}{4\pi}\int_{-\pi}^{\pi} \log f(\lambda)\, d\lambda \,. \tag{5.21}$$

Comparing (5.21) and (5.11), we conclude that *the function* $\Gamma(z)$, *defined by* (5.19), *is maximal.*

The results which have been obtained are summarized by the following theorem.

Theorem 5.3. *Let* ξ *be a linearly regular stationary process with spectral density* $f(\lambda)$,

$$\xi(t) = \int_{-\pi}^{\pi} e^{i\lambda t}\Phi(d\lambda) \,. \tag{5.22}$$

Then the stationary process $\hat{\xi}(\cdot,\tau) = \{\hat{\xi}(t,\tau)\}$, *consisting of the best linear predictions* (τ *units of time ahead*) *of the process* ξ, *is obtained from* ξ *by a linear transformation:*

$$\hat{\xi}(t,\tau) = \int_{-\pi}^{\pi} e^{i\lambda t}\hat{\varphi}(\lambda,\tau)\Phi(d\lambda) \,. \tag{5.23}$$

The spectral characteristic $\hat{\varphi}(\lambda,\tau)$ *is defined by the relation*

$$\hat{\varphi}(\lambda,\tau) = e^{i\lambda\tau}\frac{\varphi(\lambda) - \sum_0^{\tau-1} c(s)e^{-i\lambda s}}{\varphi(\lambda)} \,, \tag{5.24}$$

where $\varphi(\lambda) = \Gamma(e^{-i\lambda})$ *is the boundary value of the function* $\Gamma(z)$, *analytic in the unit disc, of the form* (5.10), *and the coefficients* $c(s)$ *are the coefficients in the power series expansion of* $\Gamma(z)$:

$$\Gamma(z) = \sum_{s=0}^{\infty} c(s)z^s \,.$$

If the spectral density $f(\lambda)$ *is a rational function of* $e^{-i\lambda}$, *then an expression for* $\Gamma(z)$ *is given by* (5.19).

Let us consider some examples of the linear extrapolation of stationary processes.

Example 5.1. Suppose that the stationary process ξ has the correlation function

$$B(t) = \sigma^2 e^{-\alpha|t|} \,, \qquad \alpha > 0 \,.$$

The spectral density $f(\lambda)$ of ξ is

$$f(\lambda) = \frac{1}{2\pi}\sum_{-\infty}^{\infty} B(t)e^{-i\lambda t} = \frac{\sigma^2}{2\pi}\frac{1-\beta^2}{|1-\beta e^{-i\lambda}|^2} \,,$$

where $\beta = e^{-\alpha}$. From this it is evident that

$$\Gamma(z) = \sigma\sqrt{1-\beta^2}\frac{1}{1-\beta z}$$

is a maximal function.

By Theorem 5.3 the best forecast $\hat{\xi}(t, \tau)$ of ξ is given by

$$\hat{\xi}(t, \tau) = \int_{-\pi}^{\pi} (1 - \beta e^{-i\lambda}) e^{i\lambda(t+\tau)} \sum_{\tau}^{\infty} \beta^s e^{-i\lambda s} \Phi(d\lambda) = \int_{-\pi}^{\pi} e^{i\lambda t} \beta^\tau \Phi(d\lambda) ,$$

where Φ is the random spectral measure of ξ, and so

$$\hat{\xi}(t, \tau) = \beta^\tau \xi(t) .$$

Example 5.2. Suppose that the stationary process ξ has a spectral density of the form

$$f(\lambda) = \frac{1}{|Q(e^{-i\lambda})|^2} , \qquad Q(z) = \sum_0^n q_k z^k ,$$

where the polynomial $Q(z)$ does not have zeros inside the unit disc. Then the function

$$\Gamma(z) = \frac{\sqrt{2\pi}}{Q(z)}$$

is maximal. If

$$\xi(t) = \int_{-\pi}^{\pi} e^{i\lambda t} \Phi(d\lambda)$$

is the spectral representation of ξ, then

$$\hat{\xi}(t, \tau) = \int_{-\pi}^{\pi} e^{i\lambda(t+\tau)} \left[\frac{1}{Q(e^{-i\lambda})} - \sum_0^{\tau-1} c(s) e^{-i\lambda s}\right] Q(e^{-i\lambda}) \Phi(d\lambda)$$

$$= \int_{-\pi}^{\pi} e^{i\lambda(t+\tau)} \left[1 - \sum_{m=0}^{\tau-1} \left(\sum_{s+k=m} c(s) q_k\right) e^{-i\lambda m} + \sum_{m=\tau}^{n+\tau-1} b_m e^{-i\lambda m}\right] \Phi(d\lambda) ,$$

where the $c(s)$ are the coefficients in the power series expansion of $1/Q(z)$: $1/Q(z) = \sum_{s=0}^{\infty} c(s) z^s$, and

$$b_m = - \sum_{\substack{s+k=m \\ s \le \tau-1}} c(s) q_k .$$

Since

$$1 = \sum_0^{\infty} c(s) z^s \sum_0^n q_k z^k = \sum_0^{\infty} \left(\sum_{s+k=m} c(s) q_k\right) z_m ,$$

then

$$c(0) q_0 = 1 , \qquad \sum_{\substack{s+k=m \\ m \ge 1}} c(s) q_k = 0 .$$

Consequently, the best forecast $\hat{\xi}(t, \tau)$ of ξ, τ units of time ahead, can be represented in the form

$$\hat{\xi}(t, \tau) = \int_{-\pi}^{\pi} e^{i\lambda(t+\tau)}\left[\sum_{\tau}^{n+\tau-1} b_m e^{-i\lambda m}\right]\Phi(d\lambda)$$

$$= \sum_{0}^{n-1} b_s \int_{-\pi}^{\pi} e^{i\lambda(t-s)}\Phi(d\lambda) = \sum_{0}^{n-1} b_s \xi(t-s) .$$

Let us consider an arbitrary stationary process ξ with spectral measure $F(d\lambda)$. We represent this measure in the form

$$F(d\lambda) = f(\lambda)\, d\lambda + \Sigma(d\lambda) , \tag{5.25}$$

where $\Sigma(d\lambda)$ is the singular part of the measure $F(d\lambda)$, concentrated on some set Δ_0 of Lebesgue measure zero.

Theorem 5.4. *If the density $f(\lambda)$ vanishes on some set of positive Lebesgue measure, or if*

$$\int_{-\pi}^{\pi} \log f(\lambda)\, d\lambda = -\infty , \tag{5.26}$$

then any stationary process ξ having spectral measure $F(d\lambda)$ will be linearly singular.

If

$$\int_{-\pi}^{\pi} \log f(\lambda)\, d\lambda > -\infty , \tag{5.27}$$

then the decomposition (5.25) *of $F(d\lambda)$ corresponds to the decomposition of the process ξ into regular and singular parts* (*cf. Theorem* 2.2):

$$\xi(t) = \eta(t) + \zeta(t) , \tag{5.28}$$

where the linearly regular process η is given by

$$\eta(t) = \int_{\bar{\Delta}_0} e^{i\lambda t}\Phi(d\lambda) , \tag{5.29}$$

and the linearly singular process ζ, by

$$\zeta(t) = \int_{\Delta_0} e^{i\lambda t}\Phi(d\lambda) . \tag{5.30}$$

Here Φ is the random spectral measure of ξ, and $\bar{\Delta}_0$ is the complement of Δ_0.

Proof. Suppose that ξ is not singular. By Theorem 2.2 ξ can be represented as the sum of mutually uncorrelated processes η and ζ which are, respectively, regular and singular. Obviously, the correlation function $B^{\xi\xi}(t)$ of ξ is also the sum of the corresponding correlation functions:

$$B^{\xi\xi}(t) = \int_{-\pi}^{\pi} e^{i\lambda t} F^{\xi\xi}(d\lambda) = B^{\eta\eta}(t) + B^{\zeta\zeta}(t) = \int_{-\pi}^{\pi} e^{i\lambda t}[F^{\eta\eta}(d\lambda) + F^{\zeta\zeta}(d\lambda)],$$

and, consequently,

$$F(d\lambda) = F^{\xi\xi}(d\lambda) = F^{\eta\eta}(d\lambda) + F^{\zeta\zeta}(d\lambda).$$

The spectral measure $F^{\eta\eta}(d\lambda)$ of the regular process η is absolutely continuous, its spectral density is almost everywhere positive, and moreover, by Theorem 5.1

$$\int_{-\pi}^{\pi} \log f^{\eta\eta}(\lambda)\, d\lambda > -\infty.$$

From this we obtain, by virtue of $f(\lambda) \geq f^{\eta\eta}(\lambda)$, that $f(\lambda)$ is almost everywhere positive and

$$\int_{-\pi}^{\pi} \log f(\lambda)\, d(\lambda) > -\infty.$$

Therefore, if the density $f(\lambda)$ of the spectral measure $F(d\lambda)$ of ξ does not satisfy (5.27), then ξ is singular.

Suppose now that (5.27) is satisfied, and let the processes η and ζ be defined by (5.29) and (5.30). Then the spectral density of η is given by $f^{\eta\eta}(\lambda) = f(\lambda)$. By Theorem 5.1 η is a regular process; since $f^{\zeta\zeta}(\lambda) = 0$, then, as was just shown, ζ is a singular process. These processes are also mutually uncorrelated, as their random spectral measures are concentrated on the disjoint sets $\overline{\Delta_0}$ and Δ_0.

Now let $\tilde{\eta}(t)$ be the perpendicular from $\xi(t)$ to the subspace $S_\xi = \bigcap_t H_\xi^-(t)$. As was shown in Theorem 2.2, the variables $\tilde{\eta}(t)$ form a regular stationary process. Since the random spectral measure of ζ is concentrated on a set Δ_0 of Lebesgue measure zero, $\tilde{\eta}$ and ζ are mutually uncorrelated,† and so the variables $\zeta(t)$ belong to the subspace S_ξ (note, from Theorem 2.2, that $H_\xi = S_\xi \oplus H_{\tilde{\eta}}$). We conclude from this that the regular process η, $\eta(t) = \xi(t) - \zeta(t)$, is subordinate to ξ; i.e., $H_\eta^-(t) \subseteq H_\xi^-(t)$. Thus, we have obtained the decomposition (2.7) of ξ into regular and singular parts.

6. Linear extrapolation of regular processes with maximal rank

We will call an n-dimensional stationary process $\xi = \{\xi_k(t)\}_{k=\overline{1,n}}$ a *process with maximal rank* if its rank coincides with its dimension (i.e.,

† Indeed, if the projections of the $\tilde{\eta}(t)$ onto H_ζ did not vanish, they would form a stationary process whose spectral measure would be concentrated on Δ_0. Hence the spectral measure of $\tilde{\eta}$ would have a singular component, contradicting the regularity of $\tilde{\eta}$.

if ξ has a spectral density $f(\lambda) = \{f_{kl}(\lambda)\}_{k=\overline{1,n}}^{l=\overline{1,n}}$ which is nondegenerate for almost all λ).

Let ξ be a process with maximal rank. Then its spectral density $f(\lambda)$ admits a factorization:

$$f(\lambda) = \frac{1}{2\pi}\Gamma(e^{-i\lambda})\overset{*}{\Gamma}(e^{-i\lambda}) , \tag{6.1}$$

where $\Gamma(e^{-i\lambda})$ is the boundary value of a matrix $\Gamma(z) = \{\Gamma_{kj}(z)\}_{k=\overline{1,n}}^{j=\overline{1,n}}$ which is analytic in the unit disc.

The determinant of $\Gamma(z)$ is an analytic function in the unit disc, satisfying the boundary condition

$$\frac{1}{(2\pi)^n}|\det \Gamma(e^{-i\lambda})|^2 = \det f(\lambda) . \tag{6.2}$$

This is a consequence of a property of analytic functions of class H_2. Namely, if $\gamma(z)$ is of class H_2, then, as we have seen earlier (cf. (4.9)), $\gamma(\rho e^{-i\lambda})$ converges in mean square to its boundary value $\gamma(e^{-i\lambda})$ as $\rho \to 1$. If, now, $\gamma(z)$ is the product of n functions $\gamma_1(z), \dots, \gamma_n(z)$ of class H_2, then

$$\lim_{\rho\to 1}\int_{-\pi}^{\pi} |\gamma(\rho e^{-i\lambda}) - \gamma(e^{-i\lambda})|^{2/n}\, d\lambda = 0 , \tag{6.3}$$

where $\gamma(e^{-i\lambda})$ is the product of the boundary values $\gamma_k(e^{-i\lambda})$ of the $\gamma_k(z)$, $k = \overline{1, n}$. This relation obviously holds for any linear combination of functions $\gamma(z)$ of this type and, in particular, for $\det \Gamma(z)$.

Lemma 6.1. *Let* $g(\lambda) = \{g_{kj}(\lambda)\}_{k=\overline{1,n}}^{j=\overline{1,n}}$ *be a positive definite integrable matrix function. Then*

$$\log \det \frac{1}{2\pi}\int_{-\pi}^{\pi} g(\lambda)\, d\lambda \geq \frac{1}{2\pi}\int_{-\pi}^{\pi} \log \det g(\lambda)\, d\lambda . \tag{6.4}$$

Proof. If A and B are positive definite matrices of order n, then, by Minkowski's inequality (see, for example, Hardy, Littlewood and Polya[*], p. 35),

$$[\det (A + B)]^{1/n} \geq [\det A]^{1/n} + [\det B]^{1/n} ,$$

and, consequently, for any non-negative numbers m_k and positive definite matrices g_k, $k = \overline{1, N}$, we have

$$\left[\det\left(\sum_1^N m_k g_k\right)\right]^{1/n} \geq \sum_1^N [\det g_k]^{1/n} m_k .$$

It follows from this that

$$\left[\det \frac{1}{2\pi}\int_{-\pi}^{\pi} g(\lambda)\, d\lambda\right]^{1/n} \geq \frac{1}{2\pi}\int_{-\pi}^{\pi} [\det g(\lambda)]^{1/n}\, d\lambda .$$

Applying the well-known inequality between the arithmetic and geometric means (*ibid*, p. 137) to the right side, we obtain (6.4).

Theorem 6.1. *For the linear regularity of a stationary process* $\boldsymbol{\xi} = \{\xi_k(t)\}_{k=\overline{1,n}}$ *having a spectral density* $f(\lambda)$ *with maximal rank, it is necessary and sufficient that*

$$\int_{-\pi}^{\pi} \log \det f(\lambda)\, d\lambda > -\infty . \tag{6.5}$$

Proof. Suppose that $\boldsymbol{\xi}$ is a regular process, and that $\Gamma(z)$ is a maximal analytic matrix satisfying the boundary condition (6.1). Since $\Gamma(z)$ is nondegenerate (by Remark 3 of Section 4) for all z, $|z| < 1$, the function $d(z) = [\det \Gamma(z)]^{1/n}$ is analytic in the unit disc and belongs to the class H_2. As $d(z)$ has no zeros in the unit disc, the function $\log(|d(z)|/\sqrt{2\pi})$ is harmonic there. Using an inequality analogous to (5.3), we obtain

$$\frac{1}{2\pi}\int_{-\pi}^{\pi}\left|\log\frac{|\det \Gamma(\rho e^{i\lambda})|^{1/n}}{\sqrt{2\pi}}\right| d\lambda \le \frac{1}{2\pi}\int_{-\pi}^{\pi}[\det f(\lambda)]^{1/n}\, d\lambda - \log\frac{|\det \Gamma(0)|^{1/n}}{\sqrt{2\pi}}$$

for all ρ, $0 \le \rho < 1$, and passing to the limit $\rho \to 1$, we have, by Fatou's lemma,

$$\begin{aligned}\frac{1}{2\pi}\int_{-\pi}^{\pi}\left|\log\frac{|\det \Gamma(e^{-i\lambda})|^{1/n}}{\sqrt{2\pi}}\right| d\lambda &= \frac{1}{2\pi}\int_{-\pi}^{\pi}|\log \det f(\lambda)|^{1/n}\, d\lambda \\ &\le \frac{1}{2\pi}\int_{-\pi}^{\pi}[\det f(\lambda)]^{1/n}\, d\lambda - \log\frac{|\det \Gamma(0)|^{1/n}}{\sqrt{2\pi}} ,\end{aligned}$$

which proves the necessity of (6.5).

Let us now consider an n-dimensional stationary process $\boldsymbol{\xi}$ whose spectral density $f(\lambda)$ satisfies condition (6.5). We note that relation (5.11) of the present chapter and Theorem 5.1 of Chapter I permit us to assert that for any almost everywhere positive integrable function $m(\lambda)$ one has the following relation:

$$\inf_P \int_{-\pi}^{\pi} |1 + P(e^{-i\lambda})|^2 m(\lambda)\, d\lambda = 2\pi \exp\left\{\frac{1}{2\pi}\int_{-\pi}^{\pi} \log m(\lambda)\, d\lambda\right\} , \tag{6.6}$$

where the infimum is taken over all polynomials $P(z)$, $P(0) = 0$.

Let $m_1(\lambda) \ge m_2(\lambda) \ge \cdots \ge m_n(\lambda) = m(\lambda)$ be the proper values of the spectral density matrix $f(\lambda)$ of $\boldsymbol{\xi}$. Obviously,

$$\log \det f(\lambda) = \sum_{k=1}^{n} \log m_k(\lambda) \le \log m(\lambda) + (n-1)\log m_1(\lambda) ,$$

and since

$$\int_{-\pi}^{\pi} m_1(\lambda)\, d\lambda \le \int_{-\pi}^{\pi}\left[\sum_{k=1}^{n} f_{kk}(\lambda)\right] d\lambda < \infty ,$$

we obtain from condition (6.5) that

$$\int_{-\pi}^{\pi} \log m(\lambda)\, d\lambda \geq \int_{-\pi}^{\pi} \log \det f(\lambda)\, d\lambda - (n-1) \int_{-\pi}^{\pi} \log m_1(\lambda)\, d\lambda > -\infty .$$

Let us consider a random variable η of the form

$$\eta = \sum_{k=1}^{n} \alpha_k \xi_k(0) .$$

The length of the perpendicular h from η onto the subspace $H_\xi^-(-1)$ can be defined by the formula

$$||h||^2 = \inf_{\alpha_k(s)} \left\| \eta - \sum_{k=1}^{n} \sum_{s \geq 1} \alpha_k(s) \xi_k(-s) \right\|^2 = \inf_{\varphi} \int_{-\pi}^{\pi} [\varphi f \overset{*}{\varphi}]\, d\lambda , \tag{6.7}$$

where $\varphi(\lambda) = \{\varphi_k(\lambda)\}^{k=\overline{1,n}}$ is the vector function with components $\varphi_k(\lambda) = \alpha_k - \sum_{s \geq 1} \alpha_k(s) e^{-i\lambda s}$. From (6.6) we have

$$\begin{aligned} ||h||^2 &= \inf_{\varphi} \int_{-\pi}^{\pi} [\varphi(\lambda) f(\lambda) \overset{*}{\varphi}(\lambda)]\, d\lambda \geq \inf_{\varphi} \int_{-\pi}^{\pi} m(\lambda) \sum_{k=1}^{n} |\varphi_k(\lambda)|^2\, d\lambda \\ &= \sum_{k=1}^{n} \inf_{\varphi_k} \int_{-\pi}^{\pi} m(\lambda) |\varphi_k(\lambda)|^2\, d\lambda = 2\pi \exp\left\{ \frac{1}{2\pi} \int_{-\pi}^{\pi} \log m(\lambda)\, d\lambda \right\} \sum_{k=1}^{n} |\alpha_k|^2 , \end{aligned} \tag{6.8}$$

from which it is evident that the dimension of the subspace $D_\xi(0)$, the orthogonal complement of $H_\xi^-(-1)$ in $H_\xi^-(0)$, equals n. Indeed, if h_k, $k = \overline{1, n}$, are the projections of the $\xi_k(0)$ on the subspace $D_\xi(0)$, and $\sum_{k=1}^{n} \alpha_k h_k = 0$ for certain numbers $\alpha_1, \ldots, \alpha_n$ not all zero, then this would contradict inequality (6.8), in which

$$\int_{-\pi}^{\pi} \log m(\lambda)\, d\lambda > -\infty .$$

Further, since $D_\xi(0)$ has dimension n, the uncorrelated process $\zeta = \{\zeta_j(t)\}_{j=\overline{1,m}}$ appearing in Wold's decomposition of the regular part of the process ξ also has dimension $m = n$. Therefore the process ζ can be obtained from ξ by means of a linear transformation with an almost everywhere nondegenerate characteristic ϕ, since $\phi f \overset{*}{\phi} = (1/2\pi) I_n$. By formula (8.14) of Chapter I, the process ξ, in turn, can be obtained from ζ by a linear transformation, which means that $H_\xi = H_\zeta$; i.e., the space H_ξ of values of ξ coincides with the space of values of its regular part; consequently, ξ is itself regular.

As was shown in Section 4, the extrapolation of a regular stationary process ξ with spectral density $f(\lambda)$ reduces to finding a maximal analytic matrix $\Gamma(z)$ satisfying the boundary condition (6.1). Unfortunately, in the multi-dimensional case, a formula analogous to, and as simple as (5.10), which would enable one to effectively compute $\Gamma(z)$

from the spectral density $f(\lambda)$, does not exist. However, the value $|\det \Gamma(0)|^2$, which allows us to select a maximal matrix $\Gamma(z)$ from the class of all analytic matrices satisfying the boundary condition (6.1), can be expressed rather easily in terms of the determinant of the spectral density.

Theorem 6.2. *Let ξ be an n-dimensional linearly regular process with maximal rank and spectral density $f(\lambda)$. Then an analytic matrix $\Gamma(z)$, satisfying the boundary condition* (6.1), *will be maximal if and only if*

$$|\det \Gamma(0)|^2 = (2\pi)^n \exp\left\{\frac{1}{2\pi}\int_{-\pi}^{\pi} \log \det f(\lambda)\, d\lambda\right\}. \tag{6.9}$$

Proof. Let $\Gamma(z)$ be maximal. Then its determinant does not vanish in the unit disc, and the function $d(z) = [\det \Gamma(z)]^{1/n}$ is analytic, of class H_2, and satisfies a boundary condition analogous to (6.2):

$$|d(e^{-i\lambda})|^2 = 2\pi[\det f(\lambda)]^{1/n}.$$

Now the modulus squared, at $z = 0$, of a maximal function which satisfies the same boundary conditions as $d(z)$ is given by (5.11); hence, in the case at hand,

$$|d(0)|^2 \leq 2\pi \exp\left\{\frac{1}{2\pi}\int_{-\pi}^{\pi} \log\,[\det f(\lambda)]^{1/n}\, d\lambda\right\}. \tag{6.10}$$

Further, let

$$\xi(t) = \sum_{-\infty}^{t} c(t-s)\zeta(s)$$

be Wold's decomposition of ξ. We define random variables $\eta^{(t)} = \{\eta_k^{(t)}\}_{k=\overline{1,n}}$ by

$$\eta^{(t)} = \xi(0) - \sum_{s=1}^{t} c(s)\zeta(-s).$$

Obviously,

$$\lim_{t\to\infty} \eta^{(t)} = c(0)\zeta(0)$$

and

$$\lim_{t\to\infty} \{E\eta_k^{(t)}\bar{\eta}_l^{(t)}\}_{k=1,n}^{l=\overline{1,n}} = \Gamma(0)\overset{*}{\Gamma}(0).$$

We have

$$\{E\eta_k^{(t)}\bar{\eta}_l^{(t)}\}_{k=1,n}^{l=\overline{1,n}} = \int_{-\pi}^{\pi} P(e^{-i\lambda})f(\lambda)\overset{*}{P}(e^{-i\lambda})\, d\lambda,$$

where the matrix function P is defined by

$$P(e^{-i\lambda}) = I_n - \sum_{s=1}^{t} c(s)\Gamma^{-1}e^{-i\lambda s}.$$

Setting $g(\lambda) = P(e^{-i\lambda})f(\lambda)\overset{*}{P}(e^{-i\lambda})$, we obtain from Lemma 6.1

$$\begin{aligned}\log\det\frac{1}{2\pi}\int_{-\pi}^{\pi} g(\lambda)\,d\lambda &\geq \frac{1}{2\pi}\int_{-\pi}^{\pi}\log[\det g(\lambda)]\,d\lambda \\ &= \frac{1}{2\pi}\int_{-\pi}^{\pi}\log|\det P(e^{-i\lambda})|^2\,d\lambda + \frac{1}{2\pi}\int_{-\pi}^{\pi}\log\det f(\lambda)\,d\lambda \\ &\geq \log|\det P(0)|^2 + \frac{1}{2\pi}\int_{-\pi}^{\pi}\log\det f(\lambda)\,d\lambda \\ &= \frac{1}{2\pi}\int_{-\pi}^{\pi}\log\det f(\lambda)\,d\lambda,\end{aligned}$$

since $P(0) = I_n$. Passing to the limit $t \to \infty$, we obtain

$$\log\frac{1}{(2\pi)^n}|\det\Gamma(0)|^2 \geq \frac{1}{2\pi}\int_{-\pi}^{\pi}\log\det f(\lambda).$$

Together with (6.10) and Lemma 6.1, this inequality proves the theorem.

As has been mentioned, an important class of stationary processes are those with spectral densities $f(\lambda)$ whose elements $f_{kl}(\lambda)$ are rational functions of $e^{-i\lambda}$. If $\boldsymbol{\xi} = \{\xi_k(t)\}_{k=\overline{1,n}}$ is such a process, and its spectral density $f(\lambda)$ is not degenerate, then $\boldsymbol{\xi}$ is regular with rank n, since the rational function $\det f(\lambda)$ will then necessarily satisfy condition (6.5) of Theorem 6.1. Let us suppose that we have succeeded in finding a matrix function $\Gamma(z)$ which is analytic in the unit disc, satisfies the boundary condition (6.1), whose elements $\Gamma_{kj}(z)$ are rational functions of z, and whose determinant does not vanish in the unit disc. In this case the function $\log(2\pi)^{-n/2}\det\Gamma(z)$ will also be analytic in the unit disc, and its real part $\log(2\pi)^{-n/2}|\det\Gamma(z)|$ will be harmonic in the unit disc and continuous on its boundary $z = e^{i\lambda}$, with the possible exception of a finite number of points, at which it will equal $-\infty$. Therefore, analogous to (5.21),

$$\log\frac{|\det\Gamma(0)|}{(2\pi)^{n/2}} = \frac{1}{4\pi}\int_{-\pi}^{\pi}\log\det f(\lambda)\,d\lambda. \tag{6.11}$$

Hence, we conclude from Theorem 6.2 that $\Gamma(z)$ is a maximal matrix. The maximal matrix $\Gamma(z)$ coincides with the matrix which figures in the representation (10.12) of Theorem 10.1, Chapter I, and can be effectively found by the methods described in Section 10, Chapter I.

Thus, the following result holds.

Theorem 6.3. *Let* $\boldsymbol{\xi} = \{\xi_k(t)\}_{k=\overline{1,n}}$ *be a linearly regular stationary* *process of maximal rank, with spectral density $f(\lambda)$ and spectral representation*

$$\xi(t) = \int_{-\pi}^{\pi} e^{i\lambda t}\Phi(d\lambda) . \tag{6.12}$$

Then the stationary process $\hat{\xi}(\cdot, \tau) = \{\hat{\xi}_k(t, \tau)\}_{k=\overline{1,n}}$, consisting of the best linear forecasts (τ steps ahead) of the process ξ, is obtained from ξ by a linear transformation:

$$\hat{\xi}(t, \tau) = \int_{-\pi}^{\pi} e^{i\lambda t}\hat{\varphi}(\lambda, \tau)\Phi(d\lambda) . \tag{6.13}$$

The spectral characteristic $\hat{\varphi}(\lambda, \tau)$ has the form

$$\hat{\varphi}(\lambda, \tau) = e^{i\lambda\tau}\left[\varphi(\lambda) - \sum_{0}^{\tau-1} c(s)e^{-i\lambda s}\right]\varphi^{-1}(\lambda) , \tag{6.14}$$

where $\varphi(\lambda) = \Gamma(e^{-i\lambda})$ is the boundary value of a matrix function $\Gamma(z)$ which is analytic in the unit disc and satisfies conditions (6.1) *and* (6.9), *and the coefficients $c(s)$ are the coefficients in the power series expansion of $\Gamma(z)$:*

$$\Gamma(z) = \sum_{s=0}^{\infty} c(s)z^s .$$

In the case where the elements of the spectral density $f(\lambda)$ are rational functions of $e^{-i\lambda}$, the matrix $\Gamma(z)$ is rational (and can be found by means of algebraic operations described in Lemma 10.3, *Chapter I, and Lemma* 6.2).

7. Linear extrapolation of stationary processes whose values form a basis

Let ξ be an n-dimensional stationary process, and H_ξ its space of values. We will say that the values $\xi_k(t)$ *form a basis*, if any element $h \in H_\xi$ can be represented in the form of a series

$$h = \sum_{k=1}^{n} \sum_{-\infty}^{\infty} a_k(t)\xi_k(t) , \tag{7.1}$$

which converges in mean square, if this representation is unique, and if the sum of the series in (7.1) does not change under arbitrary permutation of its terms.

Theorem 7.1. *If the stationary n-dimensional process ξ has a spectral density f which satisfies the condition*†

† Recall that the inequality $A \geq B$ means that the difference $A - B$ is positive definite.

$$c_1 I_n \leq f(\lambda) \leq c_2 I_n \tag{7.2}$$

for almost all λ, *for certain constants* c_1 *and* c_2, $0 < c_1 \leq c_2 < \infty$, *then its values* $\xi_k(t)$, $k = \overline{1, n}$, $-\infty < t < \infty$, *form a basis in* H_ξ.

Proof. Every element $h \in H_\xi$ can be represented in the form

$$h = \int_{-\pi}^{\pi} \varphi(\lambda) \Phi(d\lambda), \tag{7.3}$$

where $\Phi = \{\Phi_k\}_{k=\overline{1,n}}$ is the random spectral measure of $\boldsymbol{\xi}$, and $\varphi = \{\varphi_k\}^{k=\overline{1,n}}$ is some vector function in the space $L^2(F)$, i.e., such that

$$\int_{-\pi}^{\pi} [\varphi f \overset{*}{\varphi}]\, d\lambda < \infty .$$

By virtue of (7.2),

$$c_1 ||\varphi(\lambda)||^2 \leq \varphi(\lambda) f(\lambda) \overset{*}{\varphi}(\lambda) \leq c_2 ||\varphi(\lambda)||^2 ,$$

from which it is evident that every component $\varphi_k(\lambda)$, $k = \overline{1, n}$, of $\varphi(\lambda)$ is square integrable, and

$$c_1 \int_{-\pi}^{\pi} ||\varphi(\lambda)||^2 \, d\lambda \leq \boldsymbol{E} |h|^2 \leq c_2 \int_{-\pi}^{\pi} ||\varphi(\lambda)||^2 \, d\lambda . \tag{7.4}$$

We expand the functions $\varphi_k(\lambda)$, $k = \overline{1, n}$, in Fourier series:

$$\varphi_k(\lambda) = \sum_{-\infty}^{\infty} a_k(t) e^{i\lambda t}, \qquad k = \overline{1, n} . \tag{7.5}$$

Applying an inequality analogous to (7.4) to the difference

$$h - \sum_{k=1}^{n} \sum_{-N}^{N} a_k(t) \xi_k(t) ,$$

we obtain

$$\boldsymbol{E} \left| h - \sum_{k=1}^{n} \sum_{-N}^{N} a_k(t) \xi_k(t) \right|^2 \leq 2\pi c_2 \sum_{k=1}^{n} \sum_{|t|>N} |a_k(t)|^2 .$$

From this it is evident that h can be represented in the form (7.1). On the other hand, if (7.1) is some expansion of h in a series in the values of the process $\boldsymbol{\xi}$, then

$$\begin{aligned} 0 &= \lim_{N\to\infty} \boldsymbol{E} \left| h - \sum_{k=1}^{n} \sum_{-N}^{N} a_k(t) \xi_k(t) \right|^2 \\ &\geq \lim_{N\to\infty} c_1 \sum_{k=1}^{n} \int_{-\pi}^{\pi} \left| \varphi_k(\lambda) - \sum_{-N}^{N} a_k(t) e^{i\lambda t} \right|^2 d\lambda \geq 0 , \end{aligned}$$

from which we see that the coefficients $a_k(t)$ of this expansion coincide with the Fourier coefficients of the functions $\varphi_k(\lambda)$, $k = \overline{1, n}$, appearing in the representation (7.3) of h. To complete the proof of the theorem, it suffices to remark that the series in (7.5) converge to the $\varphi_k(\lambda)$, $k = \overline{1, n}$, in mean square for any permutations of their terms.

Let us turn now to the problem of the linear extrapolation of a stationary n-dimensional process $\boldsymbol{\xi}$. Let the spectral density $f(\lambda)$ of $\boldsymbol{\xi}$ satisfy condition (7.2). We may suppose, without restriction of generality, that

$$f(\lambda) = I_n + M(\lambda)\,, \qquad |||M(\lambda)||| \leq q < 1\,, \tag{7.6}$$

where $|||\cdot|||$ denotes the ordinary operator norm of an $n \times n$ matrix, since, in the contrary case, we could solve the problem of extrapolation for the process $\boldsymbol{\eta}$, $\eta(t) = \sqrt{2}\,(c_1 + c_2)^{-1/2}\xi(t)$, whose spectral density $g(\lambda) = 2(c_1 + c_2)^{-1} f(\lambda)$ does meet this requirement:

$$|||g(\lambda) - I_n||| \leq \frac{c_2 - c_1}{c_2 + c_1} < 1\,.$$

Obviously,

$$\hat{\xi}(t, \tau) = \sqrt{\frac{c_1 + c_2}{2}}\,\hat{\eta}(t, \tau)\,. \tag{7.7}$$

Thus, suppose that the spectral density $f(\lambda)$ satisfies condition (7.6). We consider the space $\boldsymbol{L}^2$ of matrix functions $\varphi(\lambda) = \{\varphi_{kj}(\lambda)\}_{k=\overline{1,n}}^{j=\overline{1,n}}$ for which

$$\int_{-\pi}^{\pi} ||\varphi(\lambda)||^2\, d\lambda < \infty \tag{7.8}$$

(each of the components $\varphi_{kj}(\lambda)$ is square integrable).

A matrix function φ from $\boldsymbol{L}^2$ can be represented in the form of a Fourier series which is convergent in mean square:

$$\begin{aligned} \varphi(\lambda) &= \sum_{-\infty}^{\infty} a(t) e^{-i\lambda t}\,, \\ a(t) &= \frac{1}{2\pi}\int_{-\pi}^{\pi} e^{i\lambda t}\varphi(\lambda)\, d\lambda\,, \end{aligned} \tag{7.9}$$

and

$$\sum_{-\infty}^{\infty} ||a(t)||^2 = \frac{1}{2\pi}\int_{-\pi}^{\pi} ||\varphi(\lambda)||^2\, d\lambda\,.$$

If we introduce a scalar product in $\boldsymbol{L}^2$ according to

$$(\varphi, \psi) = \frac{1}{2\pi}\int_{-\pi}^{\pi} \mathrm{Sp}\,[\varphi(\lambda)\overset{*}{\psi}(\lambda)]\, d\lambda\,, \tag{7.10}$$

then it becomes a Hilbert space with the norm $||\varphi|| = (\varphi, \varphi)^{1/2}$.

Let us denote by $\varphi_-(\lambda)$, $\varphi_{-0}(\lambda)$, $\varphi_0(\lambda)$, $\varphi_{0+}(\lambda)$ and $\varphi_+(\lambda)$ the matrix functions obtained from $\varphi(\lambda)$,

$$\varphi(\lambda) = \sum_{-\infty}^{\infty} a(t) e^{-i\lambda t} ,$$

in the following way:

$$\begin{aligned} &\varphi_-(\lambda) = \sum_{1}^{\infty} a(t) e^{-i\lambda t} , \quad \varphi_{-0}(\lambda) = \sum_{0}^{\infty} a(t) e^{-i\lambda t} , \\ &\varphi_0(\lambda) = a(0) , \\ &\varphi_{0+}(\lambda) = \sum_{-\infty}^{0} a(t) e^{-i\lambda t} , \quad \varphi_+(\lambda) = \sum_{-\infty}^{-1} a(t) e^{-i\lambda t} . \end{aligned} \tag{7.11}$$

We denote the collections of all matrices of these types by $\boldsymbol{L}^2_-$, $\boldsymbol{L}^2_{-0}$, $\boldsymbol{L}^2_0$, $\boldsymbol{L}^2_{0+}$ and $\boldsymbol{L}^2_+$, respectively. Obviously, $\boldsymbol{L}^2_-$, $\boldsymbol{L}^2_0$ and $\boldsymbol{L}^2_+$ are orthogonal subspaces in $\boldsymbol{L}^2$:

$$\boldsymbol{L}^2 = \boldsymbol{L}^2_- \oplus \boldsymbol{L}^2_0 \oplus \boldsymbol{L}^2_+ \qquad \boldsymbol{L}^2_{-0} = \boldsymbol{L}^2_- \oplus \boldsymbol{L}^2_0 , \qquad \boldsymbol{L}^2_{0+} = \boldsymbol{L}^2_0 \oplus \boldsymbol{L}^2_+ . \tag{7.12}$$

We further define operators B_+ and B_- on $\boldsymbol{L}^2$ by

$$\begin{aligned} B_-(\varphi) &= [\varphi(\lambda) M(\lambda)]_- , \\ B_+(\varphi) &= [M(\lambda)\varphi(\lambda)]_+ . \end{aligned} \tag{7.13}$$

Lemma 7.1. *The operators B_+ and B_- satisfy*

$$\|B_\mp\| \le q , \tag{7.14}$$

where q is the constant appearing in condition (7.6).

Proof. Since the matrix function $M(\lambda)$ is bounded, the product $\Phi = \varphi M$ belongs to $\boldsymbol{L}^2$ for any $\varphi \in \boldsymbol{L}^2$, and by condition (7.6)

$$\|\Phi(\lambda)\|^2 \le q^2 \|\varphi(\lambda)\|^2$$

for almost all λ, and, consequently,

$$\|\Phi\|^2 = \frac{1}{2\pi}\int_{-\pi}^{\pi} \|\Phi(\lambda)\|^2 \, d\lambda \le q^2 \frac{1}{2\pi}\int_{-\pi}^{\pi} \|\varphi(\lambda)\|^2 \, d\lambda = q^2 \|\varphi\|^2 . \tag{7.15}$$

Let

$$\Phi(\lambda) = \sum_{-\infty}^{\infty} b(t) e^{-i\lambda t}$$

be the Fourier series expansion of $\Phi(\lambda)$. Then

$$\|\Phi\|^2 = \sum_{-\infty}^{\infty} \|b(t)\|^2 ,$$

and from (7.15) we obtain

$$\|B_-(\varphi)\|^2 = \|\Phi_-\|^2 = \sum_1^\infty \|b(t)\|^2 \leq q^2 \|\varphi\|^2 ,$$

which proves the assertion of the lemma concerning B_-. The proof of (7.14) for B_+ is the same. ▮

It follows from Lemma 7.1 that the operators $(E + B_-)^{-1}$ and $(E + B_+)^{-1}$ exist, where E is the identity operator in $\boldsymbol{L}^2$:

$$\begin{aligned} (E + B_-)^{-1} &= E - B_- + (B_-)^2 - (B_-)^3 + \cdots , \\ (E + B_+)^{-1} &= E - B_+ + (B_+)^2 - (B_+)^3 + \cdots , \end{aligned} \tag{7.16}$$

and the series converge in the operator norm. We put

$$\begin{aligned} \Psi_{-0}(e^{-i\lambda}) &= (E + B_-)^{-1} I_n \\ &= I_n - M_- + (M_- M)_- - [(M_- M)_- M]_- + \cdots , \\ \Psi_{0+}(e^{i\lambda}) &= (E + B_+)^{-1} I_n \\ &= I_n - M_+ + (M M_+)_+ - [M(M M_+)_+]_+ + \cdots . \end{aligned} \tag{7.17}$$

Lemma 7.2. *We have the following relations*:

$$\begin{aligned} &1.\ (I_n + M)\Psi_{0+} = I_n + (M\Psi_{0+})_{-0} ; \\ &2.\ \Psi_{-0}(I_n + M) = I_n + (\Psi_{-0} M)_{0+} ; \\ &3.\ G = \Psi_{-0}(I_n + M)\Psi_{0+} = I_n + (M\Psi_{0+})_0 = I_n + (\Psi_{-0} M)_0 = G_0 . \end{aligned} \tag{7.18}$$

Proof. It is easy to see that

$$\begin{aligned} (I_n + M)\Psi_{0+} &= \Psi_{0+} + M\Psi_{0+} = \Psi_{0+} + (M\Psi_{0+})_+ + (M\Psi_{0+})_{-0} \\ &= \Psi_{0+} + B_+(\Psi_{0+}) + (M\Psi_{0+})_{-0} \\ &= (E + B_+)^{-1} I_n + B_+(E + B_+)^{-1} I_n + (M\Psi_{0+})_{-0} \\ &= I_n + (M\Psi_{0+})_{-0} . \end{aligned}$$

The verification of relation 2 is analogous. Further, using relations 1 and 2 we have

$$G = \Psi_{-0}(I_n + M)\Psi_{0+} = \Psi_{-0}[I_n + (M\Psi_{0+})_{-0}] = [I_n + (\Psi_{-0} M)_{0+}]\Psi_{0+} ,$$

from which it is evident that the matrix G belongs to both $\boldsymbol{L}^2_{-0}$ and $\boldsymbol{L}^2_{0+}$, which is possible only when $G(\lambda)$ is a constant, $G(\lambda) = G_0$, as was to be proved.

Lemma 7.3. *The matrix functions $\Psi_{-0}(e^{-i\lambda})$, $\Psi_{0+}(e^{i\lambda})$ and G are nondegenerate for almost all λ.*

Proof. Let

$$\Psi_{-0}(e^{-i\lambda}) = \sum_{t=0}^\infty c(t) e^{-i\lambda t}$$

be the Fourier series expansion of $\Psi_{-0}(e^{-i\lambda})$. Then, since

$$\sum_{t=0}^{\infty} ||c(t)||^2 < \infty ,$$

the matrix function $\Psi_{-0}(z)$,

$$\Psi_{-0}(z) = \sum_{t=0}^{\infty} c(t) z^t ,$$

will be analytic in the unit disc. Its determinant is also an analytic function, which is not identically zero because $c(0) = I_n$ and, therefore, $\det \Psi_{-0}(0) = 1$. Therefore,† the boundary value of $\det \Psi_{-0}(z)$ is different from zero almost everywhere; i.e., $\det \Psi_{-0}(e^{-i\lambda})$ is different from zero almost everywhere. The proof of the nondegeneracy of $\Psi_{0+}(e^{+i\lambda})$ for almost all λ is completely analogous. Since G is the product of the matrices Ψ_{-0}, $I_n + M$ and Ψ_{0+}, each of which is nondegenerate for almost all λ, G is, consequently, nondegenerate.

From relations (7.18) we obtain

$$\begin{aligned} \Psi_{-0}^{-1}(e^{-i\lambda}) &= [I_n + (M\Psi_{0+})_{-0}]G^{-1} \in \boldsymbol{L}_{-0}^2 , \\ \Psi_{0+}^{-1}(e^{i\lambda}) &= G^{-1}[I_n + (\Psi_{-0}M)_{0+}] \in \boldsymbol{L}_{0+}^2 . \end{aligned} \tag{7.19}$$

Lemma 7.4. *The following relations are valid*:

$$\begin{aligned} &\int_{-\pi}^{\pi} \log |\det \Psi_{-0}(e^{-i\lambda})| \, d\lambda = \int_{-\pi}^{\pi} \log |\det \Psi_{0+}(e^{i\lambda})| \, d\lambda = 0 , \\ &\int_{-\pi}^{\pi} \log \det (I_n + M) \, d\lambda = \log |\det G| . \end{aligned} \tag{7.20}$$

Proof. We consider the analytic matrix $\Psi_{-0}(z)$ (whose components belong to the class H_2) and a maximal matrix $\Gamma(z)$ which satisfies the same boundary condition as $\Psi_{-0}(z)$:

$$\Gamma(e^{-i\lambda})\overset{*}{\Gamma}(e^{-i\lambda}) = \Psi_{-0}(e^{-i\lambda})\overset{*}{\Psi}_{-0}(e^{-i\lambda}) .$$

From the results of the preceeding section it follows that

$$|\det \Psi_{-0}(0)| \le |\det \Gamma(0)| = \exp\left\{\frac{1}{2\pi}\int_{-\pi}^{\pi} \log |\det \Psi_{-0}(e^{-i\lambda})| \, d\lambda\right\} .$$

Since $\det \Psi_{-0}(0) = 1$, we obtain

$$0 \le \int_{-\pi}^{\pi} \log |\det \Psi_{-0}(e^{-i\lambda})| \, d\lambda .$$

Considering now the function $\Psi_{-0}^{-1}(z)$, we arrive in the same way at the inequality

$$0 \le \int_{-\pi}^{\pi} \log |\det \Psi_{-0}^{-1}(e^{-i\lambda})| \, d\lambda = - \int_{-\pi}^{\pi} \log |\det \Psi_{-0}(e^{-i\lambda})| \, d\lambda .$$

† See Privalov[*] or Hoffman[*].

The last two relations imply that

$$\int_{-\pi}^{\pi} \log |\det \Psi_{-0}(e^{-i\lambda})| \, d\lambda = 0 .$$

One can prove the vanishing of the second integral in the first of the relations (7.20) by the same considerations.

Finally, from the definition of G $(G = G_0)$, it is evident that

$$\det G_0 = \det \Psi_{-0}(e^{-i\lambda}) \det (I_n + M) \det \Psi_{0+}(e^{i\lambda}) ;$$

hence,

$$\begin{aligned} &\frac{1}{2\pi}\int_{-\pi}^{\pi} \log |\det (I_n + M)| \, d\lambda \\ &= \frac{1}{2\pi}\int_{-\pi}^{\pi} \log |\det \Psi_{-0}(e^{-i\lambda}) \det (I_n + M) \det \Psi_{0+}(e^{i\lambda})| \, d\lambda \\ &= \frac{1}{2\pi}\int_{-\pi}^{\pi} \log |\det G_0| \, d\lambda = \log |\det G_0| , \end{aligned}$$

which was to be proved. ▮

Lemma 7.5. *The matrix function $\Psi_{-0}(e^{-i\lambda})$ is the adjoint of $\Psi_{0+}(e^{i\lambda})$:*

$$\Psi_{-0}(e^{-i\lambda}) = \overset{*}{\Psi}_{0+}(e^{i\lambda}) , \tag{7.21}$$

and G_0 is positive definite.

Proof. Since $M(\lambda)$ is self-adjoint, $\overset{*}{M}(\lambda) = M(\lambda)$, then

$$\overset{*}{M}_-(\lambda) = M_+(\lambda) ;$$

consequently $\overset{*}{B}_-(I_n) = B_+(I_n)$. Similarly, we see that

$$\overset{*}{B}{}^m_-(I_n) = B^m_+(I_n) ,$$

which, by virtue of (7.16) and (7.17), proves (7.21). The positive definiteness of G_0 is obvious:

$$G_0 = \Psi_{-0}(I_n + M)\Psi_{0+} = \Psi_{-0}(I_n + M)\overset{*}{\Psi}_{-0} . \ ▮$$

Let $G_0^{1/2}$ denote the positive square root of G_0. The preceding lemmas show that the analytic matrix

$$\Gamma(z) = \sqrt{2\pi}\, \Psi_{-0}^{-1}(z) G_0^{1/2} \tag{7.22}$$

satisfies the boundary condition

$$\frac{1}{2\pi}\Gamma(e^{-i\lambda})\overset{*}{\Gamma}(e^{-i\lambda}) = (I_n + M) = f(\lambda) \tag{7.23}$$

and, moreover,

$$\log \left| \det \frac{\Gamma(0)}{\sqrt{2\pi}} \right|^2 = \log \det G_0 = \frac{1}{2\pi} \int_{-\pi}^{\pi} \log \det f(\lambda)\, d\lambda\,. \tag{7.24}$$

Relations (7.23) and (7.24) (cf. Theorem 6.2) imply that the matrix function $\Gamma(z)$, defined by (7.22), is maximal.

We have thus proven the following result.

Theorem 7.2. *If the spectral density* $f(\lambda)$ *meets requirement* (7.6), *then a maximal analytic matrix* $\Gamma(z)$, *satisfying the boundary condition* (7.23), *can be found from* (7.22).

Taking into consideration that the values of the corresponding process ξ form a basis in the space H_ξ, as a corollary of Theorems 6.1 and 6.3 we obtain the following theorem.

Theorem 7.3. *Let* ξ *be an n-dimensional stationary process with a spectral density f satisfying condition* (7.6). *Then the stationary process* $\hat{\xi}(\cdot, \tau) = \{\hat{\xi}_k(t, \tau)\}_{k=\overline{1,n}}$, *consisting of the best linear forecasts of* ξ (τ *steps ahead*), *is obtained from* ξ *by a moving average*:

$$\hat{\xi}(t, \tau) = \sum_{s \le t} a(t-s)\xi(s)\,. \tag{7.25}$$

The coefficients $a(s) = \{a_{kj}(s)\}_{k=\overline{1,n}}^{j=\overline{1,n}}$, $s \ge 0$, *in* (7.25) *coincide with the Fourier coefficients of the matrix function*

$$\hat{\varphi}(\lambda, \tau) = e^{i\lambda\tau}\left[\varphi(\lambda) - \sum_{0}^{\tau-1} c(s) e^{-i\lambda s}\right]\varphi^{-1}(\lambda)\,, \tag{7.26}$$

where

$$\begin{aligned} \varphi(\lambda) &= \sqrt{2\pi}\,[_n + (M\Psi_{0+})_{-0}]G_0^{-1/2}\,, \\ \Psi_{0+}(e^{i\lambda}) &= I_n - M_+ + (MM_+)_+ - [M(MM_+)_+]_+ + \cdots\,, \\ G &= \overset{*}{\Psi}_{0+} f(\lambda) \Psi_{0+}\,, \end{aligned} \tag{7.27}$$

and the $c(s)$ *are the Fourier coefficients of the matrix function* φ.

8. A general criterion for the regularity, and linear extrapolation, of processes of rank 1

As we have seen, the analytic criterion for the linear regularity of a stationary process with maximal rank, given in Theorem 6.1, is rather simple and effective. Unfortunately, this is no longer true in the general case. In order to formulate a general criterion for regularity, we need some definitions.

We have already introduced the class H_δ of analytic functions $\gamma(z)$ having the property that

$$H_\delta(\gamma) = \sup_{0 \le \rho < 1} \int_{-\pi}^{\pi} |\gamma(\rho e^{-i\lambda})|^\delta\, d\lambda < \infty\,. \tag{8.1}$$

We will say that a function $\gamma(z)$ of a complex variable z, $|z| < 1$, belongs to the class N_δ, if it can be represented as the ratio

$$\gamma(z) = \frac{\gamma_1(z)}{\gamma_2(z)} \tag{8.2}$$

of functions $\gamma_1(z)$ and $\gamma_2(z)$ of class H_δ.

The properties of functions of the classes H_δ and N_δ have been intensively studied (cf., for example, Privalov[*]). Therefore, although we require a knowledge of these properties, we will not prove them, confining ourselves to references to the specialized literature.†

From the uniqueness theorem for analytic functions it follows that a function $\gamma(z)$ of the class N_δ, having a radial limit at almost every point λ of the boundary $z = e^{-i\lambda}$,

$$\gamma(e^{-i\lambda}) = \lim_{\rho \to 1} \gamma(\rho e^{-i\lambda}), \tag{8.3}$$

is uniquely determined by its radial limit (Privalov[*]).

Theorem 8.1. *In order that a stationary n-dimensional process* ξ *be linearly regular and of rank m, it is necessary and sufficient that:*

1. ξ *have a spectral density* $f(\lambda)$ *which has rank m for almost all* λ.
2. $f(\lambda)$ *have a principal minor* $M(\lambda) = \det \{f_{i_p j_q}(\lambda)\}_{p=\overline{1,m}}^{q=\overline{1,m}}$ *which is different from zero almost everywhere, and such that*

$$\int_{-\pi}^{\pi} \log M(\lambda)\, d\lambda > -\infty .$$

3. *The functions* $\gamma_{kj}(e^{-i\lambda}) = M_{kj}(\lambda)/M(\lambda)$ *(where* $M_{kj}(\lambda)$ *denotes the determinant obtained from* $M(\lambda)$ *by replacing its* jth *row by the row* $f_{k i_p}(\lambda)$, $p = \overline{1, m}$*) be the boundary values of functions of class* N_δ *for some* $\delta > 0$.‡

Let us remark at once that, unfortunately, there is no general method for determining, from the boundary value $\gamma(e^{-i\lambda})$ of a function $\gamma(z)$, whether it belongs to a class N_δ. Thus, although the theorem clarifies the analytic nature of the regularity of a stationary process, it is not adequately effective.

Proof. Let the n-dimensional process ξ be regular. Then, by Theorem 4.1, ξ has a spectral density f satisfying condition 1, and,

† A complete proof of the properties of functions of the classes H_δ and N_δ which we need would require writing a special chapter, and since these properties will only be used in the present section, it seemed to us advisable to refer the reader to the specialized literature.

‡ As we shall see, if ξ is regular, then automatically $\delta = 2/m$.

moreover, admitting a factorization:

$$f(\lambda) = \Gamma(e^{-i\lambda})\overset{*}{\Gamma}(e^{-i\lambda}) , \tag{8.4}$$

where $\Gamma(z) = \{\Gamma_{kj}(z)\}_{k=\overline{1,n}}^{j=\overline{1,m}}$ is analytic in the unit disc. From (8.4) it is evident that every principal minor $M(\lambda) = \det \{f_{i_p j_q}(\lambda)\}_{p=\overline{1,m}}^{q=\overline{1,m}}$ of f has the form

$$M(\lambda) = \left|\det \{\Gamma_{i_p j} (e^{-i\lambda})\}_{p=\overline{1,m}}^{j=\overline{1,m}}\right|^2 , \tag{8.5}$$

and, since the function $\det \{\Gamma_{i_p j}(z)\}_{p=\overline{1,m}}^{j=\overline{1,m}}$ is analytic in the unit disc, $M(\lambda)$ is either identically zero or almost everywhere different from zero. Now the rank of the positive definite matrix f equals m for almost all λ, and therefore the sum of all its principal minors of order m is almost everywhere different from zero. Consequently, there exists some principal minor $M(\lambda)$ which is different from zero almost everywhere.

We have, further,

$$f_{kl}(\lambda) = \sum_{p=1}^{m} \theta_{ki_p}(\lambda) f_{i_p l}(\lambda) \tag{8.6}$$

for all k and l, for certain functions $\theta_{ki_p}(\lambda)$, since every row of the matrix f is a linear combination of the m rows $\{f_{i_p l}(\lambda)\}^{l=\overline{1,n}}$, $p = \overline{1, m}$, where the i_p refer to the minor $M(\lambda)$ which is nonzero almost everywhere.

It is evident from (8.4) and (8.6) that

$$\begin{aligned} \sum_{j=1}^{m} \Gamma_{kj}(e^{-i\lambda})\overline{\Gamma_{lj}(e^{-i\lambda})} &= \sum_{p=1}^{m} \theta_{ki_p}(\lambda) \sum_{j=1}^{m} \Gamma_{i_p j}(e^{-i\lambda})\overline{\Gamma_{lj}(e^{-i\lambda})} \\ &= \sum_{j=1}^{m} \left[\sum_{p=1}^{m} \theta_{ki_p}(\lambda)\Gamma_{i_p j} (e^{-i\lambda}) \right]\overline{\Gamma_{lj}(e^{-i\lambda})} \end{aligned} \tag{8.7}$$

for $l = i_1, i_2, \ldots, i_m$. But the determinant of the matrix $\{\Gamma_{i_p j}(e^{-i\lambda})\}_{p=\overline{1,m}}^{j=\overline{1,m}}$ is related to the minor $M(\lambda)$ by relation (8.5). Since $M(\lambda)$ is almost everywhere different from zero, this determinant is also different from zero almost everywhere. We must therefore have

$$\Gamma_{kj}(e^{-i\lambda}) = \sum_{p=1}^{m} \theta_{ki_p}(\lambda)\Gamma_{i_p j}(e^{-i\lambda}) \tag{8.8}$$

for all k and j. By Cramer's rule, we find from (8.6) and (8.8) that

$$\theta_{kj}(\lambda) = \frac{M_{kj}(\lambda)}{M(\lambda)} = \frac{\tilde{M}_{kj}(e^{-i\lambda})}{\tilde{M}(e^{-i\lambda})} , \tag{8.9}$$

where $\tilde{M}(z) = \det \{\Gamma_{i_p j}(z)\}_{p=\overline{1,m}}^{j=\overline{1,m}}$, and $\tilde{M}_{kj}(z)$ is obtained from $\tilde{M}(z)$ by replacing its jth row by the kth row of $\Gamma(z)$.

Since the elements $\Gamma_{kj}(z)$ of $\Gamma(z)$ are functions of the class H_2, the functions $\tilde{M}(z)$ and $\tilde{M}_{kj}(z)$ belong to the class $H_{2/m}$,† and we conclude from (8.9) that the $\gamma_{kj}(e^{-i\lambda}) = \theta_{kj}(\lambda)$ are the boundary values of functions $\gamma_{kj}(z)$ of class $N_{2/m}$. Thus, the necessity of condition 3 of the theorem is proved.

Condition 2 is also fulfilled because $M(\lambda)$ coincides with the modulus squared of the boundary value $\tilde{M}(e^{-i\lambda})$ of an analytic function $\tilde{M}(z)$ of class $H_{2/m}$ (cf. Privalov[*] or Hoffman[*]).

Let us now prove the sufficiency of conditions 1–3. If they are fulfilled, then relation (8.6) holds, where $\theta_{ki_p}(\lambda) = \gamma_{ki_p}(e^{-i\lambda})$ are the boundary values of functions $\gamma_{ki_p}(z)$ of class N_δ.

Further, by Theorem 6.1 the stationary process $\{\xi_{i_p}(t)\}_{p=\overline{1,m}}$ is regular, and therefore its spectral density $\{f_{i_p i_q}(\lambda)\}_{p=\overline{1,m}}^{q=\overline{1,m}}$ admits a factorization:

$$f_{i_p i_q}(\lambda) = \sum_{j=1}^{m} \tilde{\Gamma}_{i_p j}(e^{-i\lambda})\overline{\tilde{\Gamma}_{i_q j}(e^{-i\lambda})} . \tag{8.10}$$

Consequently,

$$\begin{aligned} f_{kj}(\lambda) &= \sum_{p=1}^{m} \theta_{ki_p}(\lambda) \sum_{j=1}^{m} \tilde{\Gamma}_{i_p j}(e^{-i\lambda})\overline{\tilde{\Gamma}_{i_q j}(e^{-i\lambda})} \\ &= \sum_{j=1}^{m} \left[\sum_{p=1}^{m} \theta_{ki_p}(\lambda)\tilde{\Gamma}_{i_p j}(e^{-i\lambda}) \right] \overline{\tilde{\Gamma}_{i_q j}(e^{-i\lambda})} . \end{aligned} \tag{8.11}$$

From the parametric representation of a function of class H_δ (see, for example, Privalov[*]) there follows the existence of a bounded analytic function $\beta(z)$,

$$|\beta(e^{-i\lambda})| = 1 \tag{8.12}$$

for almost all λ, such that the products $\alpha_{kj}(z) = \beta(z)\gamma_{kj}(z)$ (where the $\gamma_{kj}(z)$ are the functions of class N_δ appearing in condition 3 of the theorem) are analytic, and belong to some linear class of functions having the property that if a product $\prod(z)$ of functions of this class is such that

$$\int_{-\pi}^{\pi} |\prod(e^{-i\lambda})|^\delta \, d\lambda < \infty ,$$

then $\prod(z) \in H_\delta$.

Let us put

$$\Gamma_{kj}(z) = \begin{cases} \beta(z)\tilde{\Gamma}_{kj}(z) , & k = i_1, i_2, \ldots, i_m , \\ \sum_{p=1}^{m} \gamma_{ki_p}(z)\Gamma_{i_p j}(z) & \text{for remaining } k. \end{cases}$$

† This follows from the fact that if $a(z) \in H_{\delta'}$ and $b(z) \in H_{\delta''}$, then $c(z) = a(z)b(z) \in H_\delta$, where $\delta = \delta'\delta''/(\delta' + \delta'')$.

Taking into consideration that $\gamma_{kj}(e^{-i\lambda}) = \theta_{kj}(\lambda)$, we conclude from relations (8.10)—(8.12) that

$$\sum_{j=1}^{m} \Gamma_{kj}(e^{-i\lambda})\overline{\Gamma_{ej}(e^{-i\lambda})} = f_{ke}(\lambda) . \tag{8.13}$$

This equality shows that the analytic functions $\Gamma_{kj}(z)$ in fact belong to the class H_2, since the elements $f_{kk}(\lambda) = \sum_{j=1}^{m} |\Gamma_{kj}(e^{-i\lambda})|^2$, $k = \overline{1, n}$, of the spectral density are integrable.

The spectral density f of ξ therefore admits a factorization, which means that ξ is regular. ∎

Remark 1. As is evident from the proof of Theorem 8.1, if the n-dimensional process ξ is regular, then condition 3 of Theorem 8.1 must be fulfilled by all functions $\gamma_{kj}(e^{-i\lambda})$ associated with any principal minor $M(\lambda)$ satisfying condition 2.

Remark 2. An obvious corollary of Theorem 8.1 is the following fact: *A stationary n-dimensional process ξ, having a spectral density f whose elements are rational functions of $e^{-i\lambda}$, is always regular.* Indeed, the minors of f will then be rational functions of $e^{-i\lambda}$, as will also the functions $\gamma_{kj}(e^{-i\lambda})$, and a rational function always belongs to a class N_δ for some $\delta > 0$. A maximal matrix for this case will be the matrix $\Gamma(z)$ with rational elements which has rank m at all points z, $|z| < 1$ (an effective method of finding $\Gamma(z)$ from the spectral density $f(\lambda)$ is described in detail in Section 10, Chapter I).

Indeed, since any minor $M_\Gamma(z)$ of order m of the matrix $\Gamma(z)$ (and not identically zero) satisfies a boundary condition of the type (8.5), and since the function $M_\Gamma(z)$, which is rational by virtue of the rationality of $M(\lambda)$ and does not vanish, is maximal, the value $|M_\Gamma(0)|$ will be maximal; consequently $\Gamma(z)$ itself will be maximal (see Remark 2 in Section 4, Chapter II).

Let us consider in detail the case where the n-dimensional process ξ has rank 1. In this case, Theorem 8.1 can be restated in the following form.

Theorem 8.2. *An n-dimensional stationary process ξ of rank* 1 *and with spectral density f is linearly regular if and only if*

1. $\int_{-\pi}^{\pi} \log f_{jj}(\lambda)\, d\lambda > -\infty$ *for some* $j=j_0$.

2. *The ratios* $\gamma_{kj}(e^{-i\lambda}) = f_{kj}(\lambda)/f_{jj}(\lambda)$ *are the boundary values of functions of class N_δ, for some $\delta > 0$, for all* $k = \overline{1, n}$, $j = j_0$.

Obviously, if the n-dimensional process ξ is regular, each of its components ξ_k is a regular stationary process, and by Theorem 5.1

$$\int_{-\pi}^{\pi} \log f_{jj}(\lambda)\, d\lambda > -\infty$$

for all $j = \overline{1, n}$. Remark 1 above allows us to conclude that condition 2 of Theorem 8.2 must be satisfied by the functions $\gamma_{kj}(e^{-i\lambda}) = f_{kj}(\lambda)/f_{jj}(\lambda)$ for all $k, j = \overline{1, n}$.

Theorem 8.3. *A stationary process of rank* 1 *is either linearly regular or linearly stationary.*

Proof. To begin with, we note that if there is a regular process η which is subordinate to ξ, orthogonal to S_ξ and such that $H_\eta = H_\xi$, then ξ is regular. Let ξ be a stationary process of rank 1. If it is not singular, then any component, say η_1, of its regular part η is regular, orthogonal to S_ξ and subordinate to ξ. Now since ξ is of rank 1, it can be obtained by a linear transformation from some one-dimensional process ζ such that $H_\xi = H_\zeta$. The remark following Theorem 8.1 of Chapter I allows us to conclude that η_1 and ζ can each be obtained from the other by a linear transformation, so that $H_{\eta_1} = H_\zeta$. Consequently, a process ξ of rank 1 which is not singular is necessarily regular. ▮

Let us now consider an n-dimensional regular process ξ of rank 1, with spectral density f. A maximal analytic matrix, $\Gamma(z)$, satisfying the boundary condition

$$\frac{1}{2\pi}\Gamma(e^{-i\lambda})\overset{*}{\Gamma}(e^{-i\lambda}) = f(\lambda)\,, \tag{8.14}$$

will, in this case, be a column vector $\Gamma(z) = \{\Gamma_k(z)\}_{k=\overline{1,n}}$, and (8.14) means that

$$\frac{1}{2\pi}\Gamma_k(e^{-i})\Gamma^\lambda{}_l(e^{-i\lambda}) = f_{kl}(\lambda)\,, \qquad k, l = \overline{1, n}\,. \tag{8.15}$$

We will consider below the question of how the matrix $\Gamma(z)$ can be expressed in terms of the elements of the spectral density, if we consider the functions $\gamma_{kj}(z)$, $k = \overline{1, n}$, appearing in condition 2 of Theorem 8.2, as known. These functions are uniquely defined by their boundary values $\gamma_{kj}(e^{-i\lambda})$:

$$\gamma_{kj}(e^{-i\lambda}) = \frac{f_{kj}(\lambda)}{f_{jj}(\lambda)} = \frac{\Gamma_k(e^{-i\lambda})}{\Gamma_j(e^{-i\lambda})}\,, \qquad k = \overline{1, n}\,. \tag{8.16}$$

It is evident from (8.16) that it is sufficient to find only one function $\Gamma_j(z)$, since the remaining components $\Gamma_k(z)$ of the column matrix $\Gamma(z)$ can be expressed in terms of $\Gamma_j(z)$ and the $\gamma_{kj}(z)$, $k = \overline{1, n}$:

$$\Gamma_k(z) = \gamma_{kj}(z)\Gamma_j(z)\,. \tag{8.17}$$

The condition of maximality, which says that the difference $\Gamma(0)\overset{*}{\Gamma}(0) - \tilde{\Gamma}(0)\overset{*}{\tilde{\Gamma}}(0)$ is a positive definite matrix for any analytic column matrix $\tilde{\Gamma}(z) = \{\tilde{\Gamma}_k(z)\}_{k=\overline{1,n}}$ of class H_2 satisfying the boundary condition (8.14), is in the present case equivalent to the following:

$$|\Gamma_j(0)| \geq |\tilde{\Gamma}_j(0)| , \qquad j = \overline{1, n} . \tag{8.18}$$

Indeed, on the one hand, the diagonal elements of a positive definite matrix are non-negative, so that $|\Gamma_j(0)|^2 - |\tilde{\Gamma}_j(0)|^2 \geq 0$, which is (8.18). On the other hand, if (8.18) holds, then for some j, $\Gamma_j(0) \neq 0$,† and, as follows from (8.17),

$$\Gamma(0)\overset{*}{\Gamma}(0) - \tilde{\Gamma}(0)\overset{*}{\tilde{\Gamma}}(0) = (|\Gamma_j(0)|^2 - |\tilde{\Gamma}_j(0)|^2)\{\gamma_{kj}(0)\overline{\gamma_{lj}(0)}\}_{k=\overline{1,n}}^{l=\overline{1,n}}$$

which, as can be verified directly, is positive definite.

Relations (8.17) show that it is sufficient to find only one component $\Gamma_j(z)$ of a maximal matrix $\Gamma(z)$. To find $\Gamma_j(z)$, we need a theorem on the parametric representation of functions of the class H_δ (cf., for example, Privalov[*]). *Every function $\gamma(z)$ of class H_δ can be represented in the form*

$$\gamma(z) = z^m \prod_p \frac{\alpha^{(p)} - z}{1 - \overline{\alpha^{(p)}} z} \frac{|\alpha^{(p)}|}{\alpha^{(p)}} \exp\left\{-\frac{1}{2\pi}\int_{-\pi}^{\pi} \frac{e^{-i\lambda} + z}{e^{-i\lambda} - z} \sigma(d\lambda)\right\}$$
$$\times e^{i\lambda_0} \exp\left\{\frac{1}{2\pi}\int_{-\pi}^{\pi} \log|\gamma(e^{-i\lambda})| \frac{e^{-i\lambda} + z}{e^{-i\lambda} - z} d\lambda\right\}, \tag{8.19}$$

where m is the multiplicity of the zero $z = 0$ of $\gamma(z)$, the $\alpha^{(p)}$ are the remaining zeros of $\gamma(z)$, taken as many times as their multiplicities, and $\sigma(d\lambda)$ is a certain positive singular measure‡; *the infinite product in* (8.19) *converges absolutely and uniformly.*

Lemma 8.1. *Suppose that an analytic function (in the unit disc) $\gamma(z)$ can be represented in the form*

$$\gamma(z) = \exp\left\{\frac{1}{2\pi}\int_{-\pi}^{\pi} \frac{e^{-i\lambda} + z}{e^{-i\lambda} - z} \sigma(d\lambda)\right\},$$

where $\sigma(d\lambda)$ is a finite signed measure, and let $\Delta = (\lambda_1, \lambda_2)$ be an interval such that $\sigma(\{\lambda_1\}) = (\{\lambda_2\}) = 0$. Then

$$\sigma(\Delta) = \lim_{\rho\to 1} \int_{\lambda_1}^{\lambda_2} \log|\gamma(\rho e^{-i\lambda})| \, d\lambda . \tag{8.20}$$

Proof. We have

† The values $\Gamma_j(0)$, $j = \overline{1, n}$, of a maximal matrix obviously cannot all vanish, if $f(\lambda)$ is not identically zero.

‡ That is, σ is concentrated entirely on a set of Lebesgue measure zero.

$$\log|\gamma(\rho e^{-i\lambda})| = \frac{1}{2\pi}\int_{-\pi}^{\pi}\frac{1-\rho^2}{1+\rho^2-2\rho\cos(\lambda-\mu)}\sigma(d\mu)$$

and

$$\begin{aligned}\int_{\lambda_1}^{\lambda_2}\log|\gamma(\rho e^{-i\lambda})|\,d\lambda &= \int_{-\pi}^{\pi}\sigma(d\mu)\left[\frac{1}{2\pi}\int_{\lambda_1}^{\lambda_2}\frac{1-\rho^2}{1+\rho^2-2\rho\cos(\lambda-\mu)}d\lambda\right]\\ &= \int_{-\pi}^{\pi}\sigma(d\mu)\left[\frac{1}{2\pi}\int_{-\pi}^{\pi}\chi_\Delta(\lambda)\frac{1-\rho^2}{1+\rho^2-2\rho\cos(\lambda-\mu)}d\lambda\right],\end{aligned} \tag{8.21}$$

where $\chi_\Delta(\lambda)$ is the characteristic function of Δ. From well-known properties of the Poisson integral (see, for example, Privalov[*] or Hoffman[*]) it follows that

$$\lim_{\rho\to1}\frac{1}{2\pi}\int_{-\pi}^{\pi}\chi_\Delta(\lambda)\frac{1-\rho^2}{1+\rho^2-2\rho\cos(\lambda-\mu)}d\lambda = \chi_\Delta(\mu) \tag{8.22}$$

for all points μ other than λ_1 and λ_2. Since for all ρ and μ the function

$$u(\rho,\mu) = \frac{1}{2\pi}\int_{-\pi}^{\pi}\chi_\Delta(\lambda)\frac{1-\rho^2}{1+\rho^2-2\rho\cos(\lambda-\mu)}d\lambda$$

does not exceed 1, then, passing to the limit $\rho\to1$ in both sides of (8.21), we obtain relation (8.20), since by virtue of $\sigma(\{\lambda_1\}) = (\{\lambda_2\}) = 0$, the behavior of the integrand in (8.21) for $\mu=\lambda_1$ and $\mu=\lambda_2$ is unimportant. ∎

Let us turn to the definition of the column matrix $\Gamma(z) = \{\Gamma_k(z)\}_{k=\overline{1,n}}$ in terms of the spectral density f.

In accordance with the theorem on parametric representation, let

$$\begin{aligned}\Gamma_j(z) = z^{m_j}\prod_p\frac{\alpha_j^{(p)}-z}{1-\overline{\alpha_j^{(p)}}z}\frac{|\alpha_j^{(p)}|}{\alpha_j^{(p)}}\exp\left\{-\frac{1}{2\pi}\int_{-\pi}^{\pi}\frac{e^{-i\lambda}+z}{e^{-i\lambda}-z}\sigma_j(d\lambda)\right\}\\ \times\exp\left\{\frac{1}{4\pi}\int_{-\pi}^{\pi}\log f_{jj}(\gamma)\frac{e^{-i\lambda}+z}{e^{-i\lambda}-z}d\lambda\right\}.\end{aligned} \tag{8.23}$$

It is clear that the poles of the functions $\gamma_{kj}(z)$, appearing in condition 2 of Theorem 8.2, $\gamma_{kj}(z) = \Gamma_k(z)/\Gamma_j(z)$, are to be found among the zeros $\alpha_j^{(p)}$ of $\Gamma_j(z)$. If α is a zero of $\Gamma_j(z)$ of multiplicity m, then it is a pole of the same order for at least one of the functions $\gamma_{kj}(z)$, $k=\overline{1,n}$. Indeed, all of the functions $\Gamma_k(z) = \gamma_{kj}(z)\Gamma_j(z)$ would otherwise vanish at $z=\alpha$, which would contradict the maximality of $\Gamma(z)$.

Thus, *in the parametric representation* (8.23) *of* $\Gamma_j(z)$, *the number* m_j *is the maximal multiplicity of the pole* $z=0$ *of the functions* $\gamma_{kj}(z)$, $k=\overline{1,n}$, *and the* $\alpha_j^{(p)}$ *are the remaining poles of these functions, taken as many times as their maximal multiplicities.*

Further, let m_{kj} be the multiplicity of the pole $z=0$ of $\gamma_{kj}(z)$, and let the $\alpha_{kj}^{(p)}$ be its remaining poles, taken as many times as their multiplicities. We put

$$\begin{aligned} \beta_{kj}(z) &= z^{m_{kj}} \prod_p \frac{\alpha_{kj}^{(p)} - z}{1 - \overline{\alpha_{kj}^{(p)}} z} \frac{|\alpha_{kj}^{(p)}|}{\alpha_{kj}^{(p)}} , \\ \Gamma_{k0}(z) &= \exp\left\{\frac{1}{4\pi}\int_{-\pi}^{\pi} \log f_{kk}(\lambda) \frac{e^{-i\lambda} + z}{e^{-i\lambda} - z} d\lambda\right\} . \end{aligned} \tag{8.24}$$

Further, the function $a_{kj}(z)$,

$$a_{kj}(z) = \gamma_{kj}(z) \frac{\Gamma_{j0}(z)}{\Gamma_{k0}(z)} \frac{\beta_{kj}(z)}{\beta_{jk}(z)} , \tag{8.25}$$

can be represented in the form

$$a_{kj}(z) = \exp\left\{- \frac{1}{2\pi}\int_{-\pi}^{\pi} \frac{e^{-i\lambda} + z}{e^{-i\lambda} - z} \sigma_{kj}(d\lambda)\right\} , \tag{8.26}$$

where

$$\sigma_{kj}(d\lambda) = \sigma_k(d\lambda) - \sigma_j(d\lambda) . \tag{8.27}$$

Knowing the function $\gamma_{kj}(z)$, we can find $a_{kj}(z)$, and thus also the measure $\sigma_{kj}(d\lambda)$. Indeed, by Lemma 8.1, if the interval $\Delta = (\lambda_1, \lambda_2)$ is such that $\sigma_{kj}(\{\lambda_1\}) = \sigma_{kj}(\{\lambda_2\}) = 0$, then

$$\sigma_{kj}(\Delta) = \lim_{\rho \to 1} \int_{\lambda_1}^{\lambda_2} \log |a_{kj}(\rho e^{-i\lambda})| \, d\lambda . \tag{8.28}$$

It now remains to reconstruct the positive measure $\sigma_j(d\lambda)$ from the $\sigma_{kj}(d\lambda)$, $k = \overline{1, n}$. Let $\sigma_{kj}^+(d\lambda)$ and $\sigma_{kj}^-(d\lambda)$ be the positive and negative parts of $\sigma_{kj}(d\lambda)$ resulting from its Hahn decomposition:

$$\sigma_{kj}(d\lambda) = \sigma_{kj}^+(d\lambda) - \sigma_{kj}^-(d\lambda) . \tag{8.29}$$

As is known (cf., for example, Halmos[*]) this decomposition has the property that

$$\int_{-\pi}^{\pi} \sigma_{kj}^+(d\lambda) \le \int_{-\pi}^{\pi} \tilde{\sigma}_{kj}^+(d\lambda) , \qquad \int_{-\pi}^{\pi} \sigma_{kj}^-(d\lambda) \le \int_{-\pi}^{\pi} \tilde{\sigma}_{kj}^-(d\lambda) , \tag{8.30}$$

for any positive measures $\tilde{\sigma}_{kj}^+(d\lambda)$ and $\tilde{\sigma}_{kj}^-(d\lambda)$ such that $\sigma_{kj}(d\lambda) = \tilde{\sigma}_{kj}^+(d\lambda) - \tilde{\sigma}_{kj}^-(d\lambda)$. We put

$$\Sigma_j^+(d\lambda) = \sum_{k=1}^n \sigma_{kj}^+(d\lambda) , \quad p_{kj}(\lambda) = \frac{\sigma_{kj}^+(d\lambda)}{\Sigma_j^+(d\lambda)} , \quad p_j(\lambda) = \max_k \{p_{kj}(\lambda)\} , \tag{8.31}$$

and, finally,

$$\sigma_j^+(d\lambda) = p_j(\lambda) \Sigma_j^+(d\lambda) . \tag{8.32}$$

Since the measures $\sigma_k(d\lambda)$, $k = \overline{1, n}$, appearing in the parametric representation (8.23) are singular, so are the measures $\sigma_{kj}(d\lambda)$ and hence the $\sigma_{kj}^+(d\lambda)$, along with the $\sigma_k^+(d\lambda)$, $k = \overline{1, n}$. If we replace $\sigma_j(d\lambda)$, in

(8.23), by $\sigma_j^+(d\lambda)$, we obtain a function $\Gamma_j^+(z)$ of class H_2 such that the functions $\Gamma_k^+(z) = \gamma_{kj}(z)\Gamma_j^+(z)$ are analytic and of class H_2. Indeed, since $\gamma_{kj}(z) = \Gamma_k(z)/\Gamma_j(z)$, $\Gamma_k^+(z)$ can be represented in the form

$$\Gamma_k^+(z) = z^{m_k} \prod_p \frac{\alpha_k^{(p)} - z}{1 - \overline{\alpha_k^{(p)}} z} \frac{|\alpha_k^{(p)}|}{\alpha_k^{(p)}} \exp\left\{\frac{1}{4\pi}\int_{-\pi}^{\pi} \log f_{kk}(\lambda) \frac{e^{-i\lambda} + z}{e^{-i\lambda} - z} d\lambda\right\}$$

$$\times \exp\left\{\frac{1}{2\pi}\int_{-\pi}^{\pi} \frac{e^{-i\lambda} + z}{e^{-i\lambda} - z}[\sigma_j^+(d\lambda) - \sigma_{kj}(d\lambda)]\right\}, \tag{8.33}$$

where the singular measures $\sigma_j^+(d\lambda) - \sigma_{kj}(d\lambda)$, $k = \overline{1, n}$, are obviously positive. Moreover, the functions $\Gamma_k^+(z)$, $k = \overline{1, n}$, satisfy the boundary condition (8.15):

$$\frac{1}{2\pi}\Gamma_k^+(e^{-i\lambda})\overline{\Gamma_j^+(e^{-i\lambda})} = \frac{1}{2\pi}\gamma_{kj}(e^{-i\lambda})|\Gamma_j^+(e^{-i\lambda})|^2$$

$$= \frac{f_{kj}(\lambda)}{f_{jj}(\lambda)} f_{jj}(\lambda) = f_{kj}(\lambda), \qquad k, j = \overline{1, n}.$$

Further, by virtue of inequality (8.30),

$$\int_{-\pi}^{\pi} \sigma_{kj}^+(d\lambda) \le \int_{-\pi}^{\pi} \sigma_j(d\lambda)$$

for all $k = \overline{1, n}$, and, therefore,

$$\int_{-\pi}^{\pi} \sigma_j^+(d\lambda) \le \int_{-\pi}^{\pi} \sigma_j(d\lambda), \tag{8.34}$$

which means that $\Gamma_j^+(z)$ is a maximal function:

$$|\Gamma_j^+(0)| \ge |\Gamma_j(0)|. \tag{8.35}$$

This inequality shows that the column matrix $\Gamma^+(z) = \{\Gamma_k^+(z)\}_{k=\overline{1,n}}$ is in fact the sought-for maximal matrix $\Gamma(z)$.

We have thus proven the following theorem.

Theorem 8.4. *Let ξ be an n-dimensional linearly regular stationary process with spectral density f of rank* 1. *Then a maximal column matrix $\Gamma(z) = \{\Gamma(z)\}_{k=\overline{1,n}}$, satisfying the boundary condition* (8.14), *can be found from* (8.23), *where m_j is the maximal multiplicity of the pole $z = 0$ of the functions $\gamma_{kj}(z)$, $k = \overline{1, n}$, appearing in condition* 2 *of Theorem* 8.2, *the $\alpha_j^{(p)}$ are the remaining poles of these functions, taken as many times as their maximal multiplicity, and the positive singular measure $\sigma_j = \sigma_j^+$ is defined by* (8.32).

From this theorem, on the basis of the general results of Section 4 of this chapter, we have the following theorem concerning the linear extrapolation of stationary processes of rank 1:

Theorem 8.5. *Let ξ be an n-dimensional linearly regular stationary process of rank* 1, *with spectral density f and spectral representation*

$$\xi(t) = \int_{-\pi}^{\pi} e^{i\lambda t}\Phi(d\lambda) . \tag{8.36}$$

Then the stationary process $\hat{\xi}(\cdot, \tau) = \{\hat{\xi}_k(t, \tau)\}_{k=\overline{1,n}}$, *consisting of the best linear forecasts of ξ (τ steps ahead), is obtained from ξ by a linear transformation*:

$$\hat{\xi}(t, \tau) = \int_{-\pi}^{\pi} e^{i\lambda(t+\tau)}\left[\varphi(\lambda) - \sum_{0}^{\tau-1} c(s)e^{-i\lambda s}\right]\phi(\lambda)\Phi(d\lambda) . \tag{8.37}$$

Here $\varphi(\lambda) = \Gamma(e^{-i\lambda})$ *is the boundary value of a maximal column matrix* $\Gamma(z) = \{\Gamma_k(z)\}_{k=\overline{1,n}}$, *defined by* (8.17) *and* (8.23), *the coefficients* $c(s) = \{c_k(s)\}_{k=\overline{1,n}}$ *are the coefficients in the power series expansion of* $\Gamma(z)$, *and the row matrix* $\phi(\lambda) = \{\phi_k(\lambda)\}^{k=\overline{1,n}}$ *is found from the equation*

$$\sum_{k=1}^{n} \phi_k(\lambda)\varphi_k(\lambda) = 1 . \tag{8.38}$$

9. Linear filtering of stationary processes

Rather frequently the problem arises of predicting the behavior of a stationary process ξ on the basis of observations on another process η which is stationarily correlated with ξ. If the method of prediction is linear, then this problem is called the problem of *linear filtering*. More precisely, the problem of linear filtering consists of finding the projections $\hat{\xi}_k(t, \tau)$ of the unknown variables $\xi_k(t + \tau)$ on the subspace $H_\eta^-(t)$. As we shall see, linear filtering is similar to the previously considered problem of the linear extrapolation of stationary processes.

Let $f^{\xi\xi}(\lambda) = \{f_{kl}^{\xi\xi}(\lambda)\}_{k=\overline{1,n}}^{l=\overline{1,n}}$ and $f^{\eta\eta}(\lambda) = \{f_{kl}^{\eta\eta}(\lambda)\}_{k=\overline{1,m}}^{l=\overline{1,m}}$ be the spectral densities of the stationary process ξ and η, respectively, and $f^{\xi\eta}(\lambda) = \{f_{kl}^{\xi\eta}(\lambda)\}_{k=\overline{1,n}}^{l=\overline{1,m}}$ their joint spectral densities, whose existence we are assuming.

Let us assume that η has maximal rank; i.e., its spectral density $f^{\eta\eta}(\lambda)$ is nondegenerate for almost all λ. Then the projections $\tilde{\xi}_k(t)$, $k = \overline{1, n}$, of the $\xi_k(t)$ on the subspace H_η form a stationary process $\tilde{\xi} = \{\tilde{\xi}_k(t)\}_{k=\overline{1,n}}$ which is obtained from the process η,

$$\eta(t) = \int_{-\pi}^{\pi} e^{i\lambda t}\Phi(d\lambda) , \tag{9.1}$$

by a linear transformation:

$$\tilde{\xi}(t) = \int_{-\pi}^{\pi} e^{i\lambda t}\tilde{\varphi}(\lambda)\Phi(d\lambda) ; \tag{9.2}$$

the spectral characteristic of this transformation is

$$\tilde{\varphi}(\lambda) = f^{\xi\eta}(\lambda)[f^{\eta\eta}(\lambda)]^{-1} . \tag{9.3}$$

Indeed,

$$\{\boldsymbol{E}[\xi_k(t) - \tilde{\xi}_k(t)]\eta_l(s)\}_{k=\overline{1,n}}^{l=\overline{1,m}} = \int_{-\pi}^{\pi} e^{i\lambda(t-s)} f^{\xi\eta}(\lambda)\, d\lambda - \int_{-\pi}^{\pi} e^{i\lambda(t-s)}\tilde{\varphi}(\lambda) f^{\eta\eta}(\lambda)\, d\lambda$$
$$= 0$$

for any t and s.

Obviously, the projections of $\xi_k(t+\tau)$ and $\tilde{\xi}_k(t+\tau)$ on the subspace $H_\eta^-(t)$ coincide. This simple remark enables us to solve the problem of linear filtering.

Let us assume that $\boldsymbol{\eta}$ is linearly regular, and let $\boldsymbol{\zeta} = \{\zeta_j(t)\}_{j=\overline{1,m}}$ be its fundamental process,

$$\zeta(t) = \int_{-\pi}^{\pi} e^{i\lambda t} \Lambda(d\lambda) . \tag{9.4}$$

As was shown in Section 4 of this chapter, the random spectral measures $\Phi(d\lambda) = \{\Phi_k(d\lambda)\}_{k=\overline{1,m}}$ and $\Lambda(d\lambda) = \{\Lambda_j(d\lambda)\}_{j=\overline{1,m}}$ of $\boldsymbol{\eta}$ and $\boldsymbol{\zeta}$ are connected by the relation

$$\Phi(d\lambda) = \varphi(\lambda)\Lambda(d\lambda), \tag{9.5}$$

where $\varphi(\lambda) = \{\varphi_{kj})\lambda)\}_{k=\overline{1,m}}^{j=\overline{1,m}}$ is the boundary value of a maximal matrix $\Gamma(z) = \{\Gamma_{kj}(z)\}_{k=\overline{1,m}}^{j=\overline{1,m}}$ satisfying the boundary condition

$$\frac{1}{2\pi}\Gamma(e^{-i\lambda})\overset{*}{\Gamma}(e^{-i\lambda}) = f^{\eta\eta}(\lambda) . \tag{9.6}$$

From (9.2) and (9.5) we obtain

$$\tilde{\xi}(t) = \int_{-\pi}^{\pi} e^{i\lambda t}\tilde{\varphi}(\lambda)\varphi(\lambda)\Lambda(d\lambda) = \sum_{-\infty}^{\infty} a(t-s)\zeta(s) , \tag{9.7}$$

where the coefficients $a(s)$ are the Fourier coefficients of the matrix function $[\tilde{\varphi}(\lambda)\varphi(\lambda)]$:

$$a(s) = \frac{1}{2\pi}\int_{-\pi}^{\pi} e^{i\lambda s}\tilde{\varphi}(\lambda)\varphi(\lambda)\, d\lambda . \tag{9.8}$$

The moving-average representation (9.7) of $\tilde{\boldsymbol{\xi}}$ in terms of the fundamental process $\boldsymbol{\zeta}$, having the property that $H_\zeta^-(t) = H_\eta^-(t)$ for all t, enables us to find the projections $\hat{\xi}_k(t,\tau)$ of the $\xi_k(t+\tau)$ on $H_\zeta^-(t)$. Namely, $\hat{\xi}(t,\tau)$ can be represented in the form

$$\hat{\xi}(t,\tau) = \sum_{s\le t} a(t+\tau-s)\zeta(s) . \tag{9.9}$$

From this we find that

$$\hat{\xi}(t,\tau) = \int_{-\pi}^{\pi}\left[\sum_{s\le t} a(t+\tau-s)e^{i\lambda s}\right]\Lambda(d\lambda)$$
$$= \int_{-\pi}^{\pi} e^{i\lambda t}\left[\sum_{s=0}^{\infty} a(s+\tau)e^{-i\lambda s}\right]\varphi^{-1}(\lambda)\Phi(d\lambda)\,, \tag{9.10}$$

since the matrix function φ in (9.5) is nondegenerate for almost all λ.

We thus have the following result.

Theorem 9.1. *The stationary process* $\hat{\xi}(\cdot,\tau) = \{\hat{\xi}_k(t,\tau)\}_{k=\overline{1,n}}$, *consisting of the best linear forecasts of the process* ξ (τ *steps ahead*) *by means of an m-dimensional linearly regular process* η *of maximal rank which is stationarily correlated with* ξ, *is obtained from* η *by a linear transformation of the form* (9.10).

Example 9.1. Suppose that the one-dimensional stationary and stationarily correlated processes ξ and η have spectral densities of the form

$$f^{\xi\eta}(\lambda) = \frac{Be^{-i\lambda}(1-\alpha e^{-i\lambda})}{e^{-i\lambda}-\beta}\,; \qquad f^{\eta\eta}(\lambda) = \frac{A^2|1-\alpha e^{-i\lambda}|^2}{|1-\beta e^{-i\lambda}|^2}\,,$$
$$0<\alpha,\ \beta<1\,.$$

Then the function φ appearing in (9.10) is given by

$$\varphi(\lambda) = A\frac{1-\alpha e^{-i\lambda}}{1-\beta e^{-i\lambda}}\,.$$

We have

$$\frac{f^{\xi\eta}(\lambda)}{f^{\eta\eta}(\lambda)}\varphi(\lambda) = \frac{B}{A}\frac{1-\alpha e^{-i\lambda}}{1-\alpha e^{i\lambda}} = \frac{B}{A}\left[-\alpha e^{-i\lambda} + (1-\alpha^2)\sum_0^{\infty}\alpha^s e^{i\lambda s}\right],$$

from which we find that the coefficients $a(s)$ in (9.10) are

$$\alpha_0 = \frac{B}{A}(1-\alpha^2)\,, \qquad a_1 = -\alpha\frac{B}{A}\,, \qquad a_2 = a_3 = \cdots = 0\,.$$

Therefore,

$$\hat{\xi}(t,0) = \frac{B}{A^2}\int_{-\pi}^{\pi} e^{i\lambda t}\frac{(1-\alpha^2-\alpha e^{-i\lambda})(1-\beta e^{-i\lambda})}{(1-\alpha e^{-i\lambda})}\Phi(d\lambda)$$
$$= \frac{B}{A^2}\left[(1-\alpha^2)\eta(t) - (\alpha^3+\beta(1-\alpha^2))\eta(t-1) + \alpha(\beta-\alpha)\sum_{s=2}^{\infty}\alpha^s\eta(t-s)\right].$$

10. Linear interpolation of stationary processes

A problem which is related to the problems of linear extrapolation and filtering is that of the linear interpolation of stationary processes.

Let T_k, $k=\overline{1,n}$, be subsets of the set of all integers. We suppose that all the values $\xi_k(t)$ of the n-dimensional stationary process $\boldsymbol{\xi}$ are known, except for the values $\xi_k(t)$, $t \in T_k$, $k=\overline{1, n}$, and it is required to "interpolate" the unknown values $\xi_k(t)$.

If we measure the error in terms of mean square deviation, then the best linear method of interpolation consists in finding the projections of the $\xi_k(t)$, $t \in T_k$, on the closed linear manifold generated by the known variables $\xi_k(t)$, $t \notin T_k$, $k=\overline{1, n}$, which we denote by $\hat{H}(T)$.

We remark at once that, in considering the problem of linear interpolation, we may, without restriction of generality, suppose that the process $\boldsymbol{\xi}$ has a spectral density. This is easy to see (we are assuming the T_k to be finite sets) if we refer to the results of Section 5 regarding the singularity of processes having singular spectral measures.

Let A be n-dimensional vector space, and B_λ the subspace of A consisting of all vectors $b=\{b_k(\lambda)\}^{k=\overline{1,n}}$ of the form

$$b=af(\lambda)\,, \qquad a \in A\,. \tag{10.1}$$

By the expression $bf^{-1}(\lambda)$, for $b \in B_\lambda$, we will understand any of the vectors $a \in A$ satisfying (10.1).

Obviously, if two vectors a_1 and a_2 lead to the same element b in (10.1), then

$$a_1\overset{*}{b}{}'=a_2\overset{*}{b}{}' \tag{10.2}$$

for any $b'=a'f(\lambda) \in B_\lambda$, since, by virtue of the self-adjointness of the matrix $f(\lambda)$,

$$(a_1-a_2)\overset{*}{b}{}'=(a_1-a_2)[\overset{*}{\overbrace{a'f(\lambda)}}]=[(a_1-a_2)f(\lambda)]\overset{*}{a}{}'=(b-b)\overset{*}{a}{}'=0\,.$$

We define $B(T)$ as the space of vector functions $b(\lambda)=\{b_k(\lambda)\}^{k=\overline{1,n}}$, whose components $b_k(\lambda)$ are trigonometric polynomials of the form

$$b_k(\lambda)=\sum_{t\in T_k} a_k(t)\,e^{i\lambda t}\,, \tag{10.3}$$

such that $b(\lambda) \in B_\lambda$ for almost all λ, and such that $\|b\|=(b, b)^{1/2}<\infty$, where (b, b') is a scalar product in $B(T)$ defined by

$$(b, b')=\int_{-\pi}^{\pi}[b(\lambda)f^{-1}(\lambda)]\overset{*}{b}{}'(\lambda)\,d\lambda\,. \tag{10.4}$$

We denote by $\Delta(T)$ the subspace in H_ξ spanned by the differences

$$\xi_k(t)-\hat{\xi}_k(t)\,, \qquad t \in T_k\,, \qquad k=\overline{1, n}\,.$$

Lemma 10.1. *The subspace $\Delta(T)$ is isometrically isomorphic to the space $B(T)$ of vector functions.*

Proof. Let $\Phi(d\lambda) = \{\Phi_k(d\lambda)\}_{k=\overline{1,n}}$ be the random spectral measure of ξ. The elements h of the subspace $\Delta(T)$ can be represented in the form

$$h = \int_{-\pi}^{\pi} \varphi(\lambda)\Phi(d\lambda), \tag{10.5}$$

where the vector function $\varphi = \{\varphi_k\}^{k=\overline{1,n}}$ belongs to the space $L^2(F)$, i.e.,

$$\int_{-\pi}^{\pi} [\varphi f \overset{*}{\varphi}]\, d\lambda < \infty. \tag{10.6}$$

The orthogonality of h to the subspace $\hat{H}(T)$ means that

$$\boldsymbol{E} h\overline{\xi_l(t)} = \int_{-\pi}^{\pi} e^{-i\lambda t}\left[\sum_{k=1}^{n} \varphi_k(\lambda) f_{kl}(\lambda)\right] d\lambda = 0 \tag{10.7}$$

for all l and t ($l = \overline{1,n}$, $-\infty < t < \infty$) except for $t \in T_l$. If we put

$$b(\lambda) = \varphi(\lambda) f(\lambda),$$

then (10.7) shows that the vector function $b(\lambda) = \{b_k(\lambda)\}^{k=\overline{1,n}}$ belongs to the space $B(T)$:

$$b_k(\lambda) = \sum_{l=1}^{n} \varphi_l(\lambda) f_{lk}(\lambda) = \sum_{t \in T_k} a_k(t) e^{i\lambda t}, \qquad k = \overline{1,n},$$

$$\|b\|^2 = \int_{-\pi}^{\pi} [b(\lambda) f^{-1}(\lambda) \overset{*}{b}(\lambda)]\, d\lambda = \int_{-\pi}^{\pi} [\varphi(\lambda) f(\lambda) \overset{*}{\varphi}(\lambda)]\, d\lambda = \boldsymbol{E}|h|^2.$$

On the other hand, if one takes an arbitrary vector function $b(\lambda)$ from $B(T)$ and sets

$$\varphi(\lambda) = b(\lambda) f^{-1}(\lambda), \tag{10.8}$$

then

$$\int_{-\pi}^{\pi} [\varphi(\lambda) f(\lambda) \overset{*}{\varphi}(\lambda)]\, d\lambda = \int_{-\pi}^{\pi} [b(\lambda) f^{-1}(\lambda) \overset{*}{b}(\lambda)]\, d\lambda < \infty, \tag{10.9}$$

and the random variable h of the form

$$h = \int_{-\pi}^{\pi} \varphi(\lambda)\Phi(d\lambda)$$

is orthogonal to $\hat{H}(T)$:

$$\boldsymbol{E} h\overline{\xi}_l(t) = \int_{-\pi}^{\pi} e^{-i\lambda t}\left[\sum_{k=1}^{n} \varphi_k(\lambda) f_{kl}(\lambda)\right] d\lambda = \int_{-\pi}^{\pi} e^{-i\lambda t} b_l(\lambda)\, d\lambda = 0$$

for all l and t, except for $t \in T_l$. But this means that h belongs to the subspace $\Delta(T)$, and, morever, by virtue of (10.9),

$$E|h|^2 = \|b\|^2. \tag{10.10}$$

An obvious consequence of this lemma is the following theorem.

Theorem 10.1. *For linear interpolation of the stationary process ξ, with spectral density f, to be error-free, it is necessary and sufficient that*

$$B(T) = 0\,, \tag{10.11}$$

where $B(T)$ is defined above.

In the case where the spectral density f is nondegenerate for almost all λ, condition (10.11) can be formulated in the following way: *For any vector function $b(\lambda) = \{b_k(\lambda)\}^{k=\overline{1,n}}$, $b \not\equiv 0$, with components of the form* (10.3),

$$\int_{-\pi}^{\pi} [b(\lambda) f^{-1}(\lambda) \overset{*}{b}(\lambda)]\, d\lambda = \infty\,. \tag{10.12}$$

Other cases of error-free interpolation can occur in which there is no analytic condition of the type (10.12).

Example 10.1. Let ξ be a two-dimensional stationary process with spectral density

$$f(\lambda) = \{f_{kl}(\lambda)\}^{l=1,2}_{k=1,2}\,,$$

whose components have the form

$$f_{11} = f_{22} = 1\,; \qquad f_{12} = \bar{f}_{21} = e^{i\lambda}\,.$$

Obviously, $f(\lambda)$ is a degenerate matrix. Suppose that the values of ξ are unknown at some moment $t = t_0$, i.e., $T_k = \{t_0\}$ for $k = 1, 2$.

The relation $b(\lambda) \in B$, where $b(\lambda) = \{a_1 e^{i\lambda t_0}, a_2 e^{i\lambda t_0}\}$, means that the rank of the extended matrix $\tilde{f}(\lambda) = \{\tilde{f}_{kl}(\lambda)\}^{l=1,2}_{k=\overline{1,3}}$, where $\tilde{f}_{kl}(\lambda) = f_{kl}(\lambda)$ for $k, l = 1, 2$ and $\tilde{f}_{3l}(\lambda) = a_l e^{i\lambda t_0}$, $l = 1, 2$, coincides with the rank of the spectral density $f(\lambda)$. But as is easily seen, in our case the ranks of $\tilde{f}(\lambda)$ and $f(\lambda)$ coincide for almost all λ only if $a_1 = a_2 = 0$. Thus, $B(T) = 0$, and ξ can be linearly interpolated without error.

An interesting question, from the point of view of the problem of linear interpolation, is that of ascertaining when each separate random variable $\xi_k(t)$ lies outside the linear closure of the remaining values of the given stationary process ξ. Let us agree to call a process having this property a *minimal* process.

Theorem 10.2. *In order that an n-dimensional stationary process ξ with spectral density f be minimal, it is necessary and sufficient that*

$$\int_{-\pi}^{\pi} \operatorname{Tr} f^{-1}(\lambda)\, d\lambda < \infty\,. \tag{10.13}$$

Proof. The condition of minimality is equivalent to the difference

$h_k = \xi_k(t_0) - \hat{\xi}_k(t_0)$ (here $T_k = \{t_0\}$, $T_l = 0$ for $l \neq k$) being different from zero. As follows from Lemma 10.1, the random variables h_k, $k = \overline{1, n}$, give rise in each of the corresponding spaces $B(T)$ to vector functions $b_k(\lambda) = \{b_{kj}(\lambda)\}^{j=\overline{1,n}}$ with components of the form $b_{kj}(\lambda) = 0$ for $j \neq k$; $b_{kk}(\lambda) = a_k e^{i\lambda t_0}$, $a_k \neq 0$. Now, $b_k(\lambda)$ belonging to the corresponding space $B(T)$ means that adding to the matrix $f(\lambda)$ another row of the form $\{b_{kj}(\lambda)\}^{j=\overline{1,n}}$ does not increase its rank for any $k = \overline{1, n}$. It is easy to see that this can only be the case (for the vectors $b_k(\lambda)$ defined above) when $f(\lambda)$ is nondegenerate, and thus the inverse $f^{-1}(\lambda) = \{p_{kl}(\lambda)\}_{k=\overline{1,n}}^{l=\overline{1,n}}$ exists for almost all λ. Further, by (10.10)

$$\boldsymbol{E}|h_k|^2 = \|b_k\|^2 = |a_k|^2 \int_{-\pi}^{\pi} p_{kk}(\lambda)\, d\lambda < \infty \tag{10.14}$$

for all $k = \overline{1, n}$, from which follows condition (10.13) of the theorem.

The sufficiency of this condition is, by virtue of the relation (10.14), obvious.

We proceed now to a direct determination of the quantities $\hat{\xi}_k(t)$, which give the best forecast by linear interpolation.

As we already know, $\hat{\xi}_k(t_0)$ can be represented in the following form:

$$\hat{\xi}_k(t_0) = \int_{-\pi}^{\pi} \varphi_k(\lambda)\Phi\,(d\lambda)\,. \tag{10.15}$$

The problem of linear interpolation consists, essentially, of determining the vector functions $\varphi_k(\lambda) = \{\varphi_{kj}(\lambda)\}^{j=\overline{1,n}}$.

Since the difference $\xi_k(t_0) - \hat{\xi}_k(t_0)$ belongs to the space $\Delta(T)$, we obtain, from Lemma 10.1, that the vector function

$$b_k(\lambda) = [e^{i\lambda t_0}\delta_k - \varphi_k(\lambda)]f(\lambda) = \{b_{kj}(\lambda)\}^{j=\overline{1,n}}$$

belongs to the space $B(T)$, and, in particular, that

$$b_{kj}(\lambda) = \sum_{t \in T_j} a_{kj}(t)\, e^{i\lambda t}\,, \qquad j = \overline{1, n}\,.$$

Thus, the vector function $\varphi_k(\lambda)$ has the form

$$\varphi_k(\lambda) = e^{i\lambda t_0}\delta_k - b_k(\lambda) f^{-1}(\lambda)\,, \tag{10.16}$$

and the problem of linear interpolation reduces to finding the coefficients $a_{kj}(t)$ of the trigonometric polynomials $b_{kj}(\lambda)$. These coefficients can easily be found from a linear system of equations, expressing the fact that $\hat{\xi}_k(t_0)$ is orthogonal to $\Delta(T)$.

We will not write down this system of equations in the general case, but will restrict ourselves to a minimal process $\boldsymbol{\xi}$, whose spectral density satisfies condition (10.13). In this case the vector functions of the form $e^{i\lambda t}\delta_l$, $t \in T_l$, $l = \overline{1, n}$, form a basis in the space $B(T)$, and if one denotes by $h^{l,t}$ the corresponding variables in the space $\Delta(T)$, then the orthogonality of $\hat{\xi}_k(t_0)$ to $\Delta(T)$ is equivalent to the following:

$$\boldsymbol{E}\hat{\xi}_k(t_0)\overline{h^{l,t}} = \int_{-\pi}^{\pi} e^{-i\lambda t}[\hat{\varphi}_k(\lambda)f(\lambda)\overset{*}{p}_l(\lambda)]\,d\lambda = 0\,,$$
$$t \in T_l\,, \qquad l = \overline{1, n}\,, \tag{10.17}$$

where $p_l(\lambda) = \{p_{lj}(\lambda)\}^{j=\overline{1,n}}$ is the lth row of the inverse $f^{-1}(\lambda) = \{p_{lj}(\lambda)\}_{l=\overline{1,n}}^{j=\overline{1,n}}$ of $f(\lambda)$. Taking into consideration the form (10.16) of the vector function $\hat{\varphi}_k(\lambda)$, system (10.17) can be rewritten in the form

$$\begin{aligned} &\sum_{j=1}^{n} \sum_{s\in T_j} P_{jl}(s-t)a_{kj}(s) = 0 \quad \text{for} \quad t \in T_l,\ t \neq t_0,\ l \neq k\,, \\ &\sum_{j=1}^{n} \sum_{s\in T_j} P_{jk}(s-t_0)a_{kj}(s) = 1\,. \end{aligned} \tag{10.18}$$

Here the $P_{jl}(s)$ are the Fourier coefficients of the elements $p_{jl}(\lambda)$ of the matrix $f^{-1}(\lambda)$:

$$P_{jl}(s) = \frac{1}{2\pi}\int_{-\pi}^{\pi} e^{i\lambda s}p_{jl}(\lambda)\,d\lambda\,. \tag{10.19}$$

We have thus proven the following result.

Theorem 10.3. *Suppose that the spectral density f of the n-dimensional stationary process $\boldsymbol{\xi}$ satisfies* (10.13). *Then the random variables $\hat{\xi}_k(t_0)$, giving the best linear interpolation, can be found from formula* (10.15), *in which the vecter functions $\hat{\varphi}_k(\lambda)$ are determined from the system of equations* (10.18).

A particularly simple form of system (10.18) is obtained in the case where the values $\xi_k(t)$ of the process $\boldsymbol{\xi}$ are all unknown for the same times t, i.e., when the T_k coincide; $T_k = T$. Let $\hat{\xi}(t_0) = \{\hat{\xi}_k(t_0)\}_{k=\overline{1,n}}$. We have

$$\hat{\xi}(t_0) = \int_{-\pi}^{\pi} \hat{\varphi}(\lambda)\Phi\,(d\lambda)\,, \tag{10.20}$$

where, by virtue of (10.16), the matrix function $\hat{\varphi}(\lambda) = \{\hat{\varphi}_{kj}(\lambda)\}_{k=\overline{1,n}}^{j=\overline{1,n}}$ has the form

$$\hat{\varphi}(\lambda) = e^{i\lambda t_0}I_n - \sum_{s\in T} e^{i\lambda s}a(s)f^{-1}(\lambda)\,. \tag{10.21}$$

For the matrix coefficients $a(s) = \{a_{kj}(s)\}_{k=\overline{1,n}}^{j=\overline{1,n}}$ we obtain from (10.18) the following system of equations:

$$\begin{aligned} &\sum_{s\in T} a(s)P(s-t) = 0 \quad \text{for} \quad t \neq t_0\,, \\ &\sum_{s\in T} a(s)P(s-t_0) = I_n\,, \end{aligned} \tag{10.22}$$

where

$$P(s) = \frac{1}{2\pi}\int_{-\pi}^{\pi} e^{i\lambda s} f^{-1}(\lambda)\, d\lambda .$$

Let us consider one important case, in which the set T consists of only one value $t = t_0$. The system (10.22) will then appear as

$$aP = I , \tag{10.23}$$

where

$$a = \{a_{kj}(t_0)\}_{k=\overline{1,n}}^{j=\overline{1,n}}; \qquad P = P(0) .$$

We find that

$$a = P^{-1} . \tag{10.24}$$

Thus, $\hat{\xi}(t_0) = \{\hat{\xi}_k(t_0)\}_{k=\overline{1,n}}$ can be represented in the form

$$\hat{\xi}(t_0) = \int_{-\pi}^{\pi} e^{i\lambda t_0}[I_n - P^{-1}f^{-1}(\lambda)]\Phi\,(d\lambda) . \tag{10.25}$$

We put

$$h_k = \xi_k(t_0) - \hat{\xi}_k(t_0) , \qquad \sigma_{kj} = \boldsymbol{E} h_k \bar{h}_j . \tag{10.26}$$

The matrix of "errors" $\sigma^2 = \{\sigma_{kj}\}_{k=\overline{1,n}}^{j=\overline{1,n}}$ of linear interpolation is easily found from the representation (10.25):

$$\sigma^2 = 2\pi P^{-1} . \tag{10.27}$$

Let us consider in detail the linear interpolation of a *one-dimensional* stationary process ξ with spectral density $f(\lambda)$.

Theorem 10.1 allows us to conclude that *error-free linear interpolation of any finite number of values of the one-dimensional process ξ is possible if and only if*

$$\int_{-\pi}^{\pi} \frac{|\sum_k a_k e^{i\lambda k}|^2}{f(\lambda)}\, d\lambda = \infty \tag{10.28}$$

for any trigonometric polynomial $\sum_k a_k e^{i\lambda k} \not\equiv 0$.

Condition (10.28) expresses a property of the zeros of the spectral density $f(\lambda)$ of ξ.

We call a number λ_0 a zero of the function $f(\lambda)$, of finite order k (k an integer), if

$$\int_{-\pi}^{\pi} \frac{|\lambda - \lambda_0|^{k-1}}{f(\lambda)}\, d\lambda = \infty , \qquad \int_{-\pi}^{\pi} \frac{|\lambda - \lambda_0|^{k}}{f(\lambda)}\, d\lambda < \infty . \tag{10.29}$$

It is easily seen that if $f(\lambda)$ has an infinite number of zeros, then (10.28) holds for every trigonometric polynomial not identically zero.

Thus, if (10.28) does not hold for all such polynomials, $f(\lambda)$ has only a finite number, say N, of zeros, and each has finite order. Let λ_j be the zeros of $f(\lambda)$, and N_j their orders. The trigonometric polynomial

$$b_0(\lambda) = \prod_{j=1}^{N} (e^{i\lambda} - e^{i\lambda_j})^{k_j} , \tag{10.30}$$

where $k_j = [\frac{1}{2}(N_j + 1)]$, has the property that

$$\int_{-\pi}^{\pi} \frac{|b_0(\lambda)|^2}{f(\lambda)} d\lambda < \infty . \tag{10.31}$$

Obviously, $b_0(\lambda)$ is *minimal* in the sense that every trigonometric polynomial $b(\lambda)$ satisfying a condition analogous to (10.31) must necessarily have zeros at the points $z_j = e^{i\lambda_j}$ of orders at least k_j, and, consequently, must be divisible by $b_0(\lambda)$:

$$b(\lambda) = b_0(\lambda) \sum_k a_k e^{i\lambda k} . \tag{10.32}$$

Suppose that the values $\xi(t)$ of the one-dimensional process $\boldsymbol{\xi}$ are unknown for t in some "interval" $T = \{t^*, t^* + 1, \ldots, t^* + p - 1\}$. Since the elements $b(\lambda)$ of the space $B(T)$ must have the form (10.32), then $B(T) = 0$ *if the number p of unknown values $\xi(t)$, $t \in T$, does not exceed the degree $q = \sum_{j=1}^{N} k_j$ of the minimal polynomial $b_0(\lambda)$.* As is easily seen, *if $p > q$, then the dimension of the space $B(T)$, which is isometric to the "space of errors" $\Delta(T)$,* is just $p - q$.

Further, the condition of minimality (10.13) for a stationary process $\boldsymbol{\xi}$ turns out to be very simple in the one-dimensional case:

$$\int_{-\pi}^{\pi} \frac{d\lambda}{f(\lambda)} < \infty . \tag{10.33}$$

Formulas (10.15)-(10.19), which allow one to find the best interpolation, have been obtained under the condition of minimality for the process $\boldsymbol{\xi}$. For a one-dimensional process $\boldsymbol{\xi}$, the analogous formulas, in the general case when condition (10.33) need not be fulfilled, are rather simple. The minimal polynomial $b_0(\lambda)$, defined by the zeros of the spectral density $f(\lambda)$ according to (10.30), appears in these formulas. Namely, analogous to (10.15)-(10.19),

$$\hat{\xi}(t_0) = \int_{-\pi}^{\pi} \hat{\varphi}(\lambda)\Phi(d\lambda) , \tag{10.34}$$

where the function $\hat{\varphi}(\lambda)$ has the form

$$\hat{\varphi}(\lambda) = e^{i\lambda t^*}\left[e^{i\lambda(t_0 - t^*)} - \frac{b_0(\lambda)}{f(\lambda)} \sum_{k=1}^{p-q} a_k e^{i\lambda k}\right] . \tag{10.35}$$

Obviously, the functions $b^s(\lambda) = e^{i\lambda t^*} b_0(\lambda) e^{i\lambda s}$, $s = \overline{1, p - q}$, form a basis in the space $B(T)$, and the condition of orthogonality of $\hat{\xi}(t_0)$ to the subspace $\Delta(T)$ gives us $p-q$ linear equations for determining the unknown coefficients a_k, $k=\overline{1, p-q}$, in the expression (10.35):

$$\boldsymbol{E}\hat{\xi}(t_0)\bar{h}^s = \int_{-\pi}^{\pi}\left[e^{i\lambda(t_0-t^*-s)} - \frac{b_0(\lambda)}{f(\lambda)}\sum_{k=1}^{p-q} a_k e^{i\lambda(k-s)}\right] d\lambda = 0\,,$$

$$s=\overline{1, p-q}\,, \tag{10.36}$$

where the h^s are the elements of $\Delta(T)$ corresponding to the functions $b^s(\lambda)$. If we put

$$P_m = \frac{1}{2\pi}\int_{-\pi}^{\pi}\frac{b_0(\lambda)}{f(\lambda)}e^{i\lambda m}\,d\lambda\,, \tag{10.37}$$

then the system of linear equations (10.36) can be rewritten in the form

$$\sum_{k=1}^{p-q} a_k P_{k-s} = \begin{cases} 0 & \text{for} \quad s \neq t_0 - t^*\,, \\ 1 & \text{for} \quad s = t_0 - t^*\,, \end{cases} \qquad s=\overline{1, p-q}\,. \tag{10.38}$$

In the case where the process $\boldsymbol{\xi}$ is minimal and $T=\{t_0\}$, we obtain from (10.34)-(10.38) the formula for the best interpolation:

$$\hat{\xi}(t_0) = \int_{-\pi}^{\pi} e^{i\lambda t_0}\left[1 - \frac{2\pi}{\int_{-\pi}^{\pi} d\mu/f(\mu)}\,\frac{1}{f(\lambda)}\right]\Phi(d\lambda)\,; \tag{10.39}$$

and

$$\sigma = [\boldsymbol{E}|\xi(t_0) - \hat{\xi}(t_0)|^2]^{1/2} = \frac{2\pi}{(\int_{-\pi}^{\pi} d\lambda/f(\lambda))^{1/2}}\,. \tag{10.40}$$

11. Stationary processes whose values form a basis

In view of the preceding consideration of the problem of the linear approximation of a random variable h from the space H_{ξ} by the values of the stationary process $\boldsymbol{\xi}$, it is natural to ask under what conditions h can, in some reasonable sense, be represented in the form of a series

$$h \sim \sum_{k=1}^{n}\sum_{t} a_k(t)\xi_k(t)\,. \tag{11.1}$$

Let $H(T)$ be the closed linear manifold spanned by the values $\xi_k(t)$, $t \in T_k$ $(k=\overline{1, n})$ of an n-dimensional stationary process $\boldsymbol{\xi}$. We say that these values form a *conditional basis* in $H(T)$, if with each $h \in H(T)$ one can associate a series

$$L(h) = \sum_{k=1}^{n}\sum_{t\in T_k} a_k(t)\xi_k(t)\,,^{\dagger} \tag{11.2}$$

† The summation over t is carried out in the order of increasing $|t|$.

in such a way that:

1. If the series $L(h)$ converges in norm, then its sum is h; moreover, $L(\xi_k(t)) \equiv \xi_k(t)$ for all k and t;

2. Each of the coefficients $a_k(t)$ of the series $L(h)$ depends linearly and continuously on h; i.e.,

$$\lim_{p\to\infty} a_k^{(p)}(t) = a_k(t) \quad \text{if} \quad \lim_{p\to\infty} h^{(p)} = h \, , \qquad L(\alpha_1 h_1 + \beta_2 h_2) = \alpha_1 L(h_1) + \beta_2 L(h_2) \tag{11.3}$$

for any $h_1, h_2 \in H(T)$ and arbitrary numbers α_1, β_2.

Let us denote by $H_t(T)$ the subspace of $H(T)$ generated by the elements $\xi_k(s)$, $s \in T_k$ $(k = \overline{1, n})$, for which $|s| \geq t$. As we shall see below, *if the values* $\xi_k(t)$, $t \in T_k$ $(k = \overline{1, n})$ *form a conditional basis in* $H(T)$, *then*

$$\bigcap_t H_t(T) = 0 \, , \tag{11.4}$$

and the series in (11.2) *converges in the sense that*

$$h - \sum_{k=1} \sum_{\substack{s\in T_k \\ |s|<t}} a_k(s)\xi_k(s) \in H_t(T) \, . \tag{11.5}$$

Obviously, this convergence is stronger than the ordinary weak convergence of elements in a Hilbert space.

Theorem 11.1. *The system of values* $\xi_k(t)$, $t \in T_k$ $(k = \overline{1, n})$ *forms a conditional basis in* $H(T)$ *if and only if it is minimal in* $H(T)$, *i.e,, if no element* $\xi_k(t)$ *of this system belongs to the closed linear span of the remaining elements, and if, moreover,* (11.4) *is fulfilled.*

Proof. Suppose that the system $\xi_k(t)$, $t \in T_k$ $(k = \overline{1, n})$ forms a conditional basis. Then each of the coefficients $a_{k,t}(h)$ in (11.2) is a linear functional of $h \in H(T)$, and consequently there exists an element $\eta_{k,t}$ in $H(T)$ such that

$$a_{k,t}(h) = (h, \eta_{k,t}) \, . \tag{11.6}$$

Since $L(\xi_k(t)) \equiv \xi_k(t)$, we have

$$(\xi_j(s), \eta_{k,t}) = \begin{cases} 1 & \text{for } j = k, s = t \, , \\ 0 & \text{otherwise} \, . \end{cases} \tag{11.7}$$

Relation (11.7) shows that each $\eta_{k,t}$ is orthogonal to all of the $\xi_j(s)$ for $k \neq j$ or $t \neq s$. Obviously, this can only happen in the case where $\xi_k(t)$ does not belong to the closed linear span of the remaining $\xi_j(s)$, $s \in T_j$ $(j = \overline{1, n})$. Thus, the system $\xi_k(t)$, $t \in T_k$ $(k = \overline{1, n})$ is necessarily minimal.

The system $\eta_{k,t}$, $t \in T_k$ $(k = \overline{1, n})$, with the properties (11.7), is called the *conjugate system*. Condition (11.4) is obviously equivalent to the completeness of this system in the space $H(T)$.

If the conjugate system is not complete in $H(T)$ [i.e., there exists an element $h \in H(T)$, $h \neq 0$, which is orthogonal to all the $\eta_{k,t}$], then the coefficients of the corresponding series $L(h)$, given by (11.6), all vanish, which contradicts the assumption that $h = L(h)$ when the series converges. Consequently, if the values $\xi_k(t)$, $t \in T_k$ $(k = \overline{1, n})$ form a conditional basis in $H(T)$, then (11.4) holds. Conversely, if the system $\xi_k(t)$, $t \in T_k$ $(k = \overline{1, n})$ is minimal, then a conjugate system $\eta_{k,t}$, $t \in T_k$ $(k = \overline{1, n})$ exists. Indeed, each $\eta_{k,t}$ is just a suitable multiple of the perpendicular from $\xi_k(t)$ onto the closed linear span of the remaining $\xi_k(t)$ in the system $\xi_k(t)$, $t \in T_k$ $(k = \overline{1, n})$. By (11.4), the conjugate system is complete in $H(T)$; therefore every element $h \in H(T)$ is uniquely defined by its coefficients $a_k^h(t) = (h, \eta_{k,t})$, and the series $L(h)$ satisfies the conditions required of a conditional basis.

We shall consider two important cases in detail.

Let us consider the system of all values $\xi_k(t)$, $-\infty < t < \infty$, $k = \overline{1, n}$. As follows from the results of the previous section, this system is minimal and therefore satisfies condition (11.4) if and only if the spectral measure of $\boldsymbol{\xi}$ is absolutely continuous, and the spectral density $f(\lambda)$ is nondegenerate for almost all λ and

$$\int_{-\pi}^{\pi} \operatorname{Tr} f^{-1}(\lambda)\, d\lambda < \infty . \tag{11.8}$$

The elements of the conjugate system (which will now write as $\eta_k(t)$, $-\infty < t < \infty$, $k = \overline{1, n}$) form a stationary process $\boldsymbol{\eta}$ of the form

$$\eta(t) = \frac{1}{2\pi}\int_{-\pi}^{\pi} e^{i\lambda t} f^{-1}(\lambda)\Phi(d\lambda) , \tag{11.9}$$

where $\Phi(d\lambda) = \{\Phi_k(d\lambda)\}_{k=\overline{1,n}}$ is the random spectral measure of the process $\boldsymbol{\xi}$. If

$$h = \int_{-\pi}^{\pi} \varphi(\lambda)\Phi(d\lambda) \tag{11.10}$$

is the spectral representation of an element $h \in H_{\boldsymbol{\xi}}$, then its spectral characteristic $\varphi(\lambda) = \{\varphi_k(\lambda)\}^{k=\overline{1,n}}$ has integrable elements $\varphi_k(\lambda)$, and the coefficients $a_k(t)$ in the expansion (11.2) are simply the Fourier coefficients:

$$a_k(t) = \frac{1}{2\pi}\int_{-\pi}^{\pi} e^{-i\lambda t}\varphi_k(\lambda)\, d\lambda , \qquad -\infty < t < \infty , \qquad k = \overline{1, n} . \tag{11.11}$$

We thus have the following result.

Theorem 11.2. *The values $\xi_k(t)$, $-\infty < t < \infty$, $k = \overline{1, n}$, of a stationary* *process form a conditional basis in the space H_ξ if and only if condition* (11.8) *is fulfilled. In this case the coefficients in the series expansion* (11.2) *are defined by* (11.11).

Let us now consider the system of values $\xi_k(t)$, where t ranges over the nonpositive integers. As follows from the results of Section 6, this system will be minimal and will satisfy (11.4) if and only if the stationary process $\boldsymbol{\xi}$ has maximal rank and is lineary regular; the spectral condition for this is

$$\int_{-\pi}^{\pi} \log \det f(\lambda)\, d\lambda > -\infty \,. \tag{11.12}$$

We remark at once that in this case there is no simple expression for the conjugate system. Therefore we will try to find the coefficients in the expansion (11.2) of an arbitrary element by using (11.6), which was derived in the proof of Theorem 11.1.

Let $\varphi(\lambda) = \{\varphi_k(\lambda)\}^{k=\overline{1,n}}$ be the spectral characteristic of an element h in its representation (11.10), and let $\Gamma(e^{-i\lambda}) = \{\Gamma_{kj}(e^{-i\lambda})\}_{k=\overline{1,n}}^{j=\overline{1,n}}$ be the boundary value of a maximal analytic matrix satisfying the condition

$$\Gamma(e^{-i\lambda})\overset{*}{\Gamma}(e^{-i\lambda}) = \frac{1}{2\pi} f(\lambda) \tag{11.13}$$

for almost all λ (cf. Section 6).

Let

$$\begin{aligned} b_j(t) &= \frac{1}{2\pi}\int_{-\pi}^{\pi} e^{-i\lambda t} \sum_{k=1}^{n} \varphi_k(\lambda)\Gamma_{kj}(\lambda)\, d\lambda \,, \qquad t \le 0\,, \quad j = \overline{1,n}\,; \\ c_{kj}(t) &= \frac{1}{2\pi}\int_{-\pi}^{\pi} e^{-i\lambda t}\Gamma_{kj}(\lambda)\, d\lambda \,, \qquad t \le 0\,, \quad k, j = \overline{1,n}\,; \end{aligned} \tag{11.14}$$

and let $\boldsymbol{\zeta} = \{\zeta_j(t)\}_{j=\overline{1,n}}$ be a fundamental process for $\boldsymbol{\xi}$. Then

$$h = \int_{-\pi}^{\pi} \varphi(\lambda)\Phi(d\lambda) = \sum_{j=1}^{n} \sum_{-\infty}^{0} b_j(t)\zeta_j(t)\,,$$

$$\xi_k(t) = \sum_{j=1}^{n} \sum_{-\infty}^{0} c_{kj}(s)\zeta_j(t+s)\,, \qquad k = \overline{1,n}\,,$$

and

$$\begin{aligned} h - \sum_{k=1}^{n} \sum_{t+1}^{0} a_k(s)\xi_k(s) &= \sum_{j=1}^{n} \sum_{-\infty}^{0} b_j(s)\zeta_j(s) - \sum_{k=1}^{n} \sum_{t+1}^{0} a_k(s)\left[\sum_{j=1}^{n} \sum_{-\infty}^{0} c_{kj}(u)\zeta_j(u+s)\right] \\ &= \sum_{j=1}^{n} \sum_{-\infty}^{0} b_j(s)\zeta_j(s) - \sum_{j=1}^{n} \sum_{-\infty}^{n} b'_j(s)\zeta_j(s)\,, \end{aligned} \tag{11.15}$$

where

$$b'_j(s) = \sum_{k=1}^{n} \sum_{u=s}^{0} a_k(u)c_{kj}(u-s)\,, \qquad t < s \le 0\,.$$

In order that the difference $h - \sum_{k=1}^{0} \sum_{t+1}^{0} a_k(s)\xi_k(s)$ belong to the subspace $H_\xi^-(t)$ for all t, it is necessary and sufficient (as one sees from (11.15)) that

$$b_j(t) = b'_j(t) = \sum_{k=1}^{n} \sum_{s=t}^{0} c_{kj}(s-t)a_k(s) , \qquad j = \overline{1, n} , \tag{11.16}$$

for all t, $t \leq 0$. The equations obtained for the coefficients $a_k(s)$, $s \leq 0$ ($k = \overline{1, n}$) in the expansion (11.2) have a "triangular" form, and can be solved successively for $t = 0, -1, \ldots$.

It is useful to write these equations in a more revealing form:

$$\begin{gathered} \sum_{k=1}^{n} a_k(0)c_{kj}(0) = b_j(0) , \qquad j = \overline{1, n} , \\ \sum_{k=1}^{n} a_k(t)c_{kj}(0) = b_j(t) - \sum_{k=1}^{n} \sum_{s=t+1}^{0} a_k(s)c_{kj}(s-t) , \\ j = \overline{1, n} , \quad t = -1, 2, \ldots . \end{gathered} \tag{11.17}$$

We already know from Section 6 that the matrix $c(0) = \{c_{kj}(0)\}_{k=\overline{1,n}}^{j=\overline{1,n}}$ is nondegenerate:

$$\det c(0) = (2\pi)^n \exp\left\{\frac{1}{4\pi}\int_{-\pi}^{\pi} \log \det f(\lambda)\, d\lambda\right\} \neq 0$$

and each of the equations in (11.17) relative to the $a_k(t)$, $k = \overline{1, n}$, has a unique solution.

We have therefore proven the following result.

Theorem 11.3. *In order that the values* $\xi_k(t)$, $t \leq 0$ ($k = \overline{1, n}$) *form a conditional basis in the subspace* $H_\xi^-(0)$, *it is necessary and sufficient that the process* ξ *have maximal rank* n *and that it be linearly regular, i.e., that condition* (11.12) *be fulfilled. In this case the coefficients* $a_k(t)$ *in the expansion* (11.2) *of an arbitrary element* $h \in H_\xi^-(0)$ *can be determined from the system* (11.17) *of linear equations.*

III

LINEAR FORECASTING OF CONTINUOUS-PARAMETER STATIONARY PROCESSES

1. Linear extrapolation. Statement of the problem

The problem of the linear extrapolation of a continuous-parameter stationary process $\boldsymbol{\xi} = \{\xi_k(t)\}_{k=\overline{1,n}}$,

$$\xi(t) = \int_{-\infty}^{\infty} e^{i\lambda t}\Phi(d\lambda), \tag{1.1}$$

in no way differs from the discrete-parameter case (see Section 1 of the previous chapter) and consists of finding the projections $\hat{\xi}_k(t, \tau)$ of the $\xi_k(t+\tau)$, $k = \overline{1, n}$, on the subspace $H_\xi^-(t)$ which, as before, is the closed linear manifold generated by the $\xi_k(s)$, $k = \overline{1, n}$, $-\infty < s \le t$.

The random variables $\hat{\xi}(t, \tau) = \{\hat{\xi}_k(t, \tau)\}_{k=\overline{1,n}}$ form a stationary process $\hat{\boldsymbol{\xi}}(\cdot, \tau)$,

$$\hat{\xi}(t, \tau) = \int_{-\infty}^{\infty} e^{i\lambda t}\varphi(\lambda, \tau)\Phi(d\lambda) \tag{1.2}$$

(obtained from $\boldsymbol{\xi}$ by a linear transformation with spectral characteristic $\varphi(\lambda, \tau) = \{\varphi_{kl}(\lambda, \tau)\}_{k=\overline{1,n}}^{l=\overline{1,n}}$), whose values are the best linear forecasts, τ units of time ahead, of the $\xi(t)$.

2. Regularity and singularity of stationary processes

As in the discrete-parameter case, a stationary process $\boldsymbol{\xi} = \{\xi_k(t)\}_{k=\overline{1,n}}$ is said to be *linearly singular*, if

$$\hat{\xi}_k(t, \tau) = \xi_k(t + \tau), \qquad k = \overline{1, n}, \tag{2.1}$$

for all t and τ, and *linearly regular*, if

$$\lim_{\tau \to \infty} \hat{\xi}_k(t, \tau) = \boldsymbol{E}\xi_k(t), \qquad k = \overline{1, n}. \tag{2.2}$$

As before, we will assume that $\boldsymbol{E}\xi_k(t) = 0$, $k = \overline{1, n}$.

Theorem 2.1. *A stationary process* $\boldsymbol{\xi}$ *is linearly regular if and only if*

$$S_\xi = \bigcap_t H_\xi^-(t) = 0 \tag{2.3}$$

and, correspondingly, linearly singular if and only if

$$S_\xi = H_\xi. \tag{2.4}$$

Theorem 2.2. *Every stationary process* $\boldsymbol{\xi}$ *can be represented, in unique fashion, in the form*

$$\xi(t) = \eta(t) + \zeta(t), \tag{2.5}$$

where the stationary processes $\boldsymbol{\eta} = \{\eta(t)\} = \{\eta_k(t)\}_{k=\overline{1,n}}$ *and* $\boldsymbol{\zeta} = \{\zeta(t)\} = \{\zeta_k(t)\}_{k=\overline{1,n}}$ *are subordinate to* $\boldsymbol{\xi}$; *that is,*

$$H_\eta^-(t) \subseteq H_\xi^-(t), \qquad H_\zeta^-(t) \subseteq H_\xi^-(t); \tag{2.6}$$

are mutually uncorrelated; that is,

$$\boldsymbol{E}\eta_k(t)\overline{\zeta_j(s)} = 0, \qquad k, j = \overline{1, n}, \tag{2.7}$$

for any t *and* s, *and* $\boldsymbol{\eta}$ *is linearly regular, while* $\boldsymbol{\zeta}$ *is linearly singular. The* $\eta_k(t)$ *are the perpendiculars from the* $\xi_k(t)$ *to the subspace* S_ξ, *and the* $\zeta_k(t)$ *are the corresponding projections* ($k = \overline{1, n}$).

The proofs of these theorems do not differ in any way from those in the discrete-parameter case, established in Section 2, Chapter II.

Let

$$\xi(t) = \int_{-\infty}^{\infty} e^{i\lambda t} \Phi(d\lambda) \tag{2.8}$$

be the spectral representation of the stationary process $\boldsymbol{\xi} = \{\xi_k(t)\}_{k=\overline{1,n}}$. We consider the discrete-parameter stationary process $\tilde{\boldsymbol{\xi}} = \{\tilde{\xi}_k(t)\}_{k=\overline{1,n}}$ obtained in the following way:

$$\tilde{\xi}(t) = \int_{-\pi}^{\pi} e^{i\mu t} \tilde{\Phi}(d\mu), \tag{2.9}$$

where

$$\tilde{\Phi}(d\mu) = \Phi(d\lambda), \qquad \mu = 2 \operatorname{arctg} \lambda. \tag{2.10}$$

Lemma 2.1. *The following relations hold:*

$$H_\xi = H_{\tilde\xi}\ ,$$
$$H_\xi^-(0) = H_{\tilde\xi}^-(0)\ . \tag{2.11}$$

Proof. The first of these relations is evident, since H_ξ and $H_{\tilde\xi}$ coincide with the closed linear manifold generated by the values of the random spectral measures $\Phi_k(d\lambda)$ and $\tilde\Phi_k(d\lambda)$, $k=\overline{1,n}$. Further, if $\mu = 2\operatorname{arctg}\lambda$, then

$$e^{-i\mu} = \frac{1-i\lambda}{1+i\lambda} = -1 + \frac{2}{1+i\lambda} = -1 + 2\int_{-\infty}^{0} e^{i\lambda t}e^{t}\,dt\ , \tag{2.12}$$

from which it is evident that the function $e^{i\mu s}$, where s is a negative integer, can be approximated uniformly in every finite interval $(-\Lambda, \Lambda)$ by trigonometric functions $\varphi(\lambda)$ of the form

$$\varphi(\lambda) = \Big(-1 + 2\sum_{t_p\le 0} e^{i\lambda t_p}e^{t_p}\Delta_p\Big)^s\ .$$

Therefore, the quantity

$$\int_{-\infty}^{\infty} |\, e^{i\mu s} - \varphi(\lambda)\,|^2\, F_{kk}(d\lambda)\ ,$$

where $F_{kk}(d\lambda)$ is the spectral measure of the kth component ξ_k of ξ, can be made arbitrarily small for suitable choice of $\varphi(\lambda)$, and, consequently, the random variables

$$\tilde\xi_k(s) = \int_{-\pi}^{\pi} e^{i\mu s}\tilde\Phi_k(d\mu) = \int_{-\infty}^{\infty}\Big(\frac{1-i\lambda}{1+i\lambda}\Big)^{-s}\Phi_k(d\lambda) \tag{2.13}$$

can be approximated arbitrarily closely in mean square by random variables

$$h_k = \int_{-\infty}^{\infty}\varphi(\lambda)\Phi_k(d\lambda)$$

from $H_\xi^-(0)$. This means that the $\tilde\xi_k(s)$, $k=\overline{1,n}$, themselves belong to $H_\xi^-(0)$, and thus

$$H_{\tilde\xi}^-(0) \subseteq H_\xi^-(0)\ . \tag{2.14}$$

Further, the function $e^{t(1-\tilde z)/(1+\tilde z)}$ of $\tilde z$, $|\,\tilde z\,|<1$, is analytic in the unit disc and, for any fixed $t\le 0$, its modulus does not exceed 1:

$$e^{t(1-\tilde z)/(1+\tilde z)} = \sum_{s=0}^{\infty} a(s)\rho^s e^{-i\mu s}\ , \qquad \tilde z = \rho e^{-i\mu}\ . \tag{2.15}$$

Taking into account that

$$i\lambda = (1-e^{-i\mu})/(1+e^{-i\mu})\ ,$$

we find that

$$\lim_{\rho\to 1} e^{t(1-\tilde{z})/(1+\tilde{z})} = e^{i\lambda t}, \tag{2.16}$$

and, by Lebesgue's theorem,

$$\lim_{\rho\to 1}\int_{-\pi}^{\pi} | e^{i\lambda t} - e^{t(1-\tilde{z})/(1+\tilde{z})} |^2 \tilde{F}_{kk}(d\mu) = 0 \tag{2.17}$$

(where $\tilde{F}_{kk}(d\lambda)$ is the spectral measure of the kth component $\tilde{\xi}_k$ of $\tilde{\xi}$). From (2.15) and (2.17) it is evident that the random variables

$$\int_{-\pi}^{\pi} e^{t(1-\tilde{z})/(1+\tilde{z})} \Phi_k(d\mu)$$

belong to $H_{\tilde{\xi}}^{-}(0)$, and

$$\xi_k(t) = \int_{-\infty}^{\infty} e^{i\lambda t}\Phi_k(d\lambda) = \int_{-\pi}^{\pi} e^{i\lambda t}\tilde{\Phi}_k(d\mu) = \lim_{\rho\to 1}\int_{-\pi}^{\pi} e^{t(1-\tilde{z})/(1+\tilde{z})}\tilde{\Phi}_k(d\mu). \tag{2.18}$$

Consequently, the values $\xi_k(t)$, $k=\overline{1,n}$, belong to $H_{\tilde{\xi}}^{-}(0)$ (for $t \le 0$). Thus,

$$H_{\xi}^{-}(0) \subseteq H_{\tilde{\xi}}^{-}(0) \tag{2.19}$$

which, with (2.14), proves the lemma.

Lemma 2.2. *If ξ and η are stationary and stationarily correlated, then η is subordinate to ξ if and only if the processes $\tilde{\eta}$ and $\tilde{\xi}$, corresponding to η and ξ by formula* (2.9), *are in the same relationship to one another.*

Proof. The assertion is obvious because $\tilde{\eta}(0) = \eta(0)$, $H_{\xi}^{-}(0) = H_{\tilde{\xi}}^{-}(0)$, and the condition that η be subordinate to ξ is equivalent to $\eta(0) \in H_{\xi}^{-}(0)$ [respectively, $\tilde{\eta}$ subordinate to $\tilde{\xi}$ is equivalent to $\tilde{\eta}(0) \in H_{\tilde{\xi}}^{-}(0)$].

Lemma 2.3. *The processes ξ and $\tilde{\xi}$ can be linearly singular only simultaneously.*

Proof. Singularity means that $H_{\xi}^{-}(0) = H_{\xi}$ [respectively, $H_{\tilde{\xi}}^{-}(0) = H_{\tilde{\xi}}$], but, by Lemma 2.1, $H_{\xi}^{-}(0) = H_{\tilde{\xi}}^{-}(0)$ and $H_{\xi} = H_{\tilde{\xi}}$, from which follows the assertion.

Lemma 2.4. *The stationary processes ξ and $\tilde{\xi}$ can be linearly regular only simultaneously.*

Proof. If ξ is not regular, then, by Theorem 2.2, there exists a singular process ζ which is subordinate to ξ. It follows from Lemmas 2.2 and 2.3 that the corresponding process $\tilde{\zeta}$ is also singular and subordinate to $\tilde{\xi}: H_{\tilde{\zeta}}^{-}(t) \subseteq H_{\tilde{\xi}}^{-}(t)$. Since $H_{\tilde{\zeta}}^{-}(t) = H_{\tilde{\zeta}}$ for all t, the subspace

$S_{\tilde{\xi}} = \bigcap_t H_{\tilde{\xi}}^-(t)$ contains the nontrivial subspace $H_{\tilde{\zeta}}$, and this means that $\tilde{\xi}$ is not regular. Interchanging ξ and $\tilde{\xi}$ in the foregoing arguments, we find that the nonregularity of $\tilde{\xi}$ implies the nonregularity of ξ. Thus, ξ and $\tilde{\xi}$ can only be regular simultaneously. ∎

The spectral measures F and $\tilde{F}$ of ξ and $\tilde{\xi}$ are connected by the following relation:

$$\tilde{F}(d\mu) = F(d\lambda)\,,$$
$$d\mu = \frac{2}{1+\lambda^2}d\lambda\,. \tag{2.20}$$

If ξ is regular, then, by Lemma 2.4, $\tilde{\xi}$ is regular; consequently, the spectral measure $\tilde{F}(d\mu)$ will then be absolutely continuous together with $F(d\lambda)$, and the respective spectral densities $\tilde{f}(\mu)$ and $f(\lambda)$ are related according to

$$\tilde{f}(\mu) = \frac{1+\lambda^2}{2}f(\lambda)\,. \tag{2.21}$$

By Theorem 4.1 of Chapter II, the spectral density $\tilde{f}(\mu)$ has the same rank m for almost all μ, and there exists a matrix function $\tilde{\Gamma}(\tilde{z}) = \{\tilde{\Gamma}_{kj}(\tilde{z})\}_{k=\overline{1,n}}^{j=\overline{1,m}}$ which is analytic in the unit disc and whose components $\tilde{\Gamma}_{kj}(\tilde{z})$ are of class H_2, such that

$$\tilde{f}(\mu) = \frac{1}{2\pi}\tilde{\Gamma}(e^{-i\mu})\overset{*}{\tilde{\Gamma}}(e^{-i\mu})\,. \tag{2.22}$$

Let us consider the matrix function

$$\Gamma(z) = \frac{\sqrt{2}}{1+iz}\tilde{\Gamma}(\tilde{z})\,, \tag{2.23}$$

where

$$\tilde{z} = \frac{1-iz}{1+iz}\,. \tag{2.24}$$

The transformation (2.24) carries the interior of the unit disc $|\tilde{z}|<1$ into the lower half-plane $\operatorname{Im} z < 0$, and

$$z = i\frac{\tilde{z}-1}{\tilde{z}+1}\,. \tag{2.25}$$

From (2.21)–(2.23) it is evident that the matrix $\Gamma(z)$, which is analytic in the lower half-plane, satisfies the boundary condition

$$f(\lambda) = \frac{1}{2\pi}\Gamma(\lambda)\overset{*}{\Gamma}(\lambda)\,. \tag{2.26}$$

Further,

$$\Gamma(\lambda) = \frac{\sqrt{2}}{1+i\lambda}\tilde{\Gamma}(e^{-i\mu}) = \frac{\sqrt{2}}{1+i\lambda}\sum_0^\infty \tilde{c}(s)e^{-i\mu s} = \sqrt{2}\sum_0^\infty \tilde{c}(s)\frac{(1-i\lambda)^s}{(1+i\lambda)^{s+1}}, \qquad (2.27)$$

and

$$\frac{(1-i\lambda)^s}{(1+i\lambda)^{s+1}} = \sum_0^s \frac{A_k}{(1+i\lambda)^{k+1}} = \sum_0^s \frac{A_k}{k!}\int_0^\infty e^{-i\lambda t}e^{-t}t^k\,dt = \int_0^\infty e^{-i\lambda t}B_s(t)\,dt,$$
$$B_s(t) = e^{-t}\sum_0^s \frac{A_k}{k!}t^k. \qquad (2.28)$$

Since the functions $e^{i\mu s}$, $-\infty < s < \infty$, form a complete orthogonal system on the interval $[-\pi, \pi]$, and $d\mu = (2/1+\lambda^2)d\lambda$, the functions

$$\frac{\sqrt{2}}{1+i\lambda}e^{i\mu s} = \sqrt{2}\frac{(1-i\lambda)^s}{(1+i\lambda)^{s+1}}$$

form a similar system on the line $-\infty < \lambda < \infty$; thus, every square integrable function $\varphi(\lambda)$ can be expanded in a series of the following form:

$$\varphi(\lambda) = \sum_{-\infty}^\infty a(s)\frac{(1-i\lambda)^s}{(1+i\lambda)^{s+1}}, \qquad a(s) = \frac{1}{\pi}\int_{-\infty}^\infty \varphi(\lambda)\frac{(1-i\lambda)^s}{(1+i\lambda)^{s+1}}d\lambda \qquad (2.29)$$

(this series converges in mean square). Consequently, the order of the summation in (2.27) and the integration in (2.28) can be interchanged, which gives us a representation of $\Gamma(z)$ in the form

$$\Gamma(\lambda) = \int_0^\infty e^{-i\lambda t}c(t)\,dt, \qquad (2.30)$$

where

$$c(t) = \sqrt{2}\sum_0^\infty \tilde{c}(s)B_s(t), \qquad \int_{-\infty}^\infty \|c(t)\|^2\,dt = \frac{1}{2\pi}\int_{-\infty}^\infty \|\Gamma(\lambda)\|^2\,d\lambda. \qquad (2.31)$$

In turn, if the spectral density $f(\lambda)$ admits a representation (2.26) with a matrix $\Gamma(\lambda)$ of the form (2.30), $\Gamma(\lambda)$ can be expanded in a series (2.27), and the matrix $\tilde{\Gamma}(\tilde{z})$, related with $\Gamma(z)$ by (2.23), will be analytic in the unit disc with components of class H_2, and its boundary value $\tilde{\Gamma}(e^{-i\mu})$ will satisfy condition (2.22).

We shall say that the spectral density $f(\lambda)$ *admits a factorization*, if it can be represented in the form (2.26).

Taking Theorem 4.1 of the previous chapter into account, we conclude that the following result holds:

Theorem 2.3. *For the linear regularity of a stationary process* $\xi = \{\xi_k(t)\}_{k=\overline{1,n}}$ *it is necessary and sufficient that it have a spectral density* $f(\lambda) = \{f_{kl}(\lambda)\}_{k=\overline{1,n}}^{l=\overline{1,n}}$ *with constant rank for almost all* λ, *which admits a factorization.*

On the basis of the results of Section 8, Chapter II, one can give a general analytic criterion for the regularity of a stationary process. Namely, the transformation

$$\gamma(z) = \frac{\sqrt{2}}{1+iz}\tilde{\gamma}(\tilde{z}), \qquad \tilde{z} = \frac{1-iz}{1+iz}, \tag{2.32}$$

carries a function $\tilde{\gamma}(\tilde{z})$, analytic in the unit disc, into a function $\gamma(z)$, analytic in the lower half-plane; thus the class H_δ, defined in Section 4, Chapter II, goes over into a class of functions which we will also denote by H_δ. This class of functions, analytic in the lower half-plane, has been intensively studied in the specialized literature (see, for example, Hoffman[*]). The class N_δ is defined analogously.

Theorem 2.4. *For the linear regularity of a stationary process* $\xi = \{\xi_k(t)\}_{k=\overline{1,n}}$, *the following conditions are necessary and sufficient:*

1. *The spectral density* $f(\lambda) = \{f_{kl}(\lambda)\}_{k=\overline{1,n}}^{l=\overline{1,n}}$ *exists and has rank* m *for almost all* λ.
2. *There exists a principal minor* $M(\lambda) = \det\{f_{i_p i_q}(\lambda)\}_{p=\overline{1,m}}^{q=\overline{1,m}}$ *of* $f(\lambda)$ *which is almost everywhere different from zero, for which*

$$\int_{-\infty}^{\infty} \log M(\lambda)\frac{d\lambda}{1+\lambda^2} > -\infty .$$

3. *The functions* $\gamma_{kj}(\lambda) = M_{kj}(\lambda)/M(\lambda)$, *where* $M_{kj}(\lambda)$ *denotes the determinant obtained from* $M(\lambda)$ *by replacing its* jth *row by the row* $\{f_{ki_p}(\lambda)\}_{p=\overline{1,m}}$, *are the boundary values of functions of class* N_δ *for some* $\delta > 0$.

The assertion of this theorem follows in an obvious way from Theorem 8.2 of Chapter II and Lemma 2.4 of the present section.

In particular, for the linear regularity of a stationary process with maximal rank it is necessary and sufficient that

$$\int_{-\infty}^{\infty} \log \det f(\lambda)\frac{d\lambda}{1+\lambda^2} > -\infty . \tag{2.33}$$

From Theorem 2.4 it follows also that *a stationary process with a spectral density which is a rational function of* λ *is always regular.*

In conclusion we note an important fact regarding one-dimensional processes (cf. Theorem 5.4 of Chapter II). Let

$$F(d\lambda) = f(\lambda)d\lambda + \Sigma\,(d\lambda) \tag{2.34}$$

be the decomposition of the spectral measure F of the stationary process ξ into its absolutely continuous and singular parts. *If the density* $f(\lambda)$ *vanishes on some set of positive measure, or if*

$$\int_{-\infty}^{\infty} \log f(\lambda) \frac{d\lambda}{1+\lambda^2} = -\infty\,, \tag{2.35}$$

then ξ will be singular; if

$$\int_{-\infty}^{\infty} \log f(\lambda) \frac{d\lambda}{1+\lambda^2} > -\infty\,, \tag{2.36}$$

then the regular and singular parts η and ζ in the decomposition (2.5) *of ξ are given by*

$$\begin{aligned} \eta(t) &= \int_{\bar{\Delta}_0} e^{i\lambda t}\Phi(d\lambda)\,, \\ \zeta(t) &= \int_{\Delta_0} e^{i\lambda t}\Phi(d\lambda)\,, \end{aligned} \tag{2.37}$$

where $\Phi(d\lambda)$ is the random spectral measure of ξ, Δ_0 is the set of Lebesgue measure zero on which the measure $\sum(d\lambda)$ is concentrated, and $\bar{\Delta}_0$ is its complement.

3. Wold's decomposition

As we shall see below, a linearly regular process $\xi = \{\xi_k(t)\}_{k=\overline{1,n}}$ can be represented in the form of a "moving average":

$$\xi(t) = \int_{-\infty}^{t} c(t-s)\zeta(ds)\,, \qquad \zeta(dt) = \{\zeta_j(dt)\}_{j=\overline{1,m}}\,. \tag{3.1}$$

Here $\zeta(dt)$ is an uncorrelated random measure;

$$\boldsymbol{E}\,|\,\zeta_j(dt)\,|^2 = dt\,, \quad j=\overline{1,m}\,, \qquad \boldsymbol{E}\zeta_j(\Delta)\overline{\zeta_{j'}(\Delta')} = 0$$

for $j \neq j'$ for any Borel sets Δ and Δ'. This random measure can be chosen so that the closed linear manifold $H_\zeta^-(t)$ generated by the values $\zeta_j(\Delta)$, $j=\overline{1,m}$, where Δ lies in the half-line $(-\infty, t)$, coincides with the subspace $H_\xi^-(t)$:

$$H_\zeta^-(t) = H_\xi^-(t)\,. \tag{3.2}$$

We will then say that such a random measure $\zeta(dt)$ is *fundamental* for the process ξ, and call the representation (3.1) *Wold's decomposition of ξ.*

As we already know, the spectral density $f(\lambda)$ of a regular n-dimensional process ξ admits a representation in the form

$$f(\lambda) = \frac{1}{2\pi}\Gamma(\lambda)\overset{*}{\Gamma}(\lambda)\,, \tag{3.3}$$

where the matrix $\Gamma(z) = \{\Gamma_{kj}(z)\}_{k=\overline{1,n}}^{j=\overline{1,m}}$ is analytic in the lower half-plane (its components $\Gamma_{kj}(z)$ are functions of class H_2). Just as in the discrete-parameter case, among such matrices $\Gamma(z)$ there exists a *maximal*† one. (This follows at once from the definition of H_2 in the continuous-parameter case and from (2.23)).

If $\Gamma(\lambda)$ is a matrix function with components from H_2, then, as is evident from (2.30), its Fourier transform $c(t)$ vanishes for negative t.

Let $\Phi = \{\Phi_k\}_{k=\overline{1,n}}$ be the random spectral measure of ξ, and suppose that the matrix function $\phi(\lambda) = \{\phi_{jk}(\lambda)\}_{j=\overline{1,m}}^{k=\overline{1,n}}$ satisfies the equation

$$\phi(\lambda)\Gamma(\lambda) = I_m \tag{3.4}$$

for almost all λ. Then by Theorem 9.1, Chapter I, ξ can be represented in the form (3.1), where the uncorrelated random measure $\zeta(dt) = \{\zeta_j(dt)\}_{j=\overline{1,m}}$ is defined by

$$\zeta(\Delta) = \int_{-\infty}^{\infty} \frac{e^{i\lambda t_2} - e^{i\lambda t_1}}{i\lambda} \phi(\lambda)\Phi(d\lambda) \tag{3.5}$$

for any interval $\Delta = (t_1, t_2)$.

Suppose that $\Gamma(z)$ is maximal. We denote by $\Psi = \{\Psi_j\}_{j=\overline{1,m}}$ the random measure defined by

$$\Psi(d\lambda) = \frac{\sqrt{2}}{1+i\lambda}\phi(\lambda)\Phi(d\lambda)\,. \tag{3.6}$$

Then $\Psi(d\lambda)$ is such that

$$\boldsymbol{E}\,|\Psi_j(d\lambda)|^2 = \frac{d\lambda}{\pi(1+\lambda^2)}\,, \qquad \boldsymbol{E}\Psi_j(\Delta)\overline{\Psi}_{j'}(\Delta') = 0 \tag{3.7}$$

for $j \neq j'$ for any Borel sets Δ and Δ'. If $\Delta = (t_1, t_2)$, then

$$\begin{aligned} \zeta(\Delta) &= \frac{1}{\sqrt{2}}\int_{-\infty}^{\infty} \frac{e^{i\lambda t_2} - e^{i\lambda t_1}}{i\lambda}(1+i\lambda)\Psi(d\lambda) \\ &= \frac{1}{\sqrt{2}}\int_{-\infty}^{\infty} e^{i\lambda t_2}\Psi(d\lambda) - \frac{1}{\sqrt{2}}\int_{-\infty}^{\infty} e^{i\lambda t_1}\Psi(d\lambda) \\ &\quad + \frac{1}{\sqrt{2}}\int_{-\infty}^{\infty}\left[\int_{t_1}^{t_2} e^{i\lambda t}\,dt\right]\Psi(d\lambda)\,. \end{aligned} \tag{3.8}$$

We set

$$\eta(t) = \int_{-\infty}^{\infty} e^{i\lambda t}\Psi(d\lambda)\,. \tag{3.9}$$

It is evident from (3.8) that the values $\zeta_j(\Delta)$ of the random measure $\zeta = \{\zeta_j\}_{j=\overline{1,m}}$ belong to $H_\eta^-(t)$ for all $j = \overline{1,m}$ and $\Delta = (t_1, t_2)$, when $t_1 \leq$

† That is, $\Gamma(-i)\overset{*}{\Gamma}(-i) - \tilde{\Gamma}(-i)\overset{*}{\tilde{\Gamma}}(-i) \geq 0$ for any matrix function $\tilde{\Gamma}(z)$ which is analytic in the lower half-plane, has components of class H_2, and satisfies the same boundary condition (3.3) as does $\Gamma(z)$.

$t_2 \leq t$. The discrete-parameter process $\tilde{\boldsymbol{\eta}}$ corresponding to $\boldsymbol{\eta}$,

$$\tilde{\eta}(t) = \int_{-\pi}^{\pi} e^{i\mu t}\tilde{\Psi}(d\mu) , \tag{3.10}$$

where

$$\tilde{\Psi}(d\mu) = \Psi(d\lambda) ,$$
$$\mu = 2 \operatorname{arctg} \lambda ,$$

will be an uncorrelated process, because

$$\boldsymbol{E} \mid \tilde{\Psi}_j(d\mu) \mid^2 = \boldsymbol{E} \mid \Psi_j(d\lambda) \mid^2 = \frac{d\lambda}{\pi(1+\lambda^2)} = \frac{d\mu}{2\pi} . \tag{3.11}$$

We see now that $\tilde{\boldsymbol{\eta}} = \{\tilde{\eta}_j(t)\}_{j=\overline{1,m}}$ is fundamental for the process $\tilde{\boldsymbol{\xi}} = \{\tilde{\xi}_k(t)\}_{k=\overline{1,n}}$:

$$\tilde{\xi}(t) = \int_{-\pi}^{\pi} e^{i\mu t}\tilde{\Phi}(d\mu) . \tag{3.12}$$

Indeed, the matrix function $\tilde{\phi}(\mu) = \{\tilde{\phi}_{jk}(\mu)\}_{j=\overline{1,m}}^{k=\overline{1,n}}$,

$$\tilde{\phi}(\mu) = \frac{\sqrt{2}}{1+i\lambda}\phi(\lambda) ,$$

satisfies the equation

$$\tilde{\phi}(\mu)\tilde{\Gamma}(e^{-i\mu}) = I_m , \tag{3.13}$$

where $\tilde{\Gamma}(\tilde{z})$ is a maximal analytic matrix corresponding to $\tilde{\boldsymbol{\xi}}$: $\tilde{\Gamma}(e^{-i\mu}) = [(1+i\lambda)/\sqrt{2}]\Gamma(\lambda)$. That $\tilde{\boldsymbol{\eta}}$ is fundamental for $\tilde{\boldsymbol{\xi}}$ follows from

$$\tilde{\Psi}(d\mu) = \tilde{\phi}(\mu)\tilde{\Phi}(d\mu) . \tag{3.14}$$

(In this connection see Theorems 4.2 and 4.3 of the previous chapter.)

That $\tilde{\boldsymbol{\eta}}$ is fundamental for $\tilde{\boldsymbol{\xi}}$ means that $H_{\tilde{\eta}}^-(0) = H_{\tilde{\xi}}^-(0)$, from which, taking into account Lemma 2.1, we obtain $H_{\eta}^-(0) = H_{\xi}^-(0)$. Consequently, for all $j = \overline{1,m}$, $\Delta = (t_1, t_2)$ the values $\zeta_j(\Delta)$ of the uncorrelated measure $\zeta(dt)$ in representation (3.1) belong to $H_{\xi}^-(t)$ when $t_2 \leq t$. The same arguments, when carried through in the opposite direction, show that if the uncorrelated measure $\zeta(dt)$ in (3.1) is fundamental, then the matrix

$$\Gamma(z) = \int_0^{\infty} e^{-izt}c(t)\,dt , \tag{3.15}$$

which is analytic in the lower half-plane, will be maximal.

We have thus proven the following theorem:

Theorem 3.1. *A linearly regular process* $\boldsymbol{\xi} = \{\xi_k(t)\}_{k=\overline{1,n}}$,

$$\xi(t) = \int_{-\infty}^{\infty} e^{i\lambda t}\Phi(d\lambda) ,$$

with a spectral density $f(\lambda) = \{f_{kl}(\lambda)\}_{k=\overline{1,n}}^{l=\overline{1,n}}$ *of rank m can be represented in the form of a "moving average"* (3.1) *relative to some uncorrelated measure*

$$\zeta(dt) = \{\zeta_j(dt)\}_{j=\overline{1,m}} ,$$

which is fundamental if and only if the matrix function $c(t)$ *in* (3.1) *is the Fourier transform of a maximal matrix* $\Gamma(\lambda)$. *The measure* $\zeta(dt)$ *can be defined by formula* (3.5).

We leave it to the reader to prove that only a linearly regular process can be represented in the form (3.1).

4. Linear extrapolation of stationary processes

Wold's decomposition (3.1) of a linearly regular stationary process $\boldsymbol{\xi} = \{\xi_k(t)\}_{k=\overline{1,n}}$ enables us to find the projections $\hat{\xi}_k(t, \tau)$ of the $\xi_k(t+\tau)$, $k = \overline{1, n}$, on the subspace $H_\xi^-(t)$.

Namely,

$$\hat{\xi}(t, \tau) = \{\hat{\xi}_k(t, \tau)\}_{k=\overline{1,n}} = \int_{-\infty}^{t} c(t + \tau - s)\zeta(ds) . \tag{4.1}$$

Let

$$\xi(t) = \int_{-\infty}^{\infty} e^{i\lambda t}\Phi(d\lambda) \tag{4.2}$$

be the spectral representation of $\boldsymbol{\xi}$, and let $f(\lambda)$ be its spectral density. Applying the Fourier transformation to the integrand $c(s)$ and the fundamental measure $\zeta(dt)$, the expression (4.1) can be represented in the form

$$\hat{\xi}(t, \tau) = \int_{-\infty}^{\infty} e^{i\lambda t}\hat{\varphi}(\lambda, \tau)\Phi(d\lambda) . \tag{4.3}$$

Here the matrix function $\hat{\varphi}(\lambda, \tau) = \{\hat{\varphi}_{kl}(\lambda, \tau)\}_{k=\overline{1,n}}^{l=\overline{1,n}}$ is defined by

$$\hat{\varphi}(\lambda, \tau) = \varphi_\tau(\lambda)\psi(\lambda) ,$$

where

$$\varphi_\tau(\lambda) = \int_0^{\infty} e^{-i\lambda s}c(s + \tau)\, ds , \tag{4.4}$$

$$c(s) = \frac{1}{2\pi}\int_{-\infty}^{\infty} e^{i\lambda s}\Gamma(\lambda)\, d\lambda , \tag{4.5}$$

and $\Gamma(\lambda)$ is the boundary value of a maximal matrix $\Gamma(z) = \{\Gamma_{kj}(z)\}_{k=\overline{1,n}}^{j=\overline{1,m}}$ satisfying the boundary condition

$$\Gamma(\lambda)\overset{*}{\Gamma}(\lambda) = 2\pi f(\lambda) ; \tag{4.6}$$

the matrix function $\psi(\lambda) = \{\psi_{jk}(\lambda)\}_{j=\overline{1,m}}^{k=\overline{1,n}}$ satisfies the equation

$$\psi(\lambda)\Gamma(\lambda) = I_m \tag{4.7}$$

(for almost all λ).

The question of reconstructing a maximal matrix from the spectral density of a stationary process was considered in detail earlier for the discrete-parameter case. We saw that comparatively simple formulas can be obtained only for one-dimensional processes (see Section 5 of the previous chapter).

Although one can immediately indicate several methods for finding a maximal matrix $\Gamma(z)$ from condition (4.6) in rather diverse situations (in view of the possibility of reducing the continuous-parameter case to the discrete-parameter case, which was shown in Section 2), we will restrict ourselves to considering this question only for one-dimensional processes.

Thus, let ξ be a regular stationary process with spectral density $f(\lambda)$ and let $\Gamma(z)$ be a maximal function satisfying the boundary condition

$$\frac{1}{2\pi} | \Gamma(\lambda) |^2 = f(\lambda) . \tag{4.8}$$

We consider the function $\tilde{\Gamma}(\tilde{z})$ which is analytic in the unit disc:

$$\tilde{\Gamma}(\tilde{z}) = \frac{1+iz}{\sqrt{2}} \Gamma(z) , \tag{4.9}$$

where

$$\tilde{z} = \frac{1-iz}{1+iz} .$$

By virtue of the maximality of $\Gamma(z)$, this function will also be maximal, and, moreover,

$$\frac{1}{2\pi} | \tilde{\Gamma}(e^{-i\mu}) |^2 = \tilde{f}(\mu) , \tag{4.10}$$

where

$$\tilde{f}(\mu) = \frac{1+\lambda^2}{2} f(\lambda) , \quad \mu = 2 \operatorname{arctg} \lambda .$$

By formula (5.10) of the previous chapter, $\tilde{\Gamma}(\tilde{z})$ can be represented in the form

$$\tilde{\Gamma}(\tilde{z}) = \sqrt{2\pi} \exp \left\{ \frac{1}{4\pi} \int_{-\pi}^{\pi} \log \tilde{f}(\mu) \frac{e^{-i\mu} + \tilde{z}}{e^{-i\mu} - \tilde{z}} d\mu \right\} . \tag{4.11}$$

Taking into consideration that the function

$$\frac{\tilde{z}+1}{2}=\frac{1}{1+iz} \tag{4.12}$$

can be represented in the form

$$\begin{aligned}\frac{\tilde{z}+1}{2}&=\exp\left\{\frac{1}{4\pi}\int_{-\pi}^{\pi}\log\left|\frac{e^{-i\mu}+1}{2}\right|^2\frac{e^{-i\mu}+\tilde{z}}{e^{-i\mu}-\tilde{z}}d\mu\right\}\\&=\exp\left\{\frac{1}{2\pi i}\int_{-\infty}^{\infty}\log\frac{1}{1+\lambda^2}\frac{1+\lambda z}{z-\lambda}\frac{d\lambda}{1+\lambda^2}\right\}\end{aligned} \tag{4.13}$$

(see, in this regard, relations (5.19)–(5.21), Chapter II), we have

$$\begin{aligned}\Gamma(z)&=\frac{\sqrt{2}}{1+iz}\tilde{\Gamma}(\tilde{z})=\sqrt{2}\,\frac{\tilde{z}+1}{2}\sqrt{2\pi}\exp\left\{\frac{1}{4\pi}\int_{-\pi}^{\pi}\log\tilde{f}(\mu)\frac{e^{-i\mu}+\tilde{z}}{e^{-i\mu}-\tilde{z}}d\mu\right\}\\&=\sqrt{2}\exp\left\{\frac{1}{2\pi i}\int_{-\infty}^{\infty}\left(\log\frac{1}{1+\lambda^2}\right)\frac{1+\lambda z}{z-\lambda}\frac{d\lambda}{1+\lambda^2}\right\}\\&\quad\times\sqrt{2\pi}\exp\left\{\frac{1}{2\pi i}\int_{-\infty}^{\infty}\left[\log\frac{f(\lambda)(1+\lambda^2)}{2}\right]\frac{1+\lambda z}{z-\lambda}\frac{d\lambda}{1+\lambda^2}\right\}\\&=\sqrt{\pi}\exp\left\{\frac{1}{2\pi i}\int_{-\infty}^{\infty}\log f(\lambda)\frac{1+\lambda z}{z-\lambda}\frac{d\lambda}{1+\lambda^2}\right\}.\end{aligned} \tag{4.14}$$

Thus, if the one-dimensional process ξ,

$$\xi(t)=\int_{-\infty}^{\infty}e^{i\lambda t}\Phi(d\lambda)\,, \tag{4.15}$$

is linearly regular, then the stationary process $\hat{\xi}(\cdot,\tau)$, *consisting of the best linear forecasts* (τ *units of time ahead*) *of the* $\xi(t)$, *can be obtained from* ξ *by a linear transformation of the form*

$$\hat{\xi}(t,\tau)=\int_{-\infty}^{\infty}e^{i\lambda t}\frac{1}{\Gamma(\lambda)}\left[\int_0^{\infty}e^{-i\lambda s}c(s+\tau)\,ds\right]\Phi(d\lambda)\,, \tag{4.16}$$

where $\Gamma(\lambda)$ *is the boundary value of the analytic function* $\Gamma(z)$ *defined by* (4.14), *and*

$$c(s)=\frac{1}{2\pi}\int_{-\infty}^{\infty}e^{i\lambda s}\Gamma(\lambda)\,d\lambda\,. \tag{4.17}$$

Let us consider the important case in which the spectral density $f(\lambda)$ of ξ is a rational function of λ. As was shown in Section 10, Chapter I,

$$f(\lambda)=\frac{|P(\lambda)|^2}{|Q(\lambda)|^2}\,, \tag{4.18}$$

where the polynomials P and Q do not have zeros in the lower half-plane.

Let us consider the maximal function $\tilde{\Gamma}(\tilde{z})$ which is related to the sought-for function $\Gamma(z)$ by (4.9). Since under the transformation $\mu=$

$2\operatorname{arctg}\lambda$ a function which is rational in λ goes over into a function which is rational in $e^{-i\mu}$, the function $\tilde{f}(\mu)$ in (4.10) will be rational in $e^{-i\mu}$, and therefore $\tilde{\Gamma}(\tilde{z})$ is the unique, up to a constant factor, analytic function in the unit disc satisfying the boundary condition (4.10), not having zeros in this disc, and rational in $\tilde{z}$ (see formula (5.19), Chapter II). Consequently, *the maximal function* $\Gamma(z)$ *is the unique* (*up to a constant factor*) *analytic function in the lower half-plane which satisfies the boundary condition* (4.8), *has no zeros and is rational in* z. But such a function, as follows from the representation (4.18), is given by†

$$\Gamma(z) = \sqrt{2\pi}\,\frac{P(z)}{Q(z)}\,. \tag{4.19}$$

Example 4.1. Suppose that the stationary process ξ has the correlation function

$$B(t) = \sigma^2 e^{-\alpha|t|}\,, \qquad \alpha > 0\,.$$

The spectral density $f(\lambda)$ of ξ is

$$f(\lambda) = \frac{1}{2\pi}\int_{-\infty}^{\infty} e^{-i\lambda t} B(t)\,dt = \frac{\sigma^2}{\pi}\,\frac{\alpha}{\alpha^2+\lambda^2}\,.$$

It is easy to see that a maximal function $\Gamma(z)$ is

$$\Gamma(z) = \sqrt{2\alpha}\,\sigma\,\frac{1}{\alpha+iz} = \sqrt{2\alpha}\,\sigma\int_0^{\infty} e^{-izt}e^{-\alpha t}\,dt\,.$$

Consequently, the $\hat{\xi}(t,\tau)$, which give the best forecast of the $\xi(t)$, can be represented in the form

$$\hat{\xi}(t,\tau) = \int_{-\infty}^{\infty} e^{i\lambda t}\,\frac{1}{\alpha+i\lambda}\left[\int_0^{\infty} e^{-i\lambda s}e^{-\alpha(s+\tau)}\,ds\right]\Phi(d\lambda)\,,$$

where Φ is the random spectral measure of ξ. The final formula for the best forecasts is very simple:

$$\hat{\xi}(t,\tau) = e^{-\alpha\tau}\xi(t)\,.$$

In formula (4.16) for the best linear forecast there appears a function of the form

$$\int_0^{\infty} e^{-i\lambda s}c(s+\tau)\,ds\,.$$

We shall show that this function is rational in λ whenever $f(\lambda)$ is rational in λ.

Let us consider an arbitrary rational function $r(\lambda)$ of λ which is a proper fraction,

† The polynomials $P(z)$ and $Q(z)$ can easily be determined from the zeros and poles of the spectral density $f(\lambda)$.

$$r(\lambda) = \frac{P(\lambda)}{Q(\lambda)} \,.$$

As is known, $r(\lambda)$ can be represented as a linear combination of simple fractions of the form $1/(\lambda - \alpha)^\nu$, where α is a root of the polynomial $Q(\lambda)$, and the positive integer ν does not exceed the multiplicity of this root. We will therefore suppose that $r(\lambda)$ itself is given by

$$r(\lambda) = \frac{1}{(\lambda - \alpha)^\nu} \,.$$

If $r(\lambda)$ is square integrable, then the root α cannot be real; in this case

$$r(\lambda) = \int_0^\infty e^{-i\lambda s}\left[\frac{i^\nu}{(\nu - 1)!} s^{\nu-1} e^{i\alpha s}\right] ds \,,$$

when $\operatorname{Im} \alpha > 0$, and

$$r(\lambda) = \int_{-\infty}^0 e^{-i\lambda s}\left[-\frac{i^\nu}{(\nu - 1)!} s^{\nu-1} e^{i\alpha s}\right] ds \,,$$

when $\operatorname{Im} \alpha < 0$.

Suppose $\operatorname{Im} \alpha > 0$. Then the Fourier transform $a(s)$ of $r(\lambda)$ is such that for $\tau \geq 0$

$$\begin{aligned}\int_0^\infty e^{-i\lambda s} a(s + \tau)\, ds &= \int_0^\infty e^{-i\lambda s}\left[\frac{i^\nu}{(\nu - 1)!}(s + \tau)^{\nu-1} e^{i\alpha(s+\tau)}\right] ds \\ &= e^{i\alpha\tau} \sum_{k=1}^{\nu} i^{\nu-k} \frac{(k-1)!}{(\nu-1)!} C_{\nu-1}^{k-1} \tau^{\nu-k} \frac{1}{(\lambda - \alpha)^k} \,. \end{aligned} \tag{4.20}$$

If $\operatorname{Im} \alpha < 0$, then for $\tau \geq 0$, obviously,

$$\int_0^\infty e^{-i\lambda s} a(s + \tau)\, ds = 0 \,, \tag{4.21}$$

since in this case $a(s) = 0$ for positive s.

Formulas (4.20)-(4.21) allow us to conclude that *for any rational function* $r(\lambda)$ *which is square integrable, its Fourier transform* $a(s)$,

$$a(s) = \frac{1}{2\pi} \int_{-\infty}^\infty e^{i\lambda s} r(\lambda)\, d\lambda \,,$$

has the property that the function $r_\tau(\lambda)$ *of the form*

$$r_\tau(\lambda) = \int_0^\infty e^{-i\lambda s} a(s + \tau)\, ds \tag{4.22}$$

is rational in λ.

This is true, in particular, for $r(\lambda) = \Gamma(\lambda)$, since a maximal function $\Gamma(z)$ corresponding to a rational spectral density $f(\lambda)$ is rational in z.

Thus, the *spectral characteristic* $\hat{\varphi}(\lambda, \tau)$ of the linear transformation giving the best forecast,

$$\hat{\varphi}(\lambda, \tau) = \frac{1}{\Gamma(\lambda)} \int_0^\infty e^{-i\lambda s} c(s + \tau) \, ds \,, \tag{4.23}$$

is a rational function of λ, *analytic in the lower half-plane* [$\Gamma(\lambda)$ *has no zeros there*]. The condition of orthogonality of $\xi(\tau) - \hat{\xi}(0, \tau)$ to the subspace $H_\xi^-(0)$ means that

$$\boldsymbol{E}[\xi(\tau) - \hat{\xi}(0, \tau)]\overline{\xi(s)} = \int_{-\infty}^\infty e^{-i\lambda s}[e^{i\lambda\tau} - \hat{\varphi}(\lambda, \tau)] f(\lambda) \, d\lambda = 0 \tag{4.24}$$

for all $s \leq 0$, and this in turn shows that *the function* $\psi(\lambda, \tau)$,

$$\psi(\lambda, \tau) = [e^{i\lambda\tau} - \hat{\varphi}(\lambda, \tau)] f(\lambda) \,, \tag{4.25}$$

must be analytic in the upper half-plane. Indeed, the spectral density $f(\lambda)$, being rational in λ and integrable on the line, is bounded: $f(\lambda) \leq C$. The function $\hat{\varphi}(\lambda, \tau)$ satisfies the condition

$$\int_{-\infty}^\infty | \hat{\varphi}(\lambda, \tau) |^2 f(\lambda) \, d\lambda < \infty \,,$$

and, therefore,

$$\int_{-\infty}^\infty | \hat{\varphi}(\lambda, \tau) |^2 f^2(\lambda) \, d\lambda \leq C \int_{-\infty}^\infty | \hat{\varphi}(\lambda, \tau) |^2 f(\lambda) \, d\lambda < \infty \,,$$

from which it is evident that $\psi(\lambda, \tau)$ is square integrable. By virtue of relation (4.24) it can be represented in the form

$$\psi(\lambda, \tau) = \frac{1}{2\pi} \int_0^\infty e^{i\lambda s} \tilde{\psi}(s, \tau) \, ds \,,$$

and is a fortiori analytic in the upper half-plane $\operatorname{Im} \lambda > 0$.

Let

$$\hat{\varphi}(\lambda, \tau) = \frac{P_\tau(\lambda)}{Q_\tau(\lambda)} \,, \tag{4.26}$$

where the polynomials $P_\tau(\lambda)$ and $Q_\tau(\lambda)$ are irreducible. By virtue of the analyticity of $\hat{\varphi}(\lambda, \tau)$, $Q_\tau(\lambda)$ does not have zeros in the lower half-plane. From (4.25) it follows at once that the zeros of the polynomial $Q_\tau(\lambda)$ must necessarily be among the zeros of the spectral density lying in the upper half-plane.

As was already noted, the spectral density $f(\lambda)$ always has the form

$$f(\lambda) = \frac{| P(\lambda) |^2}{| Q(\lambda) |^2} \,, \tag{4.27}$$

where the polynomials P and Q do not have zeros in the lower half-plane. Consequently, *the spectral characteristic* $\hat{\varphi}(\lambda, \tau)$ *must be sought in the form*

$$\hat{\varphi}(\lambda, \tau) = \frac{\sum_0^N a_k \lambda^k}{P(\lambda)}, \tag{4.28}$$

where the degree N of the polynomial in the numerator must be less than the degree of the denominator $Q(\lambda)$ in expression (4.27) for $f(\lambda)$.

The undetermined coefficients a_k are to be chosen so that the function $\psi(\lambda, \tau)$ in (4.25) is analytic in the upper half-plane. We have

$$\psi(\lambda, \tau) = \frac{e^{i\lambda\tau} P(\lambda) - \sum_0^N a_k \lambda^k}{P(\lambda)} f(\lambda). \tag{4.29}$$

If $z_q, q = \overline{1, n}$, are the zeros of $Q(\lambda)$, with multiplicities n_q, then for the coefficients $a_k, k = \overline{0, N}$, we obtain the following system of linear equations:

$$\frac{d^l}{d\lambda^l}\left[e^{iz_q\tau} P(z_q) - \sum_0^N a_k z_q^k\right] = 0, \qquad l = \overline{0, n_q - 1}, \qquad q = \overline{1, n}. \tag{4.30}$$

[It is not hard to see that the number of unknowns a_k does not exceed the number of equations, which is equal to the degree of the polynomial $Q(\lambda)$.]

Formulas (4.28) and (4.30) enable us to find the spectral characteristic $\hat{\varphi}(\lambda, \tau)$ without calculating the Fourier transform $c(s) = (1/2\pi)\int_{-\infty}^{\infty} e^{i\lambda s}\Gamma(\lambda)\, d\lambda$, appearing in the basic formula (4.16). Of course, a similar method for finding the spectral characteristic $\hat{\varphi}(\lambda, \tau)$ is applicable in the discrete-parameter case.

Example 4.2. Let ξ be a stationary process with spectral density $f(\lambda)$ of the form

$$f(\lambda) = \frac{1}{|Q(\lambda)|^2}.$$

From formula (4.28) it is evident that in this case the spectral characteristic $\hat{\varphi}(\lambda, \tau)$ of $\hat{\xi}(t, \tau)$ is simply a polynomial:

$$\hat{\varphi}(\lambda, \tau) = \sum_0^N a_k \lambda^k.$$

Thus,

$$\hat{\xi}(t, \tau) = \int_{-\infty}^{\infty} e^{i\lambda t} \hat{\varphi}(\lambda, \tau) \Phi(d\lambda) = \sum_0^N (-i)^k a_k \xi^{(k)}(t),$$

that is, the best forecast is given by a linear combination of derivatives of ξ at the last moment t. The coefficients $a_k, k = \overline{0, N}$, are determined from the system of linear equations (4.30), which in the present case assumes the following form:

$$\frac{d^l}{d\lambda^l}\left[e^{iz_q\tau} - \sum_0^N a_k z_q^k\right] = 0\,, \qquad l = \overline{0, n_q - 1}\,; \quad q = \overline{1, n}$$

where the $z_q, q = \overline{1, n}$, are the zeros of $Q(\lambda)$.

5. Linear filtering of stationary processes

The solution of the problem of the linear filtering of continuous-parameter stationary processes differs only slightly from the corresponding solution in the discrete-parameter case, considered in Section 9, Chapter II. Namely, let $\boldsymbol{\xi} = \{\xi_k(t)\}_{k=\overline{1,n}}$ and $\boldsymbol{\eta} = \{\eta_k(t)\}_{k=\overline{1,m}}$ be multidimensional stationarily correlated processes, with spectral densities

$$f^{\xi\xi}(\lambda) = \{f_{kl}^{\xi\xi}(\lambda)\}_{k=\overline{1,n}}^{l=\overline{1,n}}\,,$$

$$f^{\eta\eta}(\lambda) = \{f_{kl}^{\eta\eta}(\lambda)\}_{k=\overline{1,m}}^{l=\overline{1,m}} \quad \text{and} \quad f^{\xi\eta}(\lambda) = \{f_{kl}^{\xi\eta}(\lambda)\}_{k=\overline{1,n}}^{l=\overline{1,m}}\,.$$

In the case where $\boldsymbol{\eta}$ is linearly regular and has maximal rank, the quantities $\hat{\xi}(t,\tau) = \{\hat{\xi}_k(t,\tau)\}_{k=\overline{1,n}}$, giving the best linear forecast for $\xi(t+\tau)$ (by means of the values $\eta_k(s), s \le t, k = \overline{1, m}$), can be represented in the form

$$\hat{\xi}(t,\tau) = \int_{-\infty}^{\infty} e^{i\lambda t}\left[\int_0^{\infty} e^{-i\lambda s} a(s+\tau)ds\right]\varphi^{-1}(\lambda)\Phi(d\lambda)\,, \tag{5.1}$$

where $\Phi(d\lambda) = \{\Phi_k(d\lambda)\}_{k=\overline{1,m}}$ is the random spectral measure of $\boldsymbol{\eta}$, the matrix function $\varphi(\lambda) = \{\varphi_{kl}(\lambda)\}_{k=\overline{1,m}}^{l=\overline{1,m}}$ is the boundary value (for $z = \lambda$) of a maximal matrix $\Gamma(z)$ satisfying the condition

$$\frac{1}{2\pi}\Gamma(\lambda)\overset{*}{\Gamma}(\lambda) = f^{\eta\eta}(\lambda)\,, \tag{5.2}$$

and the matrix function $a(s) = \{a_{kl}(s)\}_{k=\overline{1,n}}^{l=\overline{1,m}}$ is the Fourier transform of the product $f^{\xi\eta}(f^{\eta\eta})^{-1}\varphi$:

$$a(s) = \frac{1}{2\pi}\int_{-\infty}^{\infty} e^{i\lambda s} f^{\xi\eta}(\lambda)[f^{\eta\eta}(\lambda)]^{-1}\varphi(\lambda)\,d\lambda\,. \tag{5.3}$$

The proof of formula (5.1) is completely analogous to that in the discrete-parameter case, considered in Section 9, Chapter II, and we therefore omit it.

Let us consider in detail the linear filtering of processes with rational spectral densities. For such processes the spectral characteristic $\hat{\varphi}(\lambda, \tau)$ in (5.1),

$$\hat{\varphi}(\lambda,\tau) = \left[\int_0^{\infty} e^{-i\lambda s} a(s+\tau)\,ds\right]\varphi^{-1}(\lambda)\,, \tag{5.4}$$

can be found by solving a certain system of linear algebraic equations (similar to what was done in the previous section in solving the extrapolation problem).

We restrict ourselves to considering only one-dimensional processes, since, although the transition to multi-dimensional processes does not give rise to fundamental difficulties, the method itself appears rather cumbersome.

Thus, suppose that ξ and η have rational spectral densities. As in the case of linear extrapolation, *the spectral characteristic* (5.4) *of* $\hat{\xi}(t,\tau)$ *is a rational function of* λ, *analytic in the lower half-plane.* The orthogonality of $\xi(\tau)-\hat{\xi}(0,\tau)$ to the subspace $H_\eta^-(0)$ means that

$$\begin{aligned} \boldsymbol{E}[\xi(\tau)-\hat{\xi}(0,\tau)]\overline{\eta(s)} &= \int_{-\infty}^{\infty} e^{-i\lambda s}\left[e^{i\lambda\tau}\frac{f^{\xi\eta}(\lambda)}{f^{\eta\eta}(\lambda)}-\hat{\varphi}(\lambda,\tau)\right]f^{\eta\eta}(\lambda)\,d\lambda \\ &= \int_{-\infty}^{\infty} e^{-i\lambda s}[e^{i\lambda\tau}f^{\xi\eta}(\lambda)-\hat{\varphi}(\lambda,\tau)f^{\eta\eta}(\lambda)]\,d\lambda = 0 \end{aligned} \tag{5.5}$$

for all $s \le 0$. Let us note once again that the functions $f^{\xi\eta}(\lambda)$, $\hat{\varphi}(\lambda,\tau)$ and $f^{\eta\eta}(\lambda)$ are rational in λ, and relation (5.5) shows that

$$\psi(\lambda,\tau) = e^{i\lambda\tau}f^{\xi\eta}(\lambda)-\hat{\varphi}(\lambda,\tau)f^{\eta\eta}(\lambda) \tag{5.6}$$

is a function of λ, *analytic in the upper half-plane.*

Let

$$f^{\eta\eta}(\lambda) = \frac{|P(\lambda)|^2}{|Q(\lambda)|^2}, \tag{5.7}$$

where the zeros w_p, $p=\overline{1,m}$, and z_q, $q=\overline{1,n}$, of the polynomials $P(\lambda)$ and $Q(\lambda)$ lie in the upper half-plane,

$$P(\lambda) = c\prod_{p=1}^{m}(\lambda-w_p)^{m_p}, \qquad Q(\lambda)=\prod_{q=1}^{n}(\lambda-z_q)^{n_q}. \tag{5.8}$$

Let us assume that

$$f^{\xi\eta}(\lambda) = \frac{A(\lambda)}{(\lambda-\gamma_1)\cdots(\lambda-\gamma_k)(\lambda-\gamma_1')\cdots(\lambda-\gamma_l')}, \tag{5.9}$$

where $A(\lambda)$ is a polynomial in λ, the numbers γ_j, $j=\overline{1,k}$, lie in the upper half-plane, and the γ_j', $j=\overline{1,l}$, in the lower half-plane.

Obviously, $\hat{\varphi}(\lambda,\tau)$ can have poles only at the points $\lambda=w_p$, $p=\overline{1,m}$, and $\lambda=\gamma_j$, $j=\overline{1,k}$, because $\psi(\lambda,\tau)$ must be analytic in the upper half-plane. Thus, the spectral characteristic must be sought in the form

$$\hat{\varphi}(\lambda,\tau) = \frac{Q(\lambda)}{P(\lambda)}\,\frac{\sum_0^N a_j\lambda^j}{(\lambda-\gamma_1)\cdots(\lambda-\gamma_k)}; \tag{5.10}$$

here the degree N of the polynomial in the numerator is less than k, because it is required that

$$\int_{-\infty}^{\infty} | \phi(\lambda, \tau) |^2 f^{\eta\eta}(\lambda) \, d\lambda < \infty \, . \tag{5.11}$$

In order that $\phi(\lambda, \tau)$ not have poles at the points $\lambda = \gamma_j$, $j = \overline{1, k}$, the difference

$$\Delta(\lambda) = e^{i\lambda\tau} A(\lambda)\bar{Q}(\lambda) - (\lambda - \gamma_1') \cdots (\lambda - \gamma_l')\bar{P}(\lambda) \sum_0^N a_j \lambda^j \tag{5.12}$$

must vanish at these points, which gives us k equations for determining the coefficients a_k:

$$\Delta(\gamma_j) = 0 \, , \qquad j = \overline{1, k} \tag{5.13}$$

(in the case where all the zeros γ_j are simple). If some zero γ among the γ_j has multiplicity l, then one has to add to the equations (5.13) $l - 1$ equations of the form

$$\left[\frac{d^i}{d\lambda^i} \Delta(\lambda) \right]_{\lambda = \gamma} = 0 \, , \qquad i = \overline{1, l-1} \, . \tag{5.14}$$

Example 5.1. Suppose that the spectral densities of the stationary processes ξ and η have the form

$$f^{\xi\eta}(\lambda) = \frac{A}{\lambda^2 + \gamma^2} \, , \qquad f^{\eta\eta}(\lambda) = \frac{c^2(\lambda^2 + \alpha^2)}{(\lambda^2 + \beta^2)(\lambda^2 + \gamma^2)} \, ,$$

where the constants α, β, γ are positive. We see that the polynomials P and Q in the representation (5.7) of $f^{\eta\eta}(\lambda)$ are

$$P(\lambda) = c(\lambda - i\alpha) \, ,$$
$$Q(\lambda) = (\lambda - i\beta)(\lambda - i\gamma) \, .$$

Consequently, we have to put in formula (5.9)

$$A(\lambda) = A \, , \qquad \gamma_1 = i\gamma \, , \qquad \gamma_1' = -i\gamma \, .$$

From relation (5.10) it follows that the spectral characteristic $\hat{\phi}(\lambda, \tau)$ of the best linear filtering is

$$\hat{\phi}(\lambda, \tau) = a \frac{(\lambda - i\beta)}{(\lambda - i\alpha)} \, ,$$

where the coefficient a is determined from the equation (5.13):

$$a = \frac{A}{c^2} e^{-\gamma\tau} \frac{\beta + \gamma}{\alpha + \gamma} \, .$$

Thus,

$$\hat{\xi}(t, \tau) = \int_{-\infty}^{\infty} e^{i\lambda t} \hat{\phi}(\lambda, \tau) \Phi(d\lambda) = a \int_{-\infty}^{\infty} e^{i\lambda t} \frac{\lambda - i\beta}{\lambda - i\alpha} \Phi(d\lambda) \, ,$$

where $\Phi(d\lambda)$ is the random spectral measure of η. Taking into consideration that

$$\frac{\lambda - i\beta}{\lambda - i\alpha} = 1 + \frac{\beta - \alpha}{\alpha + i\lambda} = 1 + (\beta - \alpha)\int_0^\infty e^{-i\lambda s} e^{-\alpha s}\, ds \, ,$$

we obtain finally

$$\hat{\xi}(t, \tau) = \frac{A}{c^2} e^{-\gamma\tau} \frac{\beta + \gamma}{\alpha + \gamma}\left[\eta(t) + (\beta - \alpha)\int_0^\infty e^{-\alpha s}\eta(t - s)\, ds\right] .$$

6. Linear interpolation of stationary processes

Let ξ be an n-dimensional stationary process, all of whose values $\xi_k(t)$, $k = \overline{1, n}$, $-\infty < t < \infty$, are known, with the exception of the values $\xi_k(t)$, $t \in T_k$, $k = \overline{1, n}$, where the T_k are certain intervals.

The problem of the linear interpolation of the unknown values $\xi_k(t)$, $t \in T_k$, consists in finding the projections $\hat{\xi}_k(t)$ of these random variables on the subspace $\hat{H}(T)$—the closed linear manifold generated by the known variables $\xi_k(t)$, $t \notin T_k$, $k = \overline{1, n}$.

Just as in the discrete-parameter case, one can assume without restriction of generality that ξ has a spectral density $f(\lambda) = \{f_{kl}(\lambda)\}_{k=\overline{1,n}}^{l=\overline{1,n}}$. Let us denote by B_λ the set of vectors $b = \{b_k\}^{k=\overline{1,n}}$ of the form

$$b = af(\lambda) \, , \tag{6.1}$$

that is, products of an arbitrary vector $a = \{a_k\}^{k=\overline{1,n}}$ and the spectral density $f(\lambda)$. As before (see Section 10 of the previous chapter), we will understand by $bf^{-1}(\lambda)$ any vector a satisfying (6.1).

Let us consider the Hilbert space $B(T)$ of vector functions $b(\lambda) = \{b_k(\lambda)\}^{k=\overline{1,n}}$ with components $b_k(\lambda)$ of the form

$$b_k(\lambda) = \int_{T_k} e^{i\lambda t} a_k(t)\, dt \, , \tag{6.2}$$

such that $b(\lambda) \in B_\lambda$ for almost all λ and

$$\int_{-\infty}^{\infty} [b(\lambda) f^{-1}(\lambda) \overset{*}{b}(\lambda)]\, d\lambda < \infty \, , \tag{6.3}$$

with scalar product

$$(b, b') = \int_{-\infty}^{\infty} [b(\lambda) f^{-1}(\lambda) \overset{*}{b}'(\lambda)]\, d\lambda \, . \tag{6.4}$$

As in the discrete-parameter case, the following result holds.

Lemma 6.1. *The closed linear manifold $\Delta(T)$ generated by the "errors" $\xi_k(t) - \hat{\xi}_k(t)$, $t \in T_k$, $k = \overline{1, n}$, is isomorphic to the space $B(T)$.*

Proof. Let $\Phi = \{\Phi_k\}_{k=\overline{1,n}}$ be the random spectral measure of ξ. Any $h \in \Delta(T)$ can be represented in the form

$$h = \int_{-\infty}^{\infty} \varphi(\lambda)\Phi(d\lambda) , \tag{6.5}$$

where the vector function $\varphi = \{\varphi_k\}^{k=\overline{1,n}}$ satisfies the requirement

$$\int_{-\infty}^{\infty} [\varphi(\lambda)f(\lambda)\overset{*}{\varphi}(\lambda)]\, d\lambda < \infty . \tag{6.6}$$

The orthogonality of h to the subspace $\hat{H}(T)$ means that

$$\boldsymbol{E}h\overline{\xi_k(t)} = \int_{-\infty}^{\infty} e^{-i\lambda t}\left[\sum_{l=1}^{n} \varphi_l(\lambda)f_{lk}(\lambda)\right] d\lambda = 0 \tag{6.7}$$

for all $t \notin T_k$, $k = \overline{1, n}$. If we set

$$b(\lambda) = \varphi(\lambda)f(\lambda) , \tag{6.8}$$

it follows from (6.7) that the Fourier transform of the function $b_k(\lambda) = \sum_{l=1}^{n} \varphi_l(\lambda)f_{lk}(\lambda)$, a component of the vector $b(\lambda) = \{b_k(\lambda)\}^{k=\overline{1,n}}$, vanishes outside the interval T_k, and, therefore, the $b_k(\lambda)$ have the form (6.2). Moreover, the vector $b(\lambda)$ obviously belongs to the set B_λ by its very definition. The scalar product is given by the following expression:

$$(h, h') = \boldsymbol{E}h\overline{h'} = \int_{-\infty}^{\infty} [\varphi(\lambda)f(\lambda)\overset{*}{\varphi}{}'(\lambda)]\, d\lambda = \int_{-\infty}^{\infty} [b(\lambda)f^{-1}(\lambda)\overset{*}{b}{}'(\lambda)]\, d\lambda , \tag{6.9}$$

where $b'(\lambda)$ is the vector function which corresponds [by a formula analogous to (6.8)] to the random variable $h' \in \Delta(T)$. We see that the vector functions $b(\lambda)$ and $b'(\lambda)$ belong to the space $B(T)$.

If, in turn, we take an arbitrary element $b(\lambda)$ from $B(T)$, then the random variable h, related to $b(\lambda)$ by (6.8) and (6.5), will by virtue of (6.7) be orthogonal to the subspace $\hat{H}(T)$, and consequently will belong to $\Delta(T)$.

We remark that the class of functions $\gamma(\lambda)$, representable in the form

$$\gamma(\lambda) = \int_{-\tau}^{\tau} e^{i\lambda t}a(t)\, dt , \tag{6.10}$$

which is analogous to (6.2), has been studied in adequate detail (see, for example, the book by Akhiezer[*]). In particular, every such function $\gamma(z)$ is entire, of exponential type with exponent τ, i.e., such that

$$|\gamma(z)| \le C_\gamma e^{\tau|z|} . \tag{6.11}$$

The following general theorem results at once from Lemma 6.1.

Theorem 6.1. *Error-free linear interpolation of the values* $\xi_k(t)$, $t \in T_k$, $k = \overline{1, n}$, *of a stationary process* $\boldsymbol{\xi} = \{\xi_k(t)\}_{k=\overline{1,n}}$ *with spectral density* $f(\lambda)$ *is possible if and only if*

$$B(T) = 0 . \tag{6.12}$$

In particular, in the case of a one-dimensional stationary process ξ with spectral density $f(\lambda)$, condition (6.12) for error-free linear interpolation on the interval $T = (-\tau, \tau)$ can be formulated in the following way: For any nonzero entire function $\gamma(\lambda)$ of exponential type with exponent τ,

$$\int_{-\infty}^{\infty} \frac{|\gamma(\lambda)|^2}{f(\lambda)} d\lambda = \infty . \tag{6.13}$$

It must be said that in contrast with the problems of linear extrapolation and filtering, whose solution in the continuous-parameter case is completely analogous to that in the discrete-parameter case, the method of solution of the problem of the linear interpolation of a multidimensional stationary process, discussed in Section 10, Chapter II, for the discrete-parameter case, leads in the continuous-parameter case to complicated integral equations, and at present no effective solution has been found for this problem in its full generality. Therefore for its solution we shall restrict ourselves to considering only the case where the spectral density $f(\lambda) = \{f_{kl}(\lambda)\}_{k=\overline{1,n}}^{l=\overline{1,n}}$ of $\boldsymbol{\xi}$ is a rational function of λ.

Suppose that the sets T_k, $k = \overline{1, n}$, the values of the parameter for which the values $\xi_k(t)$ are unknown, are all the same interval T, and as before, let $\hat{\xi}_k(t)$ be the projection of $\xi_k(t)$ on the subspace $\hat{H}(T)$. We will seek $\hat{\xi}_k(t)$ in the form

$$\hat{\xi}_k(t) = \sum_{j=1}^{n} \int_{-\infty}^{\infty} \varphi_{kj}(\lambda)\Phi_j(d\lambda) , \tag{6.14}$$

where

$$\int_{-\infty}^{\infty} |\varphi_{kj}(\lambda)|^2 f_{jj}(\lambda)\, d\lambda < \infty \tag{6.15}$$

for all $k, j = \overline{1, n}$. It is sufficient to restrict ourselves to an interval $T = [-\tau, \tau]$.

For definiteness we consider only $\hat{\xi}_1(t)$:

$$\hat{\xi}_1(t) = \sum_{j=1}^{n} \int_{-\infty}^{\infty} \varphi_j(\lambda)\Phi_j(d\lambda) . \tag{6.16}$$

The orthogonality of the difference $\xi_1(t) - \hat{\xi}_1(t)$ to the subspace $\hat{H}(T)$ is equivalent to

$$\int_{-\infty}^{\infty} e^{i\lambda s}\left\{[e^{i\lambda t} - \varphi_1(\lambda)]f_{1k}(\lambda) - \sum_{j=2}^{n} \varphi_j(\lambda)f_{jk}(\lambda)\right\} d\lambda = 0 \tag{6.17}$$

for all $k = \overline{1, n}$ and $s \le -\tau$, $s \ge \tau$. Condition (6.17) will be fulfilled if

$$\psi_k(\lambda) = [e^{i\lambda t} - \varphi_1(\lambda)]f_{1k}(\lambda) - \sum_{j=2}^{n} \varphi_j(\lambda)f_{jk}(\lambda) , \qquad k = \overline{1, n} , \tag{6.18}$$

are entire analytic functions, representable in the form

$$\psi_k(\lambda) = e^{-i\lambda\tau}\psi_k^{(1)}(\lambda) + e^{i\lambda\tau}\psi_k^{(2)}(\lambda)\,, \tag{6.19}$$

where $\psi_k^{(1)}(\lambda)$ and $\psi_k^{(2)}(\lambda)$ are rational functions which tend to zero as $|\lambda| \to \infty$ not slower than $|\lambda|^{-2}$.

Indeed, in this case the functions $e^{i\lambda s}\psi_k(\lambda)$, for any $s, s \leq -\tau (s \geq \tau)$ will be analytic in the lower (respectively, the upper) half-plane, tending there towards zero as $|\lambda| \to \infty$ not slower than $|\lambda|^{-2}$. Applying Cauchy's theorem to these functions, we obtain

$$\int_{-\infty}^{\infty} e^{i\lambda s}\psi_k(\lambda)\,d\lambda = \lim_{\Lambda\to\infty}\int_{-\Lambda}^{\Lambda} e^{i\lambda s}\psi_k(\lambda)\,d\lambda = \lim_{\Lambda\to\infty}\int_{R_\Lambda} e^{i\lambda s}\psi_k(\lambda)\,d\lambda = 0 \tag{6.20}$$

for $s \leq -\tau, s \geq \tau$, where R_Λ denotes the semicircle of radius Λ in the appropriate half-plane, constructed on the interval $[-\Lambda, \Lambda]$ of the real axis $-\infty < \lambda < \infty$ as diameter.

Further, the quantity on the right side of (6.16) will belong to $\hat{H}(T)$, if the functions $\varphi_j(\lambda)$ are representable in the form

$$\varphi_j(\lambda) = e^{-i\lambda\tau}\varphi_j^{(1)}(\lambda) + e^{i\lambda\tau}\varphi_j^{(2)}(\lambda)\,, \qquad j = \overline{1, n}\,, \tag{6.21}$$

where $\varphi_j^{(1)}(\lambda)$ is analytic in the lower half-plane, $\varphi_j^{(2)}(\lambda)$ in the upper half-plane, and they are rational and grow, in the respective half-planes, as $|\lambda| \to \infty$, not faster than some power $|\lambda|^q$. In fact, the functions of the form

$$\frac{\varphi_j^{(1)}(\lambda)}{\left(1 + \frac{i\lambda}{n}\right)^r}\,, \qquad \frac{\varphi_j^{(2)}(\lambda)}{\left(1 - \frac{i\lambda}{n}\right)^r}\,, \qquad r \text{ an integer}, \quad r > q + 1\,,$$

are square integrable and analytic in the respective half-planes, and therefore

$$\begin{aligned} \frac{\varphi_j^{(1)}(\lambda)}{\left(1 + \frac{i\lambda}{n}\right)^r} &= \int_0^\infty e^{-i\lambda t} a_{j,n}^{(1)}(t)\,dt\,, \\ \frac{\varphi_j^{(2)}(\lambda)}{\left(1 - \frac{i\lambda}{n}\right)^r} &= \int_0^\infty e^{i\lambda t} a_{j,n}^{(2)}(t)\,dt\,, \end{aligned} \tag{6.22}$$

from which

$$\begin{aligned} &\int_{-\infty}^{\infty}\left[e^{-i\lambda\tau}\frac{\varphi_j^{(1)}(\lambda)}{\left(1 + \frac{i\lambda}{n}\right)^r} + e^{i\lambda\tau}\frac{\varphi_j^{(2)}(\lambda)}{\left(1 - \frac{i\lambda}{n}\right)^r}\right]\Phi(d\lambda) \\ &= \lim_{t\to\infty}\int_0^t [a_{j,n}^{(1)}(s)\xi_j(-\tau - s) + a_{j,n}^{(2)}(s)\xi_j(\tau + s)]\,ds \\ &= \int_0^\infty [a_{j,n}^{(1)}(s)\xi_j(-\tau - s) + a_{j,n}^{(2)}(s)\xi_j(\tau + s)]\,ds\,. \end{aligned} \tag{6.23}$$

The limit in (6.23) is understood in the sense of mean square. This limit exists, because the functions $a_{j,n}^{(1)}(s)$ and $a_{j,n}^{(2)}(s)$ are square integrable and the spectral density $f_{jj}(\lambda)$ is bounded. Passing to the limit $n \to \infty$ in (6.23), it is not difficult to see that the random variables

$$\int_{-\infty}^{\infty} [e^{-i\lambda\tau}\varphi_j^{(1)}(\lambda) + e^{i\lambda\tau}\varphi_j^{(2)}(\lambda)]\Phi_j(d\lambda), \qquad j = \overline{1, n}, \tag{6.24}$$

belong to $\hat{H}(T)$.

We will briefly consider a method which, in the case where $\det f(\lambda) > 0$, enables one to determine the rational functions $\varphi_j^{(1)}(\lambda)$, $\varphi_j^{(2)}(\lambda)$ in (6.21) in such a way that the corresponding functions $\varphi_j(\lambda)$ and $\psi_k(\lambda)$, $k = \overline{1, n}$, will satisfy the imposed requirement of analyticity.

In order that the poles of the functions $\varphi_j^{(1)}(\lambda)$ and $\varphi_j^{(2)}(\lambda)$ not be at the same time poles of the functions $\psi_k(\lambda)$, $k = \overline{1, n}$, of the form (6.18), which we wish to have analytic, we define the numerators $\omega_j^{(1)}(\lambda)$ and $\omega_j^{(2)}(\lambda)$ of the sought-for $\varphi_j^{(1)}$ and $\varphi_j^{(2)}$ so that

$$\sum_{j=1}^{n} \omega_j^{(i)}(\theta) f_{jk}(\theta) = 0, \qquad k = \overline{1, n}, \quad i = 1, 2, \tag{6.25}$$

at the poles θ of these functions $\varphi_j^{(1)}(\lambda)$ and $\varphi_j^{(2)}(\lambda)$. Equations (6.25) can have a nontrivial solution only when θ is a zero of the determinant $\det f(\lambda)$. Taking into consideration the analyticity of $\varphi_j^{(1)}(\lambda)$ in the lower half-plane, of $\varphi_j^{(2)}(\lambda)$ in the upper half-plane, and the positivity of $\det f(\lambda)$ on the real axis, we find that

$$\begin{aligned} \varphi_j^{(1)}(\lambda) &= \frac{\omega_j^{(1)}(\lambda)}{(\lambda - \theta_1) \cdots (\lambda - \theta_l)}, \\ \varphi_j^{(2)}(\lambda) &= \frac{\omega_j^{(2)}(\lambda)}{(\lambda - \bar{\theta}_1) \cdots (\lambda - \bar{\theta}_l)}, \qquad \operatorname{Im} \theta_k > 0, \end{aligned} \tag{6.26}$$

where the θ_k, $k = \overline{1, l}$, are the zeros of $\det f(\lambda)$ in the upper half-plane. Since we want

$$\int_{-\infty}^{\infty} |\varphi_j^{(i)}(\lambda)|^2 f_{jj}(\lambda)\, d\lambda < \infty, \tag{6.27}$$

the degree of the polynomials $\omega_j^{(i)}(\lambda)$ must not be greater than $L + m_j - 1$, where $2m_j$ is the difference of the degrees of the denominator and numerator of $f_{jj}(\lambda)$. The unknown coefficients of the polynomials $\omega_j^{(i)}(\lambda)$ can be determined from the condition that the functions $\psi_k(\lambda)$, $k = \overline{1, n}$, not have poles at the points α_{jk} which are the poles of the elements $f_{jk}(\lambda)$ of the spectral density $f(\lambda)$, and moreover from conditions (6.25).

The functions $\varphi_j^{(1)}(\lambda)$ and $\varphi_j^{(2)}(\lambda)$ can be represented in the form

$$\begin{aligned}\varphi_j^{(1)}(\lambda) &= \sum_{k=0}^{m_j-1} W_{j,1}^{(k)}(i\lambda)^k + w_{j,1}(\lambda)\,,\\ \varphi_j^{(2)}(\lambda) &= \sum_{k=0}^{m_j-1} W_{j,2}^{(k)}(i\lambda)^k + w_{j,2}(\lambda)\,,\end{aligned} \tag{6.28}$$

where $W_{j,1}^{(k)}$ and $W_{j,2}^{(k)}$ are certain polynomials, and the functions $w_{j,1}$ and $w_{j,2}$ are square integrable.

By virtue of the positions of the poles of these functions in the respective half-planes, the Fourier transform $c_{j,1}(s)$ of $w_{j,1}(\lambda)$ vanishes on the negative semi-axis, and $c_{j,2}(s)$, on the positive semi-axis:

$$\begin{aligned}\varphi_j^{(1)}(\lambda) &= \sum_{k=0}^{m_j-1} W_{j,1}^{(k)}(i\lambda)^k + \int_0^{\infty} e^{-i\lambda s} c_{j,1}(s)\,ds\,,\\ \varphi_j^{(2)}(\lambda) &= \sum_{k=0}^{m_j-1} W_{j,2}^{(k)}(i\lambda)^k + \int_{-\infty}^{0} e^{-i\lambda s} c_{j,2}(s)\,ds\,.\end{aligned} \tag{6.29}$$

In conclusion, we obtain the following expression for the best linear forecast:

$$\begin{aligned}\xi_1(t) = \sum_{j=1}^{n} \Bigg\{ &\sum_{k=0}^{m_j-1} [W_{j,1}^{(k)} \xi_j^{(k)}(-\tau) + W_{j,2}^{(k)} \xi_j^{(k)}(\tau)]\\ &+ \int_0^{\infty} [c_{j,1}(s)\xi_j(-\tau - s) + c_{j,2}(s)\xi_j(\tau + s)]\,ds\,.\end{aligned} \tag{6.30}$$

Example 6.1. Suppose that the stationary process $\boldsymbol{\xi}$ has a spectral density $f(\lambda)$ of the form

$$f(\lambda) = \frac{B}{\lambda^2 + \alpha^2} \qquad (\alpha > 0)\,.$$

(In Example 4.1 of this chapter we have found the formula for the best linear extrapolation of $\boldsymbol{\xi}$.)

Since in this case $f(\lambda)$ has no zeros, the functions $\varphi^{(1)}(\lambda)$ and $\varphi^{(2)}(\lambda)$ in the representation (6.21) of the spectral characteristic $\varphi(\lambda)$ are simply constants:

$$\varphi^{(1)}(\lambda) = \omega^{(1)}\,, \qquad \varphi^{(2)}(\lambda) = \omega^{(2)}\,.$$

They must be chosen so that the function $\psi(\lambda)$ in (6.18),

$$\psi(\lambda) = [e^{i\lambda t} - e^{-i\lambda\tau}\omega^{(1)} - e^{i\lambda\tau}\omega^{(2)}]f(\lambda) = B\frac{e^{i\lambda t} - e^{-i\lambda\tau}\omega^{(1)} - e^{i\lambda\tau}\omega^{(2)}}{(\lambda + i\alpha)(\lambda - i\alpha)}\,,$$

is entire. This condition gives us two equations for determining $\omega^{(1)}$ and $\omega^{(2)}$:

$$\begin{aligned}e^{\alpha\tau}\omega^{(1)} + e^{-\alpha\tau}\omega^{(2)} &= e^{-\alpha t}\,,\\ e^{-\alpha\tau}\omega^{(1)} + e^{\alpha\tau}\omega^{(2)} &= e^{\alpha t}\,.\end{aligned}$$

Solving them, we find

$$\omega^{(1)} = \frac{\sinh \alpha(\tau - t)}{\sinh 2\alpha\tau},$$

$$\omega^{(2)} = \frac{\sinh \alpha(\tau + t)}{\sinh 2\alpha\tau},$$

and, consequently, the interpolation formula has the form

$$\hat{\xi}(t) = \int_{-\infty}^{\infty} \left[e^{-i\lambda\tau} \frac{\sinh \alpha(\tau - t)}{\sinh 2\alpha\tau} + e^{i\lambda\tau} \frac{\sinh \alpha(\tau + t)}{\sinh 2\alpha\tau} \right] \Phi(d\lambda)$$

$$= \frac{\sinh \alpha(\tau - t)}{\sinh 2\alpha\tau} \xi(-\tau) + \frac{\sinh \alpha(\tau + t)}{\sinh 2\alpha\tau} \xi(\tau) .$$

7. Linear forecasting by means of the values on a finite time interval

From the point of view of practical applications, the problem of linear forecasting is evidently most interesting in the case where the values of the stationary process $\boldsymbol{\xi} = \{\xi_k(t)\}_{k=\overline{1,n}}$ are only known on a finite time interval T.

This problem consists in finding random variables $\hat{\xi}(s) = \{\hat{\xi}_k(s)\}_{k=\overline{1,n}}$, $s \notin T$, in the subspace $H(T)$ [$H(T)$ is generated by the values $\xi_k(t)$, $k = \overline{1, n}$, $t \in T$] having the property that

$$\boldsymbol{E} \| \xi(s) - \hat{\xi}(s) \|^2 = \min . \tag{7.1}$$

Each of the $\hat{\xi}_k(s)$ is the projection of $\xi_k(s)$ on $H(T)$.

Just as before, the problem consists, essentially, in finding the spectral characteristic $\varphi = \{\varphi_{kj}\}_{k=\overline{1,n}}^{j=\overline{1,n}}$ of $\hat{\xi}(s)$:

$$\hat{\xi}(s) = \int_{-\infty}^{\infty} \varphi(\lambda) \Phi(d\lambda) , \tag{7.2}$$

where $\Phi = \{\Phi_k\}_{k=\overline{1,n}}$ is the random spectral measure of $\boldsymbol{\xi}$. Concerning the matrix function $\varphi(\lambda)$, we know only that its rows $\varphi_k = \{\varphi_{kj}\}^{j=\overline{1,n}}$ are elements of the subspace $L^2_T(F)$ in $L^2(F)$†, generated by the functions of the form $e^{i\lambda t}\delta_k$, $k = \overline{1, n}$, $t \in T$.

The condition that the differences $\xi_k(s) - \hat{\xi}_k(s)$, $k = \overline{1, n}$, be orthogonal to the subspace $H(T)$ leads to the following integral equation for the spectral characteristic φ:

$$\int_{-\infty}^{\infty} e^{-i\lambda t} \varphi(\lambda) F(d\lambda) = B(s - t) , \qquad t \in T , \tag{7.3}$$

where $F = \{F_{kl}\}_{k=\overline{1,n}}^{l=\overline{1,n}}$ is the spectral measure of $\boldsymbol{\xi}$, and $B = \{B_{kl}\}_{k=\overline{1,n}}^{l=\overline{1,n}}$ is its correlation function.

† The definition of $L^2(F)$ was given in Section 7, Chapter I.

The more general problem of the linear forecasting of the unknown values of ξ by means of the values (on an interval T) of a process η stationarily correlated with ξ leads to a similar equation: instead of F and B, one has to take the joint spectral and correlation functions $F^{\xi\eta}$ and $B^{\xi\eta}$.

In solving the problem of finding the matrix function $\varphi(\lambda)$ we will consider only one important case, that in which the spectral density exists and is a rational function of λ. In this case the equation of the type (7.3) can be solved by the methods which were developed in the previous section. We will not dwell on a similar kind of solution, but shall instead consider a very effective method which reduces the integral equation (7.3) to a certain linear constant coefficient differential equation (and ultimately to some linear system of algebraic equations). For simplicity we restrict ourselves to the one-dimensional case. Thus, suppose that the spectral density $f(\lambda)$ is rational. Then it admits a representation of the form

$$f(\lambda) = \frac{|P(i\lambda)|^2}{|Q(i\lambda)|^2}, \tag{7.4}$$

where

$$P(z) = \sum_0^m p_k z^k, \qquad Q(z) = \sum_0^n q_k z^k$$

are polynomials whose roots lie in the left half-plane. We will assume that $f(\lambda) = f(-\lambda)$, as is the case for real processes, so that $P(z)$ and $Q(z)$ will have real coefficients.† Moreover, we shall suppose that $f(\lambda)$ does not vanish. This is tied up with the fact that the integral equation (7.3) would otherwise have solutions of a special type not described by the general formula which will be derived below.

We may suppose, without restriction of generality, that $T = (-\tau, \tau)$. Let us consider the integral equation of the form

$$\int_{-\infty}^{\infty} e^{-i\lambda t}\varphi(\lambda)f(\lambda)\,d\lambda = A(t), \qquad -\tau < t < \tau, \tag{7.5}$$

where the function $A(t)$, defined on the interval $(-\tau, \tau)$, has at least $2(n-m)$ continuous derivatives. It should be noted hare that the correlation function $B(t)$ of a stationary process with rational spectral density has derivatives of all orders at every point $t \neq 0$. In the integral equation (7.5) which arises in the problem of linear forecasting, the function $A(t) = B(s-t)$ enters, where either $s < -\tau$ or $s > \tau$; consequently, $A(t)$ will even be infinitely differentiable on the interal $(-\tau, \tau)$.

As will be shown below, the solution $\varphi(\lambda)$ [from the space $L_T^2(F)$]

† See Section 10, Chapter I.

of (7.5) assumes the following form†:

$$\varphi(\lambda) = e^{-i\lambda\tau} \sum_{k=0}^{n-m-1} c_k'(i\lambda)^k + e^{i\lambda\tau} \sum_{k=0}^{n-m-1} c_k''(i\lambda)^k + \int_{-\tau}^{\tau} e^{i\lambda t} c(t)\, dt\,. \qquad (7.6)$$

In this expression

$$\begin{aligned} c(t) &= \frac{1}{2\pi} Q\left(\frac{d}{dt}\right) Q\left(-\frac{d}{dt}\right) x(t)\,, \\ c_k' &= \frac{1}{2\pi} \sum_{j=m+k+1}^{n} q_j \left[Q\left(-\frac{d}{dt}\right) x^{(j-k-1)}(-\tau+0) \right], \\ c_k'' &= -\frac{1}{2\pi} \sum_{j=m+k+1}^{n} (-1)^j q_j \left[Q\left(\frac{d}{dt}\right) x^{(j-k-1)}(\tau-0) \right], \\ & k = \overline{0,\, n-m-1}\,, \end{aligned} \qquad (7.7)$$

where the function $x(t)$, $-\tau < t < \tau$ is $x(t) = p_0^{-2} A(t)$ in the case $m = 0$, and in the case $m > 0$ is the solution of the constant coefficient differential equation

$$P\left(\frac{d}{dt}\right) P\left(-\frac{d}{dt}\right) x(t) = A(t) \qquad (7.8)$$

with the boundary conditions

$$\begin{aligned} & Q\left(-\frac{d}{dt}\right) x^{(k)}(-\tau+0) = 0\,, \\ & Q\left(\frac{d}{dt}\right) x^{(k)}(\tau-0) = 0\,, \qquad k = \overline{0,\, m-1}\,. \end{aligned} \qquad (7.9)$$

Let us proceed to the derivation of formula (7.6). First we establish a parametric representation for the elements of the subspace $L_T^2(F)$.

Theorem 7.1. *If the spectral density $f(\lambda)$ is such that*

$$c_1 \le (1+\lambda^2)^r f(\lambda) \le c_2 \qquad (7.10)$$

for some integer r and positive c_1 and c_2, then the subspace $L_T^2(F)$, where $T = (-\tau, \tau)$, consists of all functions of the form

$$\varphi(\lambda) = P_1(\lambda) + P_2(\lambda) \int_{-\tau}^{\tau} e^{i\lambda t} c(t)\, dt\,, \qquad (7.11)$$

where $P_1(\lambda)$ is an arbitrary polynomial of degree $r-1$, $P_2(\lambda)$ is an arbi-

† It is not difficult to show that equation (7.5) has a solution in $L_T^2(F)$ if and only if for some $M < \infty$

$$\left| \sum_t c(t) A(t) \right|^2 \le M \int_{-\infty}^{\infty} \left| \sum_t c(t) e^{i\lambda t} \right|^2 dF(\lambda)$$

for arbitrary numbers $c(t)$, $-\tau < t < \tau$.

trary polynomial of degree r, and $c(t)$, $-\tau < t < \tau$, *is any square integrable function.*

Proof. A function $\varphi(\lambda)$ of the form (7.11) belongs to $L_T^2(F)$. Indeed, $L_T^2(F)$ contains the functions

$$(i\lambda)^k = \lim_{h\to 0} (i\lambda)^{k-1}\frac{e^{i\lambda h}-1}{h}, \qquad k = \overline{1, r-1},$$

and

$$\varphi(\lambda) = \int_{-\tau}^{\tau} e^{i\lambda t} c(t)\, dt.,$$

as well as, for smooth $c(t)$ which vanish, together with their derivatives, at the end points of the interval $(-\tau, \tau)$, the functions

$$(-i\lambda)^k \varphi(\lambda) = \int_{-\tau}^{\tau} e^{i\lambda t} c^{(k)}(t)\, dt.$$

For $k = \overline{0, r}$ one can, by a passage to the limit, go over from the functions $(-i\lambda)^k\varphi(\lambda)$ corresponding to smooth $c(t)$ to those corresponding to arbitrary square integrable $c(t)$.

Further, let us consider the elements of the form

$$\varphi_t(\lambda) = \sum_{k=0}^{r} c_k e^{i\lambda t_k},$$

where $t_1, \ldots, t_r$ are distinct and fixed, and $t_0 = t$ ranges over all values in $(-\tau, \tau)$ except for $t = t_1, \ldots, t_r$. We define the corresponding coefficients c_k from the conditions

$$\varphi_t^{(k)}(i) = 0, \qquad k = \overline{0, r-1}. \tag{7.12}$$

Let M be the closed linear manifold generated by these elements $\varphi_t(\lambda)$. Obviously M is a subspace in $L_T^2(F)$ with a finite deficiency index not exceeding r. It turns out that M consists of all functions $\psi(\lambda)$ of the form

$$\psi(\lambda) = (1 + i\lambda)^r \int_{-\tau}^{\tau} e^{i\lambda t} c(t)\, dt. \tag{7.13}$$

Indeed, by definition every $\psi(\lambda) \in M$ is the limit in mean square with weight $f(\lambda)$ of linear combinations $\psi_n(\lambda)$ of elements $\varphi_t(\lambda)$. But, by virtue of condition (7.10), this convergence is equivalent to convergence in mean square with weight $(1 + \lambda^2)^{-r}$. We have

$$\lim_{n\to\infty} \int_{-\infty}^{\infty} |\psi(\lambda) - \psi_n(\lambda)|^2 (1 + \lambda^2)^{-r}\, d\lambda$$

$$= \lim_{n\to\infty} \int_{-\infty}^{\infty} \left| \frac{\psi(\lambda)}{(1+i\lambda)^r} - \frac{\psi_n(\lambda)}{(1+i\lambda)^r} \right|^2 d\lambda = 0.$$

Obviously, linear combinations of the $\varphi_t(\lambda)$ satisfy (7.12), and this means that the ratios $\psi_n(\lambda)/(1+i\lambda)^r$ are entire analytic functions of λ of exponential type, square integrable on the real line. The well-known Paley-Wiener theorem gives us a representation for them of the form

$$\frac{\psi_n(\lambda)}{(1+i\lambda)^2} = \int_{-\tau}^{\tau} e^{i\lambda t} c_n(t)\, dt\,,$$

where the $c_n(t)$ are certain square integrable functions which vanish outside the interval $(-\tau, \tau)$. From this representation it follows at once that the ratio $\psi(\lambda)/(1+i\lambda)^r$, as the limit in mean square of the functions $\psi_n(\lambda)/(1+i\lambda)^r$, is given by

$$\frac{\psi(\lambda)}{(1+i\lambda)^r} = \int_{-\tau}^{\tau} e^{i\lambda t} c(t)\, dt\,,$$

where $c(t)$ is the limit in mean square of the $c_n(t)$. As a result we obtain the expression (7.13) for the elements $\psi(\lambda)$ of M.

To prove the theorem, it remains to note that every function $\psi(\lambda) \in M$ vanishes at the point $\lambda = i$ together with its first $r-1$ derivatives, and, consequently, no linear combination of the r linearly independent elements $\varphi_k(\lambda) = \lambda^k$, $k = \overline{0, r-1}$, belongs to M, i.e., these elements are in its complement relative to the space $L_T^2(F)$.

Lemma 7.1. *Let*

$$\varphi(\lambda) = \int_{-\tau}^{\tau} e^{i\lambda(t+\tau)} c(t)\, dt\,,$$

where $c(t)$ *is square integrable. If* $\lambda \to \infty$ *in the upper half-plane* $\operatorname{Im}\lambda \geq 0$, *then*

$$\varphi(\lambda) \to 0$$

uniformly relative to $\arg\lambda$ $(0 \leq \arg\lambda \leq \pi)$.

Proof. The assertion is obvious for smooth functions $c(t)$ having the property that $c'(-\tau) = c(\tau) = 0$, because for all λ one has the relation

$$\varphi(\lambda) = \frac{1}{-i\lambda}\int_{-\tau}^{\tau} e^{i\lambda(t+\tau)} c'(t)\, dt\,.$$

Every square integrable function $c(t)$ can be approximated arbitrarily closely in mean square by smooth functions $c_n(t)$. If

$$\varphi_n(\lambda) = \int_{-\tau}^{\tau} e^{i\lambda(t+\tau)} c_n(t)\, dt\,,$$

then

$$|\,\varphi(\lambda) - \varphi_n(\lambda)\,| \leq (2\tau)^{1/2}\left[\int_{-\tau}^{\tau} |\,c(t) - c_n(t)\,|^2\, dt\right]^{1/2},$$

from which it is evident that the difference $\varphi(\lambda) - \varphi_n(\lambda)$ can be made arbitrarily small by an appropriate choice of $c_n(t)$, uniformly for all λ, $\operatorname{Im} \lambda \geq 0$. This, plus the fact that $\varphi_n(\lambda) \to 0$ uniformly in λ as $\lambda \to \infty$, $\operatorname{Im} \lambda \geq 0$, proves the validity of the lemma.

Let $\varphi(\lambda)$ be the solution from the class $L_T^2(F)$ of the integral equation (7.5). We define a function $x(t)$ by

$$x(t) = \int_{-\infty}^{\infty} e^{-i\lambda t} \varphi(\lambda) \frac{d\lambda}{|Q(i\lambda)|^2} . \tag{7.14}$$

Obviously, $x(t)$ exists for all t, $-\infty < t < \infty$, and has everywhere $(n+m-1)$ continuous derivatives. Applying the differential operator $P(d/dt)P(-d/dt)$ to $x(t)$, we have

$$P\left(\frac{d}{dt}\right) P\left(-\frac{d}{dt}\right) x(t) = \int_{-\infty}^{\infty} e^{-i\lambda t} \varphi(\lambda) \frac{|P(i\lambda)|^2}{|Q(i\lambda)|^2} d\lambda$$

for all t. Since $\varphi(\lambda)$ is the solution of (7.5), for $-\tau < t < \tau$ the function $x(t)$ must satisfy the differential equation (7.8) [for $m = 0$ this equation becomes an identity $x(t) = A(t)/P_0^2$]. Suppose $m > 0$. We consider the expression

$$Q\left(-\frac{d}{dt}\right) x^{(k)}(t) = \int_{-\infty}^{\infty} e^{-i\lambda t} \varphi(\lambda) \frac{(-i\lambda)^k}{Q(-i\lambda)} d\lambda , \qquad k = \overline{0, m-1} .$$

Since the roots of the polynomial $Q(-i\lambda)$ lie in the lower half-plane, the integrand $\varphi(\lambda)(-i\lambda)^k/Q(-i\lambda)$ is analytic in the upper half-plane. From the representation of $\varphi(\lambda)$ in the form (7.11) and Lemma 7.1 it follows that

$$e^{i\lambda\tau} \frac{\varphi(\lambda)(-i\lambda)^k}{Q(-i\lambda)} \to 0 , \qquad k = \overline{0, m-1} ,$$

uniformly in λ as $\lambda \to \infty$, $\operatorname{Im} \lambda \geq 0$. Consequently, by a well-known lemma of Jordan,

$$Q\left(-\frac{d}{dt}\right) x^{(k)}(t) = 0 \quad \text{for} \quad t < -\tau , \quad k = \overline{0, m-1} . \tag{7.15}$$

Thanks to the continuity of the first $(n+m-1)$ derivatives of $x(t)$, we can pass to the limit $t \to -\tau$ in (7.15), which yields the first of the boundary conditions (7.9) which the function $x(t)$ under consideration must satisfy.

By completely analogous arguments,

$$Q\left(\frac{d}{dt}\right) x^{(k)}(t) = 0 \quad \text{for} \quad t > \tau , \quad k = \overline{0, m-1} , \tag{7.16}$$

and here, passing to the limit $t \to \tau$, we obtain the second of conditions (7.9).

Further, if we regard $x(t)$ as a generalized function (distribution) in the sense of L. Schwartz and apply to it the operator $Q(d/dt)Q(-d/dt)$, then we obviously obtain

$$Q\left(\frac{d}{dt}\right)Q\left(-\frac{d}{dt}\right)x(t) = \int_{-\infty}^{\infty} e^{-i\lambda t}\varphi(\lambda)\,d\lambda\,. \tag{7.17}$$

This relation shows that the solution $\varphi(\lambda)$ of equation (7.5) is the Fourier transform of the generalized function

$$y(t) = Q\left(\frac{d}{dt}\right)Q\left(-\frac{d}{dt}\right)x(t)\,. \tag{7.18}$$

Let us find this function. We set

$$u(t) = Q\left(-\frac{d}{dt}\right)x(t)\,. \tag{7.19}$$

If $m > 0$, this is an ordinary (even continuous) function of t. If for $m = 0$ we understand it in the generalized sense, then, similarly to the way in which relation (7.15) was obtained, it is easy to establish that $u(t) = 0$ for $t < -\tau$. On the interval $-\tau < t < \tau$ this function coincides with the ordinary function $Q(-d/dt)\,p_0^{-2}A(t)$. Consequently, for any m the function $u(t)$ is an ordinary function for $t < \tau$, and

$$u(t) = 0 \quad \text{for} \quad t < -\tau\,.$$

Thus,

$$y(t) = \begin{cases} 0 & \text{for} \quad t < -\tau\,, \\ Q\left(\dfrac{d}{dt}\right)u(t) & \text{for} \quad -\tau < t < \tau\,, \end{cases} \tag{7.20}$$

and as its improper component (on the half-line $t < \tau$) $y(t)$ contains only the δ-function and its derivatives at the endpoint $t = -\tau$ of the interval T. Namely,

$$y(-\tau) = \sum_{k=0}^{n-m-1} \delta^{(k)}(t+\tau)\left[\sum_{j=m+k+1}^{n} q_j u^{(j-k-1)}(-\tau+0)\right]. \tag{7.21}$$

A completely analogous situation holds for $t > -\tau$. In this case

$$y(t) = \begin{cases} Q\left(-\dfrac{d}{dt}\right)v(t) & \text{for} \quad -\tau < t < \tau\,, \\ 0 & \text{for} \quad t > \tau\,, \end{cases} \tag{7.22}$$

and

$$y(\tau) = -\sum_{k=0}^{n-m-1} \delta^{(k)}(t-\tau)\left[\sum_{j=m+k+1}^{n} (-1)^j q_j v^{(j-k-1)}(\tau-0)\right], \tag{7.23}$$

where

$$v(t) = Q\left(\frac{d}{dt}\right)x(t)\,.$$

Passing from $y(t)$ to its Fourier transform, we obtain the expression (7.6) for the solution $\varphi(\lambda)$ of the integral equation (7.5).

Example 7.1. Let us consider the stationary process ξ with

$$B(t) = \sigma^2 e^{-\alpha|t|}, \qquad \alpha > 0,$$

$$f(\lambda) = \frac{\sigma^2}{\pi}\left(\frac{\alpha}{\alpha^2 + \lambda^2}\right).$$

We shall find the best forecast $\hat{\xi}(s)$ for $\xi(s)$, $s > \tau$, by means of the values $\xi(t)$, $-\tau < t < \tau$. According to formula (7.6), the spectral characteristic $\varphi(\lambda)$ of $\hat{\xi}(s)$ will have the form

$$\varphi(\lambda) = e^{-\alpha(s-\tau)} e^{i\lambda\tau}.$$

Therefore,

$$\hat{\xi}(s) = e^{-\alpha(s-\tau)} \xi(\tau),$$

which was to be expected in view of the extrapolation formula already obtained in Example 4.1 of this chapter.

IV

RANDOM PROCESSES, STATIONARY IN THE STRICT SENSE

1. Basic concepts. Examples

As before, by an n-dimensional random process $\boldsymbol{\xi}$ we will mean a column-vector

$$\boldsymbol{\xi} = \{\xi_k(t)\}_{k=\overline{1,n}} \tag{1.1}$$

consisting of n random processes $\boldsymbol{\xi}_k$, $k = \overline{1, n}$.

Let $\boldsymbol{\xi}$ be an n-dimensional random process. We shall call the set function

$$P^{t_1,\ldots,t_N}_{\xi_{k_1},\ldots,\xi_{k_N}}(\Gamma_1, \ldots, \Gamma_N) = P\{\xi_{k_1}(t_1) \in \Gamma_1, \ldots, \xi_{k_N}(t_N) \in \Gamma_N\}\ , \tag{1.2}$$

defined for all Borel sets $\Gamma_1, \ldots, \Gamma_N$ of the complex plane R, a *finite-dimensional distribution* of $\boldsymbol{\xi}$.

We shall say that the n-dimensional random process $\boldsymbol{\xi}$ is *stationary in the strict sense,* if its finite-dimensional distributions are invariant under all shifts of the parameter t, i.e.,

$$P^{t_1,\ldots,t_N}_{\xi_{k_1},\ldots,\xi_{k_N}}(\Gamma_1, \ldots, \Gamma_N) = P^{t_1+t,\ldots,t_N+t}_{\xi_{k_1},\ldots,\xi_{k_N}}(\Gamma_1, \ldots, \Gamma_N) \tag{1.3}$$

for any N, t, $t_1, \ldots, t_N$ and $\Gamma_1, \ldots, \Gamma_N$.

Obviously, in the case where the values $\xi_k(t)$ of a strictly stationary process $\boldsymbol{\xi}$ have finite second moments $[\boldsymbol{E}|\xi_k(t)|^2 < \infty,\ k = \overline{1, n},\ -\infty < t < \infty]$, the process $\boldsymbol{\xi}$ is also stationary in the wide sense; i.e., the mathematical expectations $\boldsymbol{E}\xi_k(t)$, $k=\overline{1, n}$, do not depend upon t, and the correlation functions $B_{kl}(t, s)=\boldsymbol{E}\xi_k(t)\overline{\xi_l(s)}$, $k, l=\overline{1, n}$, depend only upon the difference $t-s$.

Example 1.1. A two-sided infinite sequence

$$\ldots, \xi(-1), \xi(0), \xi(1), \ldots$$

of independent identically distributed random variables is a strictly stationary process.

Example 1.2. A random process $\boldsymbol{\xi}$ of the form

$$\xi(t)=\rho e^{i(\lambda t+\theta)},$$

where ρ and λ are some constants, and θ is uniformly distributed on the interval $[-\pi, \pi]$, is strictly stationary. This follows from the fact that the joint distributions of the families of random variables

$$\lambda t_1+\theta, \ldots, \lambda t_n+\theta \pmod{2\pi}$$

and

$$\lambda t_1+\theta', \ldots, \lambda t_n+\theta' \pmod{2\pi}, \qquad \theta'=\theta+\lambda t$$

coincide for all $t_1, \ldots, t_n$ and any t.

2. Direct definition of random processes

Let $\boldsymbol{\xi}$ be an n-dimensional random process. We denote by $\mathfrak{A}_\xi$ the smallest σ-algebra of ω-sets of the corresponding space Ω of elementary events ω, with respect to which all of the random variables $\xi_k(t)=\xi_k(\omega, t)$ are measurable. This σ-algebra is generated by ω-sets A of the form

$$A=\{\omega: \xi_{k_1}(t) \in \Gamma_1, \ldots, \xi_{k_N}(t_N) \in \Gamma_N\}, \tag{2.1}$$

where $\Gamma_1, \ldots, \Gamma_N$ are arbitrary Borel sets in the complex plane. We will call $\mathfrak{A}_\xi$ the *σ-algebra of the random process* $\boldsymbol{\xi}$, and a set A of the form (2.1) will be called a *cylinder set*.

From now on we will only be interested in events which are defined by ω-sets from $\mathfrak{A}_\xi$. A multi-dimensional random process $\boldsymbol{\xi}=\{\xi_k(t)\}_{k=\overline{1,n}}$ can be represented as a family of vector random variables $\xi(\omega, t)=\{\xi_k(\omega, t)\}_{k=\overline{1,n}}$, depending upon the parameter t. For every fixed ω this family defines a vector function $\tilde{\omega}=\{x(t)\}$ of the parameter t: $x(t)=\xi(\omega, t)$. We will call this function a *sample function* or *trajectory* of the random process $\boldsymbol{\xi}$.

Let us consider the space $\tilde{\Omega}$ of all functions $\tilde{\omega}=\{x(t)\}$ of the parameter t, taking on values in n-dimensional complex space $R^{(n)}[x(t)=\{x_k(t)\}_{k=\overline{1,n}}]$, and the smallest σ-algebra $\tilde{\mathfrak{A}}$ of $\tilde{\omega}$-sets, containing the sets $\tilde{A}$ of the form

$$\tilde{A} = \{\tilde{\omega} : x_{k_1}(t_1) \in \Gamma_1, \ldots, x_{k_N}(t_N) \in \Gamma_N\} , \tag{2.2}$$

where $\Gamma_1, \ldots, \Gamma_N$ are arbitrary Borel sets in the complex plane. We shall also call sets of this form cylinder sets.

Let us consider the mapping T of the space Ω of elementary events into the space $\tilde{\Omega}$, by which each ω is carried into the corresponding sample function $x(t) = \xi(\omega, t)$.

Lemma 2.1. *The family of ω-sets A of the form*

$$A = \{\omega : T\omega \in \tilde{A}\} , \quad \tilde{A} \in \tilde{\mathfrak{A}} , \tag{2.3}$$

forms a σ-algebra which coincides with $\mathfrak{A}_\xi$.

Proof. Since $\tilde{\mathfrak{A}}$ is a σ-algebra of sets, the inverse images of the sets $\tilde{A} \in \tilde{\mathfrak{A}}$ with respect to the mapping T form a σ-algebra in Ω, which we denote by $\mathfrak{A}'$. We shall show that $\mathfrak{A}'$ is the smallest σ-algebra containing all inverse images of cylinder sets $\tilde{A}$ of the form (2.2). For this it is sufficient to show that every σ-algebra $\mathfrak{B}$ which contains the inverse images of all cylinder sets $\tilde{A}$ also contains $\mathfrak{A}'$. Let us consider such a σ-algebra $\mathfrak{B}$, and the collection $\tilde{\mathfrak{B}}$ of all sets in $\tilde{\Omega}$ whose inverse images with respect to T lie in $\mathfrak{B}$. Obviously, $\tilde{\mathfrak{B}}$ is a σ-algebra, and $\tilde{\mathfrak{A}} \subseteq \tilde{\mathfrak{B}}$ since $\tilde{\mathfrak{B}}$ contains all cylinder sets A. Consequently, all inverse images of sets from $\tilde{\mathfrak{A}}$ lie in $\mathfrak{B}$; but these inverse images form the σ-algebra $\mathfrak{A}'$, which is thus the smallest σ-algebra containing the inverse images of cylinder sets $\tilde{A}$.

But these inverse images are just the sets A of the form (2.1), and therefore $\mathfrak{A}' = \mathfrak{A}_\xi$.

If we now define a probability measure $\tilde{P}$ on the σ-algebra $\tilde{\mathfrak{A}}$ by means of the relation

$$\tilde{P}(\tilde{A}) = P(T^{-1}\tilde{A}) , \tag{2.4}$$

(where P is the probability measure on Ω, and $T^{-1}A$ denotes the inverse image of A with respect to the mapping T), and for each t we define a random variable $\tilde{\xi}(\tilde{\omega}, t)$ by

$$\tilde{\xi}(\tilde{\omega}, t) = x(t) , \quad \text{if} \quad \tilde{\omega} = \{x(t)\} , \tag{2.5}$$

then the collection of all $\tilde{\xi}$ will be an n-dimensional random process, whose finite-dimensional distributions coincide with the corresponding distributions of the original process. In this sense one can say that the random processes $\boldsymbol{\xi}$ and $\tilde{\boldsymbol{\xi}}$ have the same probabilistic properties.

We will henceforth say that a process $\boldsymbol{\xi} = \{\xi_k(t)\}_{k=\overline{1,n}}$ is *directly defined*,† if the space Ω of elementary events is an appropriate space

† Such processes are called *processes of function space type* in Doob[*].

$\tilde{\Omega}$ of functions $\tilde{\omega} = \{x(t)\}$, $x(t) = \{x_k(t)\}_{k=\overline{1,n}}$, and the values $\xi(\omega, t) = \tilde{\xi}(\tilde{\omega}, t)$ have the form (2.5).

A random process $\boldsymbol{\xi} = \{\xi_k(t)\}_{k=\overline{1,n}}$ can be directly defined by means of a compatible family of functions $P^{t_1,\dots,t_N}_{k_1,\dots,k_N}(\Gamma_1, \dots, \Gamma_N)$ of Borel sets $\Gamma_1, \dots, \Gamma_N$ in the complex plane (the indices $k_1, \dots, k_N$ assume values in the set $\{1, \dots, n\}$; $t_1, \dots, t_N$ are any values of the parameter; and N is any positive integer). These functions are assumed to be countably additive in each of their arguments, and for $\Gamma_1 = \cdots = \Gamma_N = R$ assume the value 1; their values do not change under a simultaneous permutation of their indices and arguments; i.e.,

$$P^{t_{i_1},\dots,t_{i_N}}_{k_{i_1},\dots,k_{i_N}}(\Gamma_{i_1}, \dots, \Gamma_{i_N}) = P^{t_1,\dots,t_N}_{k_1,\dots,k_N}(\Gamma_1, \dots, \Gamma_N) , \tag{2.6}$$

and, moreover,

$$P^{t_1,\dots,t_{N-1},t_N}_{k_1,\dots,k_{N-1},k_N}(\Gamma_1, \dots, \Gamma_{N-1}, R) = P^{t_1,\dots,t_{N-1}}_{k_1,\dots,k_{N-1}}(\Gamma_1, \dots, \Gamma_{N-1}) . \tag{2.7}$$

Namely, with the help of these functions one can define a probability measure $P(d\omega)$ in the space Ω of all vector functions $\omega = \{x(t)\}$ of the parameter t ($x(t) = \{x_k(t)\}_{k=\overline{1,n}}$) with values in n-dimensional complex space. The measure $P(d\omega)$ is defined on the smallest σ-algebra $\mathfrak{A}$ containing all cylinder sets, and†

$$P\{x_{k_1}(t_1) \in \Gamma_1, \dots, x_{k_N}(t_N) \in \Gamma_N\} = P^{t_1,\dots,t_N}_{k_1,\dots,k_N}(\Gamma_1, \dots, \Gamma_N) . \tag{2.8}$$

The multi-dimensional random variables $\xi(\omega, t) = \{\xi_k(\omega, t)\}_{k=\overline{1,n}}$, which make up the random process $\boldsymbol{\xi}$, are defined by relations analogous to (2.5); the finite-dimensional distributions of the random process $\boldsymbol{\xi}$ coincide with the corresponding set functions $P^{t_1,\dots,t_N}_{k_1,\dots,k_N}(\Gamma_1, \dots, \Gamma_N)$.

Example 2.1. *Real Gaussian stationary process.* Suppose that we are given a real matrix function $B(t) = \{B_{kl}(t)\}^{l=\overline{1,n}}_{k=\overline{1,n}}$ of a parameter t, satisfying the following condition of positive definiteness: for any positive integer N

$$\sum_{p,q=1}^{N} c_p c_q B_{k_p k_q}(t_p - t_q) \geq 0 \tag{2.9}$$

for any $t_1, \dots, t_N$, $k_1, \dots, k_N$, and arbitrary real numbers $c_1, \dots, c_N$.

By virtue of the fact that the matrix $B = \{B_{k_p k_q}(t_p - t_q)\}^{q=\overline{1,N}}_{p=\overline{1,N}}$ is positive definite, the function

$$\varphi(u_1, \dots, u_N) = \exp\left\{-\frac{1}{2}\sum_{p,q=1}^{N} u_p u_q B_{k_p k_q}(t_p - t_q)\right\} \tag{2.10}$$

is the characteristic function of some N-dimensional Gaussian distribution with distribution function

† In this connection, see, e.g., Kolmogorov[*] or Halmos[*].

$$F_{k_1,\ldots,k_N}^{t_1,\ldots,t_N}(x_1, \ldots, x_N) .$$

If the matrix $\{B_{k_p k_q}(t_p - t_q)\}_{p=\overline{1,N}}^{q=\overline{1,N}}$ is nondegenerate, then this distribution function has a density of the form

$$f_{k_1,\ldots,k_N}^{t_1,\ldots,t_N}(x_1, \ldots, x_N) = (2\pi)^{-N/2} D^{-1/2} \exp\left\{-\frac{1}{2} \sum_{p,q=1}^{N} a_{pq} x_p x_q\right\} , \tag{2.11}$$

where the matrix $\{a_{pq}\}_{p=\overline{1,N}}^{q=\overline{1,N}}$ is the inverse of B, and D is the determinant of B.

Obviously, the relations

$$P_{k_1,\ldots,k_N}^{t_1,\ldots,t_N}(\Gamma_1, \ldots, \Gamma_N) = \int_{\Gamma_1} \cdots \int_{\Gamma_N} dF_{k_1,\ldots,k_N}^{t_1,\ldots,t_N}(x_1, \ldots, x_N) \tag{2.12}$$

define a compatible family of functions $P_{k_1,\ldots,k_N}^{t_1,\ldots,t_N}(\Gamma_1, \ldots, \Gamma_N)$ of Borel sets $\Gamma_1, \ldots, \Gamma_N$ of the real line.

As the matrix $\{B_{k_p k_q}(t_p - t_q)\}_{p=\overline{1,N}}^{q=\overline{1,N}}$ depends only upon the differences $t_p - t_q$ (in addition, of course, to the choice of N and $k_1, \ldots, k_N$), the Guassian process $\boldsymbol{\xi}$ defined by the matrix function $B(t)$ will be strictly stationary; i.e., the requirement (1.3) will be fulfilled.

The mean of the process $\boldsymbol{\xi}$ thus defined will equal zero, and its correlation function coincides with the matrix function $B(t)$.

Example 2.2. *Complex Gaussian stationary process.* Suppose that a matrix function $B(t) = \{B_{kl}(t)\}_{k=\overline{1,n}}^{l=\overline{1,n}}$ satisfies conditions similar to (2.9):

$$\sum_{p,q=1}^{N} c_p \bar{c}_q B_{k_p k_q}(t_p - t_q) \geq 0 . \tag{2.13}$$

Then by means of this matrix function one can define a random process $\boldsymbol{\xi} = \{\xi_k(t)\}_{k=\overline{1,n}}$ which is strictly stationary, and such that

$$\boldsymbol{E}\xi(t) = 0 , \qquad \boldsymbol{E}\xi(t)\overset{*}{\xi}(s) = B(t-s) , \tag{2.14}$$

and the joint finite-dimensional distributions of its real and imaginary parts $\boldsymbol{\xi}^1 = \{\xi_k^1(t)\}_{k=\overline{1,n}}$ and $\boldsymbol{\xi}^2 = \{\xi_k^2(t)\}_{k=\overline{1,n}}$ are Gaussian; moreover,

$$\boldsymbol{E}\xi_k(t)\xi_l(s) = 0 , \qquad k, l = \overline{1, n} , \tag{2.15}$$

for all t and s.

To do this, it suffices to directly define the $2n$-dimensional real process $\{\xi_k^l(t)\}_{k=\overline{1,n};\, l=1,2}$.

We observe that if the random process $\boldsymbol{\xi}$ satisfies conditions (2.14) and (2.15), then

$$\begin{aligned} \boldsymbol{E}\xi_k^1(t)\xi_l^1(s) &= \boldsymbol{E}\xi_k^2(t)\xi_l^2(s) = \tfrac{1}{2}\,\mathrm{Re}\, B_{kl}(t-s)\,, \\ -\boldsymbol{E}\xi_k^1(t)\xi_l^2(s) &= \boldsymbol{E}\xi_k^2(t)\xi_l^1(s) = \tfrac{1}{2}\,\mathrm{Im}\, B_{kl}(t-s)\,. \end{aligned} \tag{2.16}$$

Conversely, it is easily seen that (2.16), in turn, implies (2.14) and (2.15). Consequently, in order to directly define the $2n$-dimensional process $\{\xi_k^l(t)\}_{k=\overline{1,n};\, l=1,2}$ by means of a compatible family of Gaussian distributions, as was done in the previous example, it is sufficient to verify the "positive definiteness" (2.9) of the matrix function $B'(t) = \{B'_{kl}(t)\}_{k=\overline{1,2n}}^{l=\overline{1,2n}}$:

$$B'(t) = \begin{pmatrix} \frac{1}{2}\,\mathrm{Re}\, B(t) & -\frac{1}{2}\,\mathrm{Im}\, B(t)\,, \\ \frac{1}{2}\,\mathrm{Im}\, B(t) & \frac{1}{2}\,\mathrm{Re}\, B(t) \end{pmatrix}.$$

Obviously this property need only be verified for $N' = 2N$, $t_p = t_{p+N}$ and $k_p = k_{p+N}$ $(p = \overline{1, N})$, since this can always be achieved by an appropriate increase in the number of indices. We then have

$$\sum_{p,q=1}^{2N} c_p c_q B'_{k_p k_q}(t_p - t_q) = \frac{1}{2} \sum_{p,q=1}^{N} (c_p - ic_{N+p})(c_q + ic_{N+q}) B_{k_p k_q}(t_p - t_q) \geq 0$$

by virtue of the "positive definiteness" of the matrix function $B(t)$. The requirement (2.15) which we impose upon the complex Gaussian process $\boldsymbol{\xi}$ may appear strange to the reader. This requirement is occasioned by the desire to preserve a very important property of real Gaussian random variables, namely, that if two such variables are uncorrelated, then they are independent. In the complex case one has this property only if a condition of type (2.15) holds.

3. The shift transformation associated with a stationary process

Let $\boldsymbol{\xi}$ be an n-dimensional strictly stationary process. We consider the mapping T of the space Ω of elementary events ω into the space $\tilde{\Omega}$ of all vector functions $\tilde{\omega} = \{x(t)\}$ of the parameter t $(x(t) = \{x_k(t)\}_{k=\overline{1,n}})$, by which each ω is carried into the corresponding sample function, and we consider, for each τ, the mapping $\tilde{S}_\tau$ of $\tilde{\Omega}$ onto itself, defined by

$$\tilde{S}_\tau \tilde{\omega} = \{x(t+\tau)\}\,, \qquad \tilde{\omega} = \{x(t)\}\,. \tag{3.1}$$

It is easy to see that for each τ the transformation $\tilde{S}_\tau$ is one-to-one, and that the image $\tilde{S}_\tau \tilde{A}$ of any set $\tilde{A}$ in the σ-algebra $\tilde{\mathfrak{A}}$, generated by the cylinder sets in $\tilde{\Omega}$, also belongs to $\tilde{\mathfrak{A}}$; in particular,

$$\begin{aligned} &\tilde{S}_\tau \{\tilde{\omega} \colon x_{k_1}(t_1) \in \Gamma_1, \ldots, x_{k_N}(t_N) \in \Gamma_N\} \\ &\qquad = \{\tilde{\omega} \colon x_{k_1}(t_1 - \tau) \in \Gamma_1, \ldots, x_{k_N}(t_N - \tau) \in \Gamma_N\}\,. \end{aligned} \tag{3.2}$$

As a transformation of sets in the σ-algebra $\tilde{\mathfrak{A}}$, $\tilde{S}_\tau$ is also a one-to-one mapping of $\tilde{\mathfrak{A}}$ onto itself, and preserves relations between sets:

$$\begin{aligned} \tilde{S}_\tau\Big(\bigcap_{k=1}^{\infty} \tilde{A}_k\Big) &= \bigcap_{k=1}^{\infty} (\tilde{S}_\tau \tilde{A}_k)\,, \\ \tilde{S}_\tau\Big(\bigcup_{k=1}^{\infty} \tilde{A}_k\Big) &= \bigcup_{k=1}^{\infty} (\tilde{S}_\tau \tilde{A}_k)\,, \\ \tilde{S}_\tau(\tilde{\Omega} - \tilde{A}) &= \tilde{\Omega} - \tilde{S}_\tau \tilde{A}\,, \end{aligned} \tag{3.3}$$

and $\tilde{S}_\tau \tilde{A}_1 \subseteq \tilde{S}_\tau \tilde{A}_2$ if $\tilde{A}_1 \subseteq \tilde{A}_2$.

Moreover, the transformations $\tilde{S}_\tau$ are related, for different values of τ, by the group relation

$$\tilde{S}_{\tau_1} \cdot \tilde{S}_{\tau_2} = \tilde{S}_{\tau_1+\tau_2}. \tag{3.4}$$

We now define a transformation S_τ of sets from the σ-algebra $\mathfrak{A}_\xi$ of the stationary process ξ. Namely, every ω-set $A \in \mathfrak{A}_\xi$ is the inverse image (see Lemma 2.1) of some $\tilde{\omega}$-set $\tilde{A} \in \tilde{\mathfrak{A}}$; we set

$$S_\tau A = T^{-1}(\tilde{S}_\tau \tilde{A})\,. \tag{3.5}$$

Generally speaking, S_τ is not uniquely defined by (3.5); i.e., a given set A can be the inverse image of various sets $\tilde{A}$. However, as we will see below, any two versions of $S_\tau A$ differ only by an ω-set of probability zero.

We note that S_τ carries cylinder sets into cylinder sets (strictly speaking, one version of the transform of a cylinder set is a cylinder set):

$$\begin{aligned} &S_\tau \{\omega\colon \xi_{k_1}(t_1) \in \Gamma_1, \ldots, \xi_{k_N}(t_N) \in \Gamma_N\} \\ &\quad = \{\omega\colon \xi_{k_1}(t_1 - \tau) \in \Gamma_1, \ldots, \xi_{k_N}(t_N - \tau) \in \Gamma_N\}\,. \end{aligned} \tag{3.6}$$

The transformation S_τ is called a *shift*.

Lemma 3.1. *The shift transformations S_τ are measure preserving:*

$$P(S_\tau A) = P(A) \tag{3.7}$$

for any version of $S_\tau A$, where $A \in \mathfrak{A}_\xi$.

Proof. It is obviously sufficient to show that

$$\tilde{P}(\tilde{S}_\tau \tilde{A}) = \tilde{P}(\tilde{A})\,, \qquad \tilde{A} \in \tilde{\mathfrak{A}}\,, \tag{3.8}$$

where the measure $\tilde{P}$ is defined on $\tilde{\mathfrak{A}}$ by

$$\tilde{P}(\tilde{A}) = P(T^{-1}\tilde{A})\,, \qquad \tilde{A} \in \tilde{\mathfrak{A}}\,.$$

By virtue of the strict stationarity of ξ, (3.8) holds for all cylinder set $\tilde{A}$. In the general case

$$\tilde{P}(\tilde{A}) = \inf \sum_j \tilde{P}(\tilde{A}_j)\,,$$

where the infimum is taken over all finite or countable families $\{\tilde{A}_j\}$ of cylinder sets such that $\bigcup_j \tilde{A}_j \supseteq \tilde{A}$. Thus

$$\tilde{P}(\tilde{S}_\tau \tilde{A}) \leq \inf \sum_j \tilde{P}(\tilde{S}_\tau A_j) = \inf \sum_j \tilde{P}(\tilde{A}_j) = \tilde{P}(\tilde{A}) ,$$

where the infimum is taken over the same family as before, since $\bigcup_j \tilde{A}_j \supseteq \tilde{A}$ implies $\bigcup_j S_\tau \tilde{A}_j \supseteq S_\tau \tilde{A}$, and (3.8) holds for cylinder sets. Applying the transformation $\tilde{S}_{-\tau}$ to the set $\tilde{S}_\tau \tilde{A}$, we obtain

$$\tilde{P}(\tilde{A}) = \tilde{P}(\tilde{S}_{-\tau}(\tilde{S}_\tau \tilde{A})) \leq \tilde{P}(\tilde{S}_\tau \tilde{A}) .$$

Comparing this with the inequality above, we have

$$\tilde{P}(\tilde{S}_\tau \tilde{A}) = \tilde{P}(\tilde{A})$$

for any $\tilde{A} \in \tilde{\mathfrak{A}}$.

Lemma 3.2. *The shift transformation S_τ is uniquely defined up to ω-sets of measure zero; i.e., if A_i and A_2 are distinct versions of $S_\tau A$, then*

$$P(A_1 \circ A_2) = 0 , \tag{3.9}$$

where $A_1 \circ A_2$ denotes the symmetric difference $(A_1 - A_2) \cup (A_2 - A_1)$.

Proof. The existence of distinct versions of $S_\tau A$ means that there exist distinct sets $\tilde{A}'$ and $\tilde{A}''$ in $\tilde{\mathfrak{A}}$ whose inverse images with respect to T are the set A:

$$A = T^{-1}A' = T^{-1}A'' ,$$

and such that

$$A_1 = T^{-1}(\tilde{S}_\tau \tilde{A}') , \qquad A_2 = T^{-1}(\tilde{S}_\tau \tilde{A}'') .$$

But then $A = T^{-1}(\tilde{A}' \cap \tilde{A}'')$, and so one version of $S_\tau A$ is just the set

$$T^{-1}(\tilde{S}_\tau(\tilde{A}' \cap \tilde{A}'')) = T^{-1}(\tilde{S}_\tau \tilde{A}') \cap T^{-1}(\tilde{S}_\tau \tilde{A}'') = A_1 \cap A_2 .$$

Since, by Lemma 3.1,

$$P(A) = P(A_1) = P(A_2) = P(A_1 \cap A_2) ,$$

obviously $P(A_1 \circ A_2) = 0$. ▮

By virtue of properties (3.3) one can say that the shift transformations S_τ preserve relations between sets:

$$\begin{gathered} S_\tau\left(\bigcap_{k=1}^{\infty} A_k\right) = \bigcap_{k=1}^{\infty} (S_\tau A_k) , \\ S_\tau\left(\bigcup_{k=1}^{\infty} A_k\right) = \bigcup_{k=1}^{\infty} (S_\tau A_k) , \\ S_\tau(\Omega - A) = \Omega - S_\tau A , \\ S_\tau A_1 \subseteq S_\tau A_2 \quad \text{if} \quad A_1 \subseteq A_2 , \end{gathered} \tag{3.10}$$

but with the stipulation that relations (3.10) are true only up to ω-sets of measure zero. It is obvious that with the same stipulation, the group relation

$$S_{\tau_1} \cdot S_{\tau_2} = S_{\tau_1+\tau_2} \tag{3.11}$$

is valid.

Furthermore, by identifying any two random variables which differ only on a set having probability zero, we can define a shift transformation U_τ of random variables which are measurable with respect to the σ-algebra $\mathfrak{A}_\xi$ of the process $\boldsymbol{\xi}$. Namely, for a random variable

$$\chi_A(\omega) = \begin{cases} 1 & \text{for} \quad \omega \in A\,, \\ 0 & \text{for} \quad \omega \notin A \end{cases} \qquad (A \in \mathfrak{A}_\xi)\,, \tag{3.12}$$

we set

$$U_\tau \chi_A = \chi_{S_{-\tau}A}\,; \tag{3.13}$$

if

$$\eta = \Sigma\, c_k \chi_{A_k}\,, \tag{3.14}$$

then we define $U_\tau \eta$ by

$$U_\tau \eta = \Sigma\, c_k U_\tau \chi_{A_k}\,. \tag{3.15}$$

It follows from (3.13) that

$$\{\omega: U_\tau \eta \in \Gamma\} = S_{-\tau}\{\omega: \eta \in \Gamma\} \tag{3.16}$$

for any random variable η of the form (3.14).

Suppose that a sequence η_k, $k = 1, 2, \ldots,$ of random variables of the form (3.14) converges in probability. We consider the corresponding sequence η'_k, $k = 1, 2, \ldots,$ of "shifted" variables $\eta'_k = U_\tau \eta_k$. By virtue of the invariance of the probability measure P and property (3.16),

$$P\{|\eta'_k - \eta'_l| > \varepsilon\} = P\{|\eta_k - \eta_l| > \varepsilon\} \to 0 \tag{3.17}$$

as $k, l \to \infty$ for any $\varepsilon > 0$; i.e., the sequence $\{\eta'_k\}$ also converges in probability.

Now every random variable which is measurable with respect to the σ-algebra $\mathfrak{A}_\xi$ can be represented as the limit in probability of a sequence $\{\eta_k\}$ of random variables of the form (3.14). By (3.17) the sequence of "shifted" variables $\eta'_k = U_\tau \eta_k$ will converge in probability to some random variable η'; we put

$$U_\tau \eta = \eta'\,. \tag{3.18}$$

The transformation U_τ is well defined by (3.18); if one chooses another sequence $\{\zeta_k\}$ which converges in probability to η, then the sequence $\zeta'_k = U_\tau \zeta_k$, $k = 1, 2, \ldots,$ will converge in probability to the same limit

η'. This is obvious from the consideration of the sequence η_1, ζ_1, η_2, ζ_2, ..., which clearly converges in probability to η.

Finally, it is easy to see that property (3.16) carries over to arbitrary random variables η which are measurable with respect to $\mathfrak{A}_\xi$.

Since the transformations S_τ preserve relations between sets [cf. (3.10)], the U_τ preserve relations between random variables. Namely,

$$\begin{aligned} U_\tau(c_1\eta_1 + c_2\eta_2) &= c_1(U_\tau\eta_1) + c_2(U_\tau\eta_2) , \\ U_\tau(\eta_1\eta_2) &= (U_\tau\eta_1)(U_\tau\eta_2) , \\ U_\tau\bar{\eta} &= \overline{(U_\tau\eta)} . \end{aligned} \tag{3.19}$$

These properties are obvious for η_1, η_2 of the form (3.12); for arbitrary η_1, η_2 they follow from the usual passage to the limit. It is also obvious that

$$U_{\tau_1}U_{\tau_2} = U_{\tau_1+\tau_2} . \tag{3.20}$$

Further, it is easily seen that if η is a given random variable, measurable with respect to $\mathfrak{A}_\xi$, then the family of random variables $\eta(t) = \eta(\omega, t)$, depending upon the parameter t,

$$\eta(t) = U_t\eta , \tag{3.21}$$

constitutes a *strictly stationary random process*. If $\boldsymbol{\xi} = \{\xi_k(t)\}_{k=\overline{1,n}}$ is the original random process, then, obviously,

$$\xi_k(t) = U_t\xi_k(0) , \qquad k = \overline{1, n} . \tag{3.22}$$

We deduce from this that if the random variable η is a Borel function of the values $\xi_{k_1}(t_1), \ldots, \xi_{k_N}(t_N)$ of the process $\boldsymbol{\xi}$, then

$$\begin{aligned} \eta(t) = U_t\eta &= U_t\eta[\xi_{k_1}(t_1), \ldots, \xi_{k_N}(t_N)] \\ &= \eta[\xi_{k_1}(t_1 + t), \ldots, \xi_{k_N}(t_N + t)] . \end{aligned} \tag{3.23}$$

Let us mention still another property of the shift transformations S_τ and U_τ, namely:

$$\int_A \eta(\omega)P(d\omega) = \int_{S_\tau^{-1}A} U_\tau\eta(\omega)P(d\omega) \tag{3.24}$$

for any random variable $\eta = \eta(\omega)$ which is measurable with respect to $\mathfrak{A}_\xi$, and for any set $A \in \mathfrak{A}_\xi$.

This property is obvious for η of the form (3.12), and is easily carried over to the general case.

4. On the measurability of the group of shift transformations

We denote by $\boldsymbol{H}_\xi$ the Hilbert space of random variables h, $\boldsymbol{E}|h|^2 < \infty$, which are measurable with respect to the σ-algebra $\mathfrak{A}_\xi$, with the scalar product

$$(h_1, h_2) = \boldsymbol{E} h_1 \overline{h_2} . \tag{4.1}$$

The properties of the shift transformations U_t described above show that these transformations form a group of unitary transformations in $\boldsymbol{H}_\xi$.

It will be important for us to determine what simple requirements, imposed upon the random process $\boldsymbol{\xi}$, lead to the separability of the Hilbert space $\boldsymbol{H}_\xi$ and the measurability of the family $\{U_t\}$ (in the continuous-parameter case).

Let $\boldsymbol{\xi}$ be an n-dimensional real discrete-parameter process. It is obvious that the family of all random variables of the form $\varphi[\xi_{k_1}(t_1), \ldots, \xi_{k_N}(t_N)]$, where $\varphi(x_1, \ldots, x_N)$ is a continuous function which vanishes outside a bounded set in R^N, is everywhere dense in $\boldsymbol{H}_\xi$.

We choose intervals $\Gamma_1, \ldots, \Gamma_N$ of length $2\pi L$ (L an integer) on the coordinate axes $x_1, \ldots, x_N$ of R^N such that the function $\varphi(x_1, \ldots, x_N)$ vanishes outside the cube $D = \Gamma_1 \times \cdots \times \Gamma_N$, and, moreover,

$$P^{t_1, \ldots, t_N}_{\xi_{k_1}, \ldots, \xi_{k_N}}(\Gamma_1, \ldots, \Gamma_N) \geq 1 - \delta , \tag{4.2}$$

where δ will be specified later. Now φ can be uniformly approximated in the cube D by trigonometric polynomials of the form

$$P = \sum_{u_1, \ldots, u_N} c(u_1, \ldots, u_N) e^{iL^{-1} \sum_{k=1}^{N} x_k u_k} \tag{4.3}$$

with rational coefficients $c(u_1, \ldots, u_N)$ ($u_1, \ldots, u_N$ are integers). For any $\varepsilon > 0$ one can find a polynomial P such that

$$|\varphi(x_1, \ldots, x_N) - P(e^{ix_1}, \ldots, e^{ix_N})| \leq \left(\frac{\varepsilon}{2}\right)^{1/2} \tag{4.4}$$

for $x_1 \in \Gamma_1, \ldots, x_N \in \Gamma_N$. Choosing δ in (4.2) equal to

$$\frac{\varepsilon}{2}\left[\max |\varphi(x_1, \ldots, x_N)| + \left(\frac{\varepsilon}{2}\right)^{1/2}\right]^{-2} ,$$

we obtain

$$\boldsymbol{E}|\varphi[\xi_{k_1}(t_1), \ldots, \xi_{k_N}(t_N)] - P[e^{i\xi_{k_1}(t_1)}, \ldots, e^{i\xi_{k_N}(t_N)}]|^2$$
$$= \int_{R^N} |\varphi - P|^2 P^{t_1, \ldots, t_N}_{\xi_{k_1}, \ldots, \xi_{k_N}}(dx_1, \ldots, dx_N) \leq \varepsilon . \tag{4.5}$$

Indeed, inside the cube $\Gamma_1 \times \cdots \times \Gamma_N$ the function $|\varphi - P|^2$ does not exceed $\varepsilon/2$, and outside this cube $|\varphi - P|^2 = |P|^2$, which does not exceed $[\max|\varphi| + (\varepsilon/2)^{1/2}]^2$ (because the trigonometric polynomial P is periodic), and

$$P^{t_1, \ldots, t_N}_{\xi_{k_1}, \ldots, \xi_{k_N}}(R^N - D) \leq [\max |\varphi| + (\varepsilon/2)^{1/2}]^2 .$$

Thus we see that the countable set of "trigonometric polynomials"

$$P = P[e^{i\xi_{k_1}(t_1)}, \ldots, e^{i\xi_{k_N}(t_N)}]$$

with rational coefficients is everywhere dense in $\boldsymbol{H}_\xi$.

In the case of an n-dimensional complex process ξ, the separability of $\boldsymbol{H}_\xi$ is proved in the same way, except that instead of the process ξ one considers the $2n$-dimensional real process consisting of the real and imaginary parts of ξ.

We have thus established that *in the discrete-parameter case,* $\boldsymbol{H}_\xi$ *is always separable.*

The situation is different in the continuous-parameter case; here $\boldsymbol{H}_\xi$ need not be separable. In order to insure separability, we are forced to impose certain requirements on the process ξ. One such condition is *stochastic continuity*: for any $\varepsilon > 0$

$$\lim_{s \to t} P\{||\xi(s) - \xi(t)|| > \varepsilon\} = 0 \tag{4.6}$$

for all t [(4.6) always holds formally in the discrete-parameter case].

In fact, if $\varphi(x_1, \ldots, x_N)$ is any bounded continuous function, then, if ξ is stochastically continuous, the random variable $\varphi[(\xi_{k_1}(s_1), \ldots, \xi_{k_N}(s_N)]$ converges in probability to $\varphi[\xi_{k_1}(t_1), \ldots, \xi_{k_N}(t_N)]$ as $s_1 \to t_1, \ldots, s_N \to t_N$. But for bounded random variables, convergence in probability coincides with convergence in the mean:

$$\lim_{s_1 \to t_1, \ldots, s_N \to t_N} \boldsymbol{E}|\varphi[\xi_{k_1}(s_1), \ldots, \xi_{k_N}(s_N)] - \varphi[\xi_{k_1}(t_1), \ldots, \xi_{k_N}(t_N)]|^2 = 0\,. \tag{4.7}$$

From this we conclude, in particular, that $\boldsymbol{H}_\xi$ is generated by random variables which are functions of the values $\xi_k(t)$, $k = \overline{1, n}$, taken at rational t only.

Therefore, under condition (4.6) the continuous-parameter case reduces to the discrete-parameter case, so that under this condition the space $\boldsymbol{H}_\xi$ will be separable.

We will further call a process $\xi = \{\xi(\omega, t)\}$ *measurable,* if the function $\xi(\omega, t)$ is measurable with respect to the pair (w, t) (in the continuous-parameter case; in the discrete-parameter case every process is formally measurable).

We shall say that two random processes ξ and $\tilde{\xi}$ are *equivalent,* if

$$P\{\tilde{\xi}(t) \neq \xi(t)\} = 0 \tag{4.8}$$

for all t.

Theorem 4.1. *If the random process* ξ *is stochastically continuous, then there exists a measurable process* $\tilde{\xi}$ *which is equivalent to it.*

For the proof of this assertion, we subdivide an arbitrary interval $[t_1, t_2]$ of length 1 into equal parts by means of points

$$t_1 = t^0 < t^1 < \cdots < t^m = t_2,$$

and consider the random processes $\boldsymbol{\xi}^m$, $m = 1, 2, \ldots$, of the form

$$\xi^m(\omega, t) = \xi(\omega, t^k), \qquad t^{k-1} < t \leq t^k, \qquad k = \overline{1, m}. \tag{4.9}$$

Let $\mu(d\omega, dt) = P(d\omega) \cdot dt$. From the stationarity of $\boldsymbol{\xi}$ and its stochastic continuity, we have

$$\begin{aligned} &\mu\{(\omega, t): ||\xi^{m_1}(\omega, t) - \xi^{m_2}(\omega, t)|| > \varepsilon\} \\ &\leq (t_2 - t_1) \sup_{|t-s|<\max(1/m_1, 1/m_2)} P\{||\xi(t) - \xi(s)|| > \varepsilon\} \to 0, \end{aligned} \tag{4.10}$$

as $m_1, m_2 \to \infty$, from which it is evident that the sequence of measurable functions (of (ω, t)) $\xi^m(\omega, t)$, $m = 1, 2, \ldots$, converges in μ-measure to some measurable function $\tilde{\xi}(w, t)$, which, for almost every fixed $t \in [t_1, t_2]$, is a random variable coinciding with $\xi(t)$ with probability 1. Finally, replacing $\tilde{\xi}(\omega, t)$ by $\xi(\omega, t)$ at the exceptional values of t (which form a Borel set of measure zero), we obtain as a result a measurable random process whose value, at any fixed t, coincides with probability 1 with the corresponding value of the original process $\boldsymbol{\xi}$. ∎

Further, if $\boldsymbol{\xi}$ is a measurable process, then any process $\boldsymbol{\eta}$ of the form

$$\eta(t) = \varphi[\xi_{k_1}(t_1 + t), \ldots, \xi_{k_N}(t_N + t)] = U_t\varphi[\xi_{k_1}(t_1), \ldots, \xi_{k_N}(t_N)], \tag{4.11}$$

(where the function $\varphi(x_1, \ldots, x_N)$ is, say, continuous and bounded) is also measurable.

Since the random variables of the form $\varphi[\xi_{k_1}(t_1), \ldots, \xi_{k_N}(t_N)]$ are everywhere dense in $\boldsymbol{H}_\xi$, there follows from this, in particular, the measurability of the family $\{U_t\}$ of unitary operators. i.e., the numerical function $(U_t h_1, h_2)$ is measurable in t for any elements $h_1, h_2 \in \boldsymbol{H}_\xi$. Moreover, if the process ξ is stochastically continuous, then any process $\boldsymbol{\eta}$, $\eta(t) = U_t\eta_0$, $\eta_0 \in \boldsymbol{H}_\xi$, is continuous in quadratic mean:

$$\lim_{s\to t} \|\eta(t) - \eta(s)\| = 0. \tag{4.12}$$

In fact, by virtue of the unitarity of U_t, every such process $\boldsymbol{\eta}$ is the uniform (in t) limit in quadratic mean of processes of the form (4.11), for which we have already established the continuity property (4.12) [see relation (4.7)].

It follows from (4.12) that the values of each stationary process $\boldsymbol{\eta}$, $\eta(t) = U_t\eta_0$, can be so chosen that the process $\boldsymbol{\eta}$ will be measurable. With probability 1, the trajectory of such a process will be a measurable function of t, integrable over any finite interval $[t_1, t_2]$. This follows from Fubini's theorem, since

$$\int_{t_1}^{t_2} \boldsymbol{E}|\eta(t)|dt \leq (t_2 - t_1)[\boldsymbol{E}|\eta(0)|^2]^{1/2} \tag{4.13}$$

and

$$\int_{t_1}^{t_2} \boldsymbol{E}\eta(t)dt = \boldsymbol{E}\int_{t_1}^{t_2} \eta(\omega, t)dt . \tag{4.14}$$

The integral $\int_{t_1}^{t_2}\eta(\omega, t)\,dt$ coincides with probability 1 with the value of the integral $\int_{t_1}^{t_2}\eta(t)\,dt$, defined in Section 2 of Chapter I, for processes which are separable in the wide sense.

5. The ergodic theorem

In the case where the space $\boldsymbol{H}_\xi$ is separable and the family $\{U_t\}$ of shift operators is measurable, a simultaneous spectral resolution of the U_t exists:

$$U_t = \int e^{i\lambda t} E(d\lambda) , \tag{5.1}$$

where $E(d\lambda)$ is the corresponding family of projection operators (an operator-valued measure), and the limits of integration are $-\pi$, π in the discrete-parameter case, and $-\infty$, ∞ in the continuous-parameter case (see, for example, Riesz-Nagy[*], Section 137).

This representation gives rise to a spectral representation

$$\eta(t) = \int e^{i\lambda t}\Phi^\eta(d\lambda) \tag{5.2}$$

of the stationary process $\boldsymbol{\eta}$, $\eta(t) = U_t\eta_0$ ($\eta_0 \in \boldsymbol{H}_\xi$) in the form of a stochastic integral with respect to the random measure $\Phi^\eta(d\lambda) = E(d\lambda)\eta_0$.

We have already considered such a representation for wide-sense stationary processes in Chapter I, and it was shown in Section 4 of Chapter I that the "time averages"

$$\frac{1}{t-s}H(s, t) = \begin{cases} \dfrac{1}{t-s}\sum_s^t \eta(u) , \\ \dfrac{1}{t-s}\int_s^t \eta(u)du \end{cases} \tag{5.3}$$

converge in quadratic mean to the variable $\Phi^\eta(0)$.

For strictly stationary processes, the question of the convergence of the "time averages" $H(s, t)/(t - s)$ can be substantially sharpened.

In order to formulate the appropriate theorem, we need a new concept—that of an invariant set. A set A, $A \in \mathfrak{A}_\xi$, is said to be *invariant*, if for any t one has

$$S_t A = A \tag{5.4}$$

up to a set of probability zero (this set will, in general, depend upon t).

The collection of all invariant sets obviously forms a σ-algebra, which we will denote by $\mathfrak{J}$.

The notion of invariance for random variables is defined similarly; i.e., the random variable η is invariant, if for each t,

$$U_t \eta = \eta \tag{5.5}$$

with probability 1.

It is easily seen that a random variable η is invariant if and only if it is measurable with respect to the σ-algebra $\mathfrak{J}$ of invariant sets.

Theorem 5.1. *Let η be any random variable which is measurable with respect to $\mathfrak{A}_\xi$ and has a finite expectation ($\boldsymbol{E}|\eta| < \infty$). Set $\eta(t) = U_t \eta$ and define $H(s, t)$ according to* (5.3). *Then, for each fixed s,*

$$\lim_{t-s\to\infty} \frac{1}{t-s} H(s, t) = \boldsymbol{E}(\eta|\mathfrak{J}) \tag{5.6}$$

with probability 1, *where $\boldsymbol{E}(\eta|\mathfrak{J})$ is the conditional expectation of η relative to the σ-algebra $\mathfrak{J}$ of invariant sets. Moreover, if*

$$\boldsymbol{E}|\eta|^\delta < \infty \tag{5.7}$$

for some $\delta \geq 1$, then, for each fixed s,

$$\lim_{t-s\to\infty} \boldsymbol{E}\left|\frac{1}{t-s} H(s, t) - \boldsymbol{E}(\eta|\mathfrak{J})\right|^\delta = 0 . \tag{5.8}$$

Proof. The proof will be carried out in a number of steps.

Suppose that the parameter t assumes only integer values. We shall show that the sequence $(1/t)H(0, t)$, $t = 1, 2, \ldots$, converges with probability 1. Let us assume the contrary. Then one can find two numbers $\alpha < \beta$ such that the probability that simultaneously

$$\underline{\lim}_{t\to\infty} \frac{1}{t} H(0, t) < \alpha , \qquad \overline{\lim}_{t\to\infty} \frac{1}{t} H(0, t) > \beta \tag{5.9}$$

will be positive. In fact, if $A_{\alpha\beta}$ denotes the ω-set for which (5.9) is fulfilled, then the ω-set A for which $\lim_{t\to\infty} (1/t)H(0, t)$ does not exist is clearly the union of the $A_{\alpha\beta}$ when α and β assume all rational values, and, therefore,

$$0 < P(A) \leq \sum_{\alpha,\beta} P(A_{\alpha\beta}) ,$$

where the summation is over all rational α, β, $\alpha < \beta$. Thus, $P(A_{\alpha\beta}) > 0$ for some α, β.

We must now show that the assumption that (5.9) can hold with positive probability leads to a contradiction. Thus, suppose $P(A_{\alpha\beta}) > 0$ for some α, β. Let us denote by $A^s_{\alpha\beta}$ the ω-set on which (5.9) holds, and in addition $(1/t_0)H(0, t_0) > \beta$ for some t_0, $t_0 \leq s$. Obviously,

$$\lim_{s\to\infty} A^s_{\alpha\beta} = A_{\alpha\beta} , \qquad \lim_{s\to\infty} P(A^s_{\alpha\beta}) = P(A_{\alpha\beta}) ,$$

and $P(A^s_{\alpha\beta}) > 0$ for sufficiently large s. Now for each $\omega \in A^s_{\alpha\beta}$ we define $\tau^* = \tau^*(\omega)$ as the smallest value of t, $0 \leq t \leq s$, for which $(1/t)H(0, t) > \beta$, and $\tau = \tau(\omega)$ as the smallest value of r, $0 \geq r \geq \tau^* - s$, such that

$$\frac{1}{\tau^* - r}H(r, \tau^*) > \beta , \qquad \frac{1}{t - r}H(r, t) \leq \beta \quad \text{for} \quad r < t < \tau^* .$$

In turn, the existence, for a given $\omega \in A_{\alpha\beta}$, of numbers τ and τ^* with these properties implies that $\omega \in A^s_{\alpha\beta}$. In fact,

$$H(\tau, \tau^*) = H(\tau, 0) + H(0, \tau^*) ,$$

where, by assumption,

$$H(\tau, \tau^*) > (\tau^* - \tau)\beta , \qquad H(\tau, 0) \leq -\tau\beta ,$$
$$0 < \tau^* \leq s , \qquad 0 \geq \tau \geq \tau^* - s ,$$

from which it necessarily follows that $H(0, \tau^*) > \tau^*\beta$, which means that $\omega \in A^s_{\alpha\beta}$.

Thus, $A^s_{\alpha\beta}$ is the union of the nonintersecting sets $B_{pq} = A_{\alpha\beta} \cap \{\tau = -p, \tau^* = -p + q\}$, $q = \overline{1, s}$, $p = \overline{0, q-1}$:

$$A^s_{\alpha\beta} = \bigcup_{p,q} B_{pq} .$$

The set $A_{\alpha\beta}$ is obviously invariant, and

$$U_p H(-p, -p + q) = H(0, q) .$$

Therefore, $S_p^{-1} B_{pq} = B_{0q}$, and by virtue of property (3.24) we have

$$\begin{aligned} \int_{A^s_{\alpha\beta}} \eta P(d\omega) &= \sum_{p,q} \int_{B_{pq}} \eta P(d\omega) = \sum_{p,q} \int_{B_{0q}} \eta(p) P(d\omega) = \sum_q \int_{B_{0q}} H(0, q) P(d\omega) \\ &\geq \sum_q q\beta P(B_{0q}) = \sum_{p,q} P(B_{pq})\beta = P(A^s_{\alpha\beta})\beta \end{aligned} \tag{5.10}$$

[for $\omega \in B_{0q}$ we have, by assumption, $H(0, q) > q\beta$].

Passing to the limit $s \to \infty$ in (5.10), we obtain

$$\int_{A_{\alpha\beta}} \eta P(d\omega) \geq P(A_{\alpha\beta})\beta . \tag{5.11}$$

In exactly the same way we prove the reverse inequality

$$\int_{A_{\alpha\beta}} \eta P(d\omega) \leq P(A_{\alpha\beta})\alpha \,. \tag{5.12}$$

But (5.11) and (5.12) are in contradiction with $\alpha < \beta$ and $P(A_{\alpha\beta}) > 0$. We were led to this contradiction by assuming that $\lim_{t\to\infty} (1/t)H(0, t)$ does not exist with probability 1; therefore this assumption is incorrect.

Now suppose that t is a continuous parameter. Obviously,

$$\begin{aligned} \overline{\lim_{t\to\infty}} \frac{1}{t}\int_0^t \eta(u)\,du &= \overline{\lim_{N\to\infty}} \frac{1}{N} \sum_0^{N-1} \int_k^{k+1} \eta(u)\,du \,, \\ \underline{\lim_{t\to\infty}} \frac{1}{t}\int_0^t \eta(u)\,du &= \underline{\lim_{N\to\infty}} \frac{1}{N} \sum_0^{N-1} \int_k^{k+1} \eta(u)\,du \,, \end{aligned} \tag{5.13}$$

where N assumes integer values. But the right sides of (5.13) coincide with probability 1, because the integrals $\eta'(k) = \int_k^{k+1}\eta(u)\,du$ form a strictly stationary discrete-parameter process. Thus, $\lim_{t\to\infty} (1/t)\int_0^t \eta(u)\,du$ exists with probability 1.

It is not hard to see, further, that $\lim_{t\to\infty} (1/t)H(0, t)$ is an invariant random variable: for any fixed s

$$U_s \lim_{t\to\infty} \frac{1}{t} H(0, t) = \lim_{t\to\infty} \frac{1}{t} H(s, t + s) = \lim_{t\to\infty} \frac{1}{t} H(0, t)$$

with probability 1.

Let us first assume that η is essentially bounded; i.e., with probability 1 $|\eta| \leq N < \infty$. Then obviously $|\eta(t)| \leq N$ and $(1/t)|H(0, t)| \leq N$. In this case, for any invariant set A we have, on the one hand,

$$\lim_{t\to\infty} \int_A \frac{1}{t} H(0, t)P(d\omega) = \int_A \left[\lim_{t\to\infty} \frac{1}{t} H(0, t) \right] P(d\omega) \,,$$

and, on the other,

$$\int_A \frac{1}{t} H(0, t)P(d\omega) = \begin{cases} \dfrac{1}{t} \sum\limits_0^{t-1} \int_A \eta(u)P(d\omega) = \dfrac{1}{t} \sum\limits_0^{t-1} \int_A \eta(0)P(d\omega) = \int_A \eta P(d\omega), \\ \dfrac{1}{t} \int_0^t \int_A \eta(u)P(d\omega)\,du = \dfrac{1}{t} \int_0^t \int_A \eta(0)P(d\omega)\,du = \int_A \eta P(d\omega) \,. \end{cases}$$

These relations show that with probability 1

$$\lim_{t\to\infty} \frac{1}{t} H(0, t) = \boldsymbol{E}(\eta|\mathfrak{J}) \,. \tag{5.14}$$

At the same time, for η essentially bounded, it is clear that (5.14) implies (5.8).

Suppose, now, only that $\boldsymbol{E}|\eta|^\delta < \infty$ for some $\delta \geq 1$. For any $\varepsilon > 0$

one can find a bounded random variable η_ε such that

$$E|\eta - \eta_\varepsilon|^\delta \leq \varepsilon .$$

Let us denote the "time averages" for η and η_ε by $H(0, t)/t$ and $H_\varepsilon(0, t)/t$ respectively. By Hölder's inequality we have

$$\left|\frac{1}{t}[H(0, t) - H_\varepsilon(0, t)]\right|^\delta \leq \begin{cases} \dfrac{1}{t}\sum_{1}^{t-1} |\eta(u) - \eta_\varepsilon(u)|^\delta , \\ \dfrac{1}{t}\int_0^t |\eta(u) - \eta_\varepsilon(u)|^\delta du . \end{cases}$$

Thus, by virtue of the stationarity of the processes $\{\eta(t)\}$ and $\{\eta_\varepsilon(t)\}$,

$$E\left|\frac{1}{t}H(0, t) - \frac{1}{t}H_\varepsilon(0, t)\right|^\delta \leq E|\eta - \eta_\varepsilon|^\delta \leq \varepsilon . \tag{5.15}$$

Finally,

$$\begin{aligned} E|E(\eta|\mathfrak{F}) - E(\eta_\varepsilon|\mathfrak{F})|^\delta &= E|E(\eta - \eta_\varepsilon|\mathfrak{F})|^\delta \\ &\leq E[E(|\eta - \eta_\varepsilon|^\delta|\mathfrak{F})] = E|\eta - \eta_\varepsilon|^\delta \leq \varepsilon , \end{aligned} \tag{5.16}$$

and, by what was just proved,

$$E\left|\frac{1}{t}H_\varepsilon(0, t) - E(\eta_\varepsilon|\mathfrak{F})\right|^\delta \leq \varepsilon \tag{5.17}$$

for sufficiently large t; i.e., $t \geq t_\varepsilon$. Comparing (5.15), (5.16), and (5.17) and using Minkowski's inequality, we obtain

$$\begin{aligned} \left[E\left|\frac{1}{t}H(0, t) - E(\eta|\mathfrak{F})\right|^\delta\right]^{1/\delta} &\leq \left[E\left|\frac{1}{t}H(0, t) - \frac{1}{t}H_\varepsilon(0, t)\right|^\delta\right]^{1/\delta} \\ &+ \left[E\left|\frac{1}{t}H_\varepsilon(0, t) - E(\eta_\varepsilon|\mathfrak{F})\right|^\delta\right]^{1/\delta} + [E|E(\eta_\varepsilon|\mathfrak{F}) - E(\eta|\mathfrak{F})|^\delta]^{1/\delta} \leq 3\varepsilon^{1/\delta} \end{aligned}$$

for all $t \geq t_\varepsilon$. Consequently, in view of the arbitrariness of ε, relation (5.8) holds, and with it Theorem 5.1, since (5.8) implies the validity of (5.14) for any η such that $E|\eta| < \infty$.

An important corollary can be deduced from Theorem 5.1. Namely, for any random variable η, $E|\eta| < \infty$, for every real λ_0 (and fixed s)

$$\lim_{t-s\to\infty} \frac{1}{t-s} \sum_{s}^{t-1} e^{-i\lambda_0 u}\eta(u) = \tilde{\eta}(\lambda_0) \tag{5.18}$$

(in the discrete-parameter case)

$$\lim_{t-s\to\infty} \frac{1}{t-s} \int_s^t e^{-i\lambda_0 u}\eta(u)\, du = \tilde{\eta}(\lambda_0) \tag{5.19}$$

(in the continuous-parameter case), with probability 1.

The limit random variable $\tilde{\eta}(\lambda_0)$ is a "proper function" of the shift transformations U_t: for each t

$$U_t\tilde{\eta}(\lambda_0) = e^{i\lambda_0 t}\tilde{\eta}(\lambda_0) \tag{5.20}$$

with probability 1. If $\boldsymbol{E}|\eta|^\delta < \infty$ for some $\delta \geq 1$, then

$$\lim_{t-s\to\infty} \boldsymbol{E}\left|\frac{1}{t-s}\sum_s^{t-1} e^{-i\lambda_0 u}\eta(u) - \tilde{\eta}(\lambda_0)\right|^\delta = 0 \tag{5.21}$$

or, respectively,

$$\lim_{t-s\to\infty} \boldsymbol{E}\left|\frac{1}{t-s}\int_s^t e^{-i\lambda_0 u}\eta(u)\,du - \tilde{\eta}(\lambda_0)\right|^\delta = 0\,. \tag{5.22}$$

It is obvious that if the limit $\tilde{\eta}(\lambda_0)$ exists, then it satisfies the requirement (5.20).

To prove relations (5.18)-(5.22), we introduce a new random variable θ which is uniformly distributed on the interval $[-\pi, \pi]$ and which is independent of the process $\boldsymbol{\xi}$. Precisely speaking, we introduce a new space $\Omega' = \Omega \times [-\pi, \pi]$ with the probability measure $P' = P \times l$, where l is normalized Lebesgue measure on $[-\pi, \pi]$, and θ is defined by $\theta(\omega') = \lambda$ for $\omega' = (\omega, \lambda)$.

Let us consider, on this new space Ω', the random process $\boldsymbol{\eta}'$, $\eta'(t) = e^{-i(\lambda_0 t+\theta)}\eta(t)$. Obviously $\boldsymbol{\eta}'$ is strictly stationary, and $\boldsymbol{E}|\eta'(t)| = \boldsymbol{E}|\eta(t)| < \infty$. Now

$$\lim_{t-s\to\infty} \frac{1}{t-s}\sum_1^{t-1} \eta'(u) = e^{-i\theta} \lim_{t-s\to\infty} \frac{1}{t-s}\sum_s^{t-1} e^{-i\lambda_0 u}\eta(u)\,,$$

or, respectively,

$$\lim_{t-s\to\infty} \frac{1}{t-s}\int_s^t \eta'(u)\,du = e^{-i\theta} \lim_{t-s\to\infty} \frac{1}{t-s}\int_s^t e^{-i\lambda_0 u}\eta(u)\,du\,.$$

Since, by Theorem 5.1, the left sides converge with probability 1 in Ω' as $t - s \to \infty$, the existence, with probability 1 in Ω, of the limit in (5.18) or (5.19) follows at once. The validity of (5.21) and, respectively, (5.22) also follows easily from Theorem 5.1.

6. Metric transitivity. Examples

A strictly stationary process $\boldsymbol{\xi} = \{\xi_k(t)\}_{k=\overline{1,n}}$ is said to be *metrically transitive* if every set which is invariant relative to the shift transformations S_t has probability either zero or 1. Obviously, the requirement of metric transitivity of $\boldsymbol{\xi}$ is equivalent to the requirement that every invariant random variable equals a constant with probability 1.

In the case of a metrically transitive process $\boldsymbol{\xi}$, the "time averages" $H(s, t)/(t - s)$ which appear in the ergodic theorem simply converge to the mathematical expectation $\boldsymbol{E}\eta$ of the random variable η. It is easily seen that the converse is true; that is, if

$$\lim_{t-s\to\infty} \frac{1}{t-s} H(s, t) = \boldsymbol{E}(\eta|\mathfrak{J}) = \boldsymbol{E}\eta \tag{6.1}$$

for any random variable η with finite expectation, then the algebra $\mathfrak{J}$ of invariant sets is trivial (it consists only of sets whose probability is either zero or 1), which means that $\boldsymbol{\xi}$ is metrically transitive.

Let us note some properties of invariant random variables. We denote by $\mathfrak{A}_u^v$ the σ-algebra generated by sets of the form

$$\{\omega: \xi_{k_1}(t_1) \in \Gamma_1, \ldots, \xi_{k_N}(t_N) \in \Gamma_N\} ,$$

where $u \leq t_k \leq v$ for all $k = \overline{1, N}$, and set

$$\begin{aligned} \mathfrak{A}^- &= \lim_{v\to-\infty} \mathfrak{A}_{-\infty}^v , \\ \mathfrak{A}^+ &= \lim_{u\to\infty} \mathfrak{A}_u^\infty . \end{aligned} \tag{6.2}$$

Lemma 6.1. *Given any invariant random variable η, there exist random variables η^- and η^+ which are measurable with respect to $\mathfrak{A}^-$ and $\mathfrak{A}^+$, respectively, and such that $\eta = \eta^- = \eta^+$ with probability* 1.

Proof. It is sufficient to show that every invariant random variable η coincides, with probability 1, with some random variables which are measurable with respect to the σ-algebras $\mathfrak{A}_{-\infty}^v$ and $\mathfrak{A}_u^\infty$, respectively, for any u and v.

Let ε and δ be arbitrary positive numbers. For any η which is measurable with respect to $\mathfrak{A}_\xi$, one can find s and t and a random variable η_ε, measurable with respect to $\mathfrak{A}_s^t$, such that

$$P\{|\eta - \eta_\varepsilon| > \delta\} < \varepsilon .$$

If η is invariant, then also

$$P\{|\eta - U_{v-t}\eta_\varepsilon| > \delta\} < \varepsilon ; \qquad P\{|\eta - U_{u-s}\eta_\varepsilon| > \delta\} < \varepsilon .$$

But the random variables $U_{v-t}\eta_\varepsilon$ and $U_{u-s}\eta_\varepsilon$ are obviously measurable with respect to $\mathfrak{A}_{-\infty}^v$ and $\mathfrak{A}_u^\infty$, respectively. Since ε and δ are arbitrary, we conclude from the preceding inequalities that η is the limit in probability of random variables which are measurable with respect to $\mathfrak{A}_{-\infty}^v$ and $\mathfrak{A}_u^\infty$, and therefore coincides, with probability 1, with random variables which are measurable with respect to these σ-algebras.

Example 6.1. Let $\{\xi(t)\}$ be a two-sided infinite sequence of independent identically distributed random variables.

Let us consider an arbitrary set $A \in \mathfrak{A}^+$. For every $\varepsilon > 0$ we choose a set $A_\varepsilon \in \mathfrak{A}_s^t$ (s and t depend upon ε) such that the probability measure of the symmetric difference of A and A_ε does not exceed ε. Obviously,

$$\lim_{\varepsilon\to 0} P(A \cap A_\varepsilon) = P(A) .$$

But A and A_ε are independent; that is,

$$P(A \cap A_\varepsilon) = P(A)P(A_\varepsilon) ,$$

while

$$\lim_{\varepsilon\to 0} P(A \cap A_\varepsilon) = P(A) \lim_{\varepsilon\to 0} P(A_\varepsilon) = [P(A)]^2 .$$

Comparing the two expressions obtained for $\lim_{\varepsilon\to 0} P(A \cap A_\varepsilon)$, we see that $P(A)$ can only equal either zero or 1. Together with Lemma 6.1, this shows that the algebra $\mathfrak{J}$ of invariant sets is trivial, and the sequence $\{\xi(t)\}$ forms a metrically transitive process. In particular, if the $\xi(t)$ have a mathematical expectation $m = \boldsymbol{E}\xi(t)$, then with probability 1

$$\lim_{t-s\to\infty} \frac{1}{t-s} \sum_{s}^{t-1} \xi(u) = m \quad (s \text{ fixed}) . \tag{6.3}$$

This result is the well-known strong law of large numbers.

Example 6.2. Let $\xi = \{\xi_k(t)\}_{k=\overline{1,n}}$ be a *Gaussian stationary process* with zero mean.

As was shown in Section 2 of this chapter, such a process is defined by its correlation function $B(t)$ or its spectral measure $F(d\lambda)$, which is connected with $B(t)$, as we already know, by the relation

$$B(t) = \int e^{i\lambda t} F(d\lambda) .$$

We shall show that a necessary and sufficient condition for the metric transitivity of $\boldsymbol{\xi}$ is that the spectral measure $F(d\lambda)$ be continuous; that is, that the spectral measure of each point λ be zero.

Metric transitivity means that for any random variable $\eta \in \boldsymbol{H}_\xi$ the time averages $H(s, t)/(t-s)$, defined by (5.3), converge to the expectation $\boldsymbol{E}\eta$. To prove our assertion, we must verify this for all $\eta \in \boldsymbol{H}_\xi$. It is obviously sufficient to verify it only for a set of random variables which is everywhere dense in $\boldsymbol{H}_\xi$, and, without restriction of generality, we may suppose $\boldsymbol{\xi}$ to be a real process.

We have already seen in Section 4 of this chapter that the set of "trigonometric polynomials" of the form

$$\eta = \sum_{u_1,\dots,u_N} c(u_1, \dots, u_N) \exp\left\{i \sum_{j=1}^{N} \xi_{k_j}(t_j) u_j\right\}$$

is everywhere dense in $\boldsymbol{H}_\xi$. Because of the linearity of the operation of "time averaging," it is sufficient to consider only the "monomials"

$$\eta = \exp\left\{ i \sum_{j=1}^{N} \xi_{k_j}(t_j) u_j \right\}.$$

We will further suppose that ξ is one-dimensional; the proof of our assertion on metric transitivity in the multi-dimensional case, which remains in principle the same, would be outwardly more cumbersome because of the amount of unavoidable notation.

Thus, let us consider a random variable η of the form

$$\eta = \exp\left\{ i \sum_{j=1}^{N} \xi(t_j) u_j \right\}.$$

As is well-known,†

$$m = \boldsymbol{E}\eta = \boldsymbol{E}\left[\exp\left\{ i \sum_{j=1}^{N} \xi(t_j) u_j \right\} \right] = \exp\left\{ -\frac{1}{2} \sum_{k,j=1}^{N} B(t_k - t_j) u_k u_j \right\},$$

where $B(t)$ is the correlation function of ξ. We set

$$\eta_0 = \eta - m, \qquad \eta(t) = U_t \eta, \qquad \eta_0(t) = U_t \eta_0.$$

The correlation function $B_0(t)$ of the process $\{\eta_0(t)\}$ is

$$B_0(t) = \boldsymbol{E}\eta_0(t)\bar{\eta}_0 = \boldsymbol{E}\eta(t)\bar{\eta} - m^2.$$

If we show that

$$B_0(t) = \int e^{i\lambda t} F_0(d\lambda),$$

where $F_0(\{0\}) = 0$, then it follows from the results of Section 6, Chapter I, that we will have proven the ergodicity of the process η_0. Since η is an arbitrary variable of the type being considered, this will mean that ξ is metrically transitive.

We have

$$\boldsymbol{E}\eta(t)\bar{\eta} = \boldsymbol{E}\left[\exp\left\{ i \sum_{k=1}^{N} (\xi(t_k + t) - \xi(t_k)) u_k \right\} \right]$$

$$= \exp\left\{ -\frac{1}{2} \sum_{k,j=1}^{N} C_{kj}(t) u_k u_j \right\},$$

where

$$C_{kj}(t) = \boldsymbol{E}[\xi(t_k + t) - \xi(t_k)][\xi(t_j + t) - \xi(t_j)], \qquad k, j = \overline{1, N}.$$

It is easy to compute that

$$C_{kj}(t) = 2B(t_k - t_j) - B(t + t_k - t_j) - B(t + t_j - t_k).$$

† $\boldsymbol{E}\eta$ is the value of the characteristic function of the N-dimensional normal distribution of the variable $\{\xi(t_1), \cdots, \xi(t_N)\}$ at the point $(u_1, \ldots, u_N)$.

Further,

$$D_{kj}(t) = B(t + t_k - t_j) + B(t + t_j - t_k)$$
$$= \int e^{i\lambda t}[e^{i\lambda(t_k - t_j)} + e^{i\lambda(t_j - t_k)}]F(d\lambda) = 2\int e^{i\lambda t}\cos\lambda(t_k - t_j)F(d\lambda) ,$$

where $F(d\lambda)$ is the spectral measure of ξ, and

$$D(t) = \int \frac{1}{2}\sum_{k,j=1}^{N} D_{kj}(t)u_k u_j = \int e^{i\lambda t}\left[\sum_{k,j=1} u_k u_j \cos\lambda(t_k - t_j)\right]F(d\lambda) .$$

The function $\cos\lambda t$ is positive definite. Let

$$G(d\lambda) = \left[\sum_{k,j=1}^{N} u_k u_j \cos\lambda(t_k - t_j)\right]F(d\lambda) .$$

Then

$$D(t) = \int e^{i\lambda t}G(d\lambda) , \qquad \boldsymbol{E}\eta(t)\bar{\eta} = m^2 \exp\{D(t)\} ,$$

and

$$B_0(t) = m^2[e^{D(t)} - 1] = m^2 \sum_{k=1}^{\infty} \frac{[D(t)]^k}{k!} .$$

The function $[D(t)]^k$ can be represented in the form

$$[D(t)]^k = \int e^{i\lambda t}G_k(d\lambda) ,$$

where $G_k(d\lambda)$ is the kth convolution of the measure $G(d\lambda)$:

$$G_{k+1}(\Delta) = \int G(\Delta - \lambda)G_k(d\lambda) , \qquad G_1(d\lambda) = G(d\lambda) ,$$

for any Borel set Δ.

We have

$$B_0(t) = m^2 \sum_{k=1}^{\infty} \frac{[D(t)]^k}{k!} = m^2 \sum_{k=1}^{\infty} \frac{1}{k!}\int e^{i\lambda t}G_k(d\lambda)$$
$$= \int e^{i\lambda t}\left[m^2 \sum_{k=1}^{\infty} \frac{1}{k!}G_k(d\lambda)\right] = \int e^{i\lambda t}F_0(d\lambda) ,$$

from which

$$F_0(d\lambda) = m^2 \sum_{k=1}^{\infty} \frac{1}{k!}G_k(d\lambda) .$$

If the spectral measure $F(d\lambda)$ of ξ is continuous, then obviously $G_k(d\lambda)$, and with it also the spectral measure $F_0(d\lambda)$ of η_0, is continuous. We have therefore proved that the continuity of the spectral measure of a Gaussian process is a sufficient condition for its metric transitivity.

If now the spectral measure $F(\{\lambda_0\})$ of some point λ_0 is different from zero, then the value $\Phi(\{\lambda_0\})$ of the random spectral measure of ξ is a proper function of the shift operators U_t:

$$U_t\Phi(\{\lambda_0\}) = e^{i\lambda_0 t}\Phi(\{\lambda_0\}) .$$

If ξ were metrically transitive, then the random variable $|\Phi(\{\lambda_0\})|^2$ would have to be a constant with probability 1 (see Lemma 7.1, below). But, by Theorem 6.1 of Chapter I, $\Phi(\{\lambda_0\})$ is the limit (in the mean) of the Gaussian random variables $(1/t)H(0, t)$, the time averages of the wide-sense stationary process η, $\eta(t) = e^{i\lambda_0 t}\xi(t)$, and is therefore a Gaussian random variable with mean zero (as ξ was assumed to have mean zero). Consequently, $|\Phi(\{\lambda_0\})|^2$ could not be a nonzero constant, which contradiction shows that ξ cannot be metrically transitive.

Let us turn to the consideration of a general stationary process ξ. It turns out that the property of metric transitivity is a spectral property of the family $\{U_t\}$ of unitary shift operators in the space $\boldsymbol{H}_\xi$.

We recall that a real number λ is said to be an eigenvalue of the unitary group $\{U_t\}$, if there exists a nonzero element $\eta \in \boldsymbol{H}_\xi$ (a proper function) for which

$$U_t\eta = e^{i\lambda t}\eta \tag{6.4}$$

for all t. The collection of elements satisfying (6.4) forms a subspace in $\boldsymbol{H}_\xi$; when this subspace has dimension 1, the eigenvalue λ is said to be *simple*.

Theorem 6.1. *In order that the stationary process ξ be metrically transitive, it is necessary and sufficient that every eigenvalue of the unitary family $\{U_t\}$ be simple.*

Proof. The sufficiency of the condition is trivial, since the constant random variables are invariant; that is, 0 is an eigenvalue. Since it is simple, there are no invariant random variables besides the constants.

Suppose that ξ is metrically transitive, and some eigenvalue λ has two linearly independent proper functions η_1 and η_2:

$$U_t\eta_k = e^{i\lambda t}\eta_k , \qquad k = 1, 2 . \tag{6.5}$$

From (3.19) we obtain

$$U_t(\eta_1\bar{\eta}_2) = U_t\eta_1\overline{U_t\eta_2} = \eta_1\bar{\eta}_2 , \tag{6.6}$$

that is, the product $\eta_1\bar{\eta}_2$ is an invariant random variable. Consequently, by Lemma 7.1 below, it is a constant, together with $|\eta_1|$ and $|\eta_2|$, which contradicts the linear independence of η_1 and η_2. Thus, λ cannot have two linearly independent proper functions, and is therefore simple. ∎

7. Metrically transitive stationary processes with discrete spectra

Let us first consider some properties of the proper functions of the shift operators U_t of a metrically transitive stationary process $\boldsymbol{\xi} = \{\xi_k(t)\}_{k=\overline{1,n}}$.

Let η_λ be a proper function corresponding to the eigenvalue λ:

$$U_t\eta_\lambda = e^{i\lambda t}\eta_\lambda \,. \tag{7.1}$$

Lemma 7.1. *The random variable* $\rho_\lambda = |\eta_\lambda|$ *is a constant with probability* 1.

Proof. By virtue of properties (3.19),

$$U_t\bar{\eta}_\lambda = e^{-i\lambda t}\bar{\eta}_\lambda \,, \qquad U_t\rho_\lambda^2 = U_t\eta_\lambda\bar{\eta}_\lambda = \rho_\lambda^2 \,, \tag{7.2}$$

and we see that ρ_λ^2 is invariant. By virtue of the metric transitivity of $\boldsymbol{\xi}$, it is a constant with probability 1. Consequently, ρ_λ is also a constant with probability 1. ∎

Thus, if

$$\eta_\lambda = \rho_\lambda e^{i\theta_\lambda} \tag{7.3}$$

is the polar decomposition of the proper function η_λ, then

$$U_t\eta_\lambda = \rho_\lambda e^{i[\lambda t + \theta_\lambda]} \,. \tag{7.4}$$

Let us now consider some arbitrary finite collection Λ_N of eigenvalues which, for certain integers m_λ, satisfy the relation

$$\sum_{\lambda \in \Lambda_N} m_\lambda \lambda \equiv 0 \qquad (\text{mod } 2\pi) \tag{7.5}$$

(in the discrete-parameter case),

$$\sum_{\lambda \in \Lambda_N} m_\lambda \lambda = 0 \tag{7.6}$$

(in the continuous-parameter case).

Lemma 7.2. *If the eigenvalues* λ, $\lambda \in \Lambda_N$, *satisfy* (7.5) *in the discrete-parameter case, or* (7.6) *in the continuous-parameter case, and* η_λ, $\lambda \in \Lambda_N$, *are corresponding proper functions, then the random variables* $\theta_\lambda = \arg \eta_\lambda$ *satisfy, with probability* 1, *the relation*

$$\sum_{\lambda \in \Lambda_N} m_\lambda \theta_\lambda \equiv \varphi \qquad (\text{mod } 2\pi) \,, \tag{7.7}$$

where φ *is some constant.*

Proof. The random variable η of the form

$$\eta = \exp\left\{i \sum_{\lambda \in \Lambda_N} m_\lambda \theta_\lambda\right\} = \prod_{\lambda \in \Lambda_N} [e^{i\theta_\lambda}]^{m_\lambda}$$

is invariant, because

$$U_t\eta = \exp\left\{i \sum_{\lambda \in \Lambda_N} m_\lambda[\theta_\lambda + \lambda t]\right\} = \exp\left\{it \sum_{\lambda \in \Lambda_N} m_\lambda \lambda\right\}\eta = \eta ,$$

and therefore η must be a constant. Consequently, the variable

$$\varphi = \arg \eta \equiv \sum_{\lambda \in \Lambda_N} m_\lambda \theta_\lambda \qquad (\mathrm{mod}\ 2\pi)$$

must be a constant. ▮

Let us consider a one-dimensional stationary process $\boldsymbol{\xi}$ with a discrete spectrum, that is, such that $\boldsymbol{E}|\xi(t)|^2 < \infty$, and whose spectral representation has the form

$$\xi(t) = \sum_{\lambda \in \Lambda} e^{i\lambda t}\Phi(\{\lambda\}) . \tag{7.8}$$

(Here the summation is extended over a discrete set Λ, the spectrum of $\boldsymbol{\xi}$.)

Theorem 7.1. *A necessary and sufficient condition for the metric transitivity of a stationary one-dimensional process $\boldsymbol{\xi}$ with a discrete spectrum Λ is the following: For any $\lambda \in \Lambda$ the variable $\rho_\lambda = |\Phi(\{\lambda\})|$ is a constant with probability* 1, *and if Λ_N is any subset of Λ for which integers m_λ, $\lambda \in \Lambda_N$, exist satisfying* (7.5) *in the discrete-parameter case, or* (7.6) *in the continuous-parameter case, then* (7.7) *holds with φ a constant, where $\theta_\lambda = \arg \Phi(\{\lambda\})$.*

Proof. Each $\Phi(\{\lambda\})$ belongs to $\boldsymbol{H}_\xi$ and is a proper function of the U_t with eigenvalue λ. As a consequence of this and Lemma 7.2, the conditions of the theorem are necessary.

Suppose that the conditions of the theorem hold. In this case the set of all linear combinations of random variables of the form

$$\eta = \exp\left\{i \sum_{\lambda \in \Lambda_N} m_\lambda \theta_\lambda\right\} , \tag{7.9}$$

where Λ_N is an arbitrary finite set of points in Λ, is everywhere dense in $\boldsymbol{H}_\xi$. In fact, the set of all continuous functions, with compact supports, of finite numbers of the $e^{i\theta_\lambda}$ are obviously everywhere dense in $\boldsymbol{H}_\xi$, and such functions can be expanded in uniformly convergent series with terms of the form (7.9).

In view of this, to prove the metric transitivity of the process $\boldsymbol{\xi}$ it is sufficient to show that every stationary process $\boldsymbol{\eta}$, $\eta(t) = U_t\eta_0$, where η_0 is of the form (7.9), is ergodic.

Suppose, for example, that t is a discrete parameter. Then Λ is a subset of the interval $[-\pi, \pi]$. Obviously, η_0 is an eigenfunction of the U_t, with eigenvalue λ_0, where

$$\lambda_0 \equiv \sum_{\lambda \in \Lambda_N} m_\lambda \lambda \qquad (\text{mod } 2\pi) .$$

The correlation function of η is $B(t) = e^{i\lambda_0 t}$, from which one sees that the spectral measure of η is concentrated at the point λ_0, and so, by Theorem 6.1 of Chapter I, η is ergodic, if $\lambda_0 \neq 0$. If $\lambda_0 = 0$, then η_0 is a constant, since by (7.7) $\arg \eta_0$ is a constant;

$$\arg \eta_0 \equiv \sum_{\lambda \in \Lambda_N} m_\lambda \theta_\lambda \qquad (\text{mod } 2\pi) .$$

The same arguments hold in the continuous-parameter case, only

$$\lambda_0 = \sum_{\lambda \in \Lambda_N} m_\lambda \lambda . \quad \blacksquare$$

We see that the probability measure $P(d\lambda)$ on the σ-algebra $\mathfrak{A}_\xi$ of a metrically transitive stationary process ξ of the form (7.8) (with a discrete spectrum Λ) is uniquely defined by specifying the positive numbers

$$\rho_\lambda = |\Phi(\{\lambda\})| , \tag{7.10}$$

for which

$$\sum_{\lambda \in \Lambda} \rho_\lambda^2 = \boldsymbol{E}|\xi(t)|^2 < \infty ,$$

and the finite-dimensional joint distributions of the random variables

$$\theta_\lambda = \arg \Phi(\{\lambda\}) , \qquad \lambda \in \Lambda . \tag{7.11}$$

Let us clarify the nature of these distributions. This can be done most effectively by turning to the basic notions of the theory of commutative locally compact topological groups.†

Let K denote the one-dimensional torus (the additive topological group of real numbers θ, in which any two numbers which are equal mod 2π are identified).

Let us number the points of the spectrum Λ of the stationary process ξ in a sequence $\{\lambda_k\}$, $k = 1, 2, \ldots$, and denote by K^Λ the direct product of countably many replicas of K. The infinite-dimensional torus K^Λ is the additive topological group of all sequences $\theta = \{\theta_k\}$, $k = 1, 2, \ldots$, of real numbers θ_k, where we do not distinguish between numbers which are equal mod 2π. The system of neighborhoods of the topological space K^Λ is defined by the system of all cylinder sets Γ of the form

$$\Gamma = \{\theta : \theta_{k_1} \in \Gamma_1, \ldots, \theta_{k_N} \in \Gamma_N\} , \tag{7.12}$$

where $k_1, \ldots, k_N$ is an arbitrary finite family of positive integers, and $\Gamma_1, \ldots, \Gamma_N$ are neighborhoods in the one-dimensional torus K.

† For the reader who is not familiar with these notions, we recommend the book by Pontryagin.[*]

The sequence of random variables θ_{λ_k}, $k = 1, 2, \ldots$, induces a probability measure $P(d\theta)$ in K^Λ:

$$P(\Gamma) = P\{\theta_{\lambda_{k_1}} \in \Gamma_1, \ldots, \theta_{\lambda_{k_N}} \in \Gamma_N\}$$

for any neighborhood Γ of the form (7.12). The problem consists in clarifying the nature of this measure.

Let G denote the closure in K of the set of points $\theta = \{\lambda_k t\}$, where t ranges over all of its values as a parameter (either all integers or all real numbers). Obviously, G is a closed subgroup of K^Λ. The probability measure $P(d\theta)$ is invariant relative to translations by the elements of this subgroup, since, by virtue of the stationarity of ξ, the finite-dimensional distributions of the random variables $\{\theta_{\lambda_k}\}$, $k = 1, 2, \ldots$, are identical to those of the random variables $\{\theta_{\lambda_k} + \lambda_k t\}$, $k = 1, 2, \ldots$, for any t. Describing the measure $P(d\theta)$ reduces, essentially, to describing the subgroup G.

Let us consider the character group M of K^Λ. This group is the additive group of all sequences $m = \{m_k\}$, $k = 1, 2, \ldots$, of integers, where only a finite number of the m_k are different from zero.

Every element $m \in M$ defines a homomorphism of K^Λ into the group K:

$$m(\theta) = \sum_k m_k \theta_k \,. \tag{7.13}$$

The subgroup G is uniquely specified by its annihilator (M, G), that is, the collection of characters m such that

$$m(\theta) = 0\,, \qquad \theta \in G\,. \tag{7.14}$$

While the structure of the subgroup G is rather difficult to describe, the structure of its annihilator (M, G) is very simply described. Namely, (M, G) consists, obviously, of just those points $m = \{m_k\}$ for which

$$\sum_k m_k \lambda_k \equiv 0 \qquad (\mathrm{mod}\ 2\pi) \tag{7.15}$$

in the discrete-parameter case, or

$$\sum_k m_k \lambda_k = 0 \tag{7.16}$$

in the continuous-parameter case.

Further, since ξ is metrically transitive, any set $\Gamma \subseteq K^\Lambda$ which is invariant relative to translation by the elements $\theta \in G$ must have P-measure either zero or 1. Let us denote by G_θ the coset with respect to G obtained by adding the elements of the subgroup G with some element $\theta \in K^\Lambda$; $G_\theta = G + \theta$. Every coset G_θ is an invariant set, and any invariant set is the union of sets of the form G_θ. We assert that the probability measure $P(d\theta)$ is concentrated on one coset G_θ. To show this, we note that the factor group K^{Λ}/G is a regular compact space with a Borel measure P such that the measure of any Borel set in K^{Λ}/G equals 0 or 1. The system of all closed subsets of K^{Λ}/G having measure 1 has the finite intersection property. The intersection of the members of this system of closed sets has measure 1 and consists of a single point G_θ; $P(G_\theta) = 1$.

Indeed, if this intersection F were such that $P(F) < 1$, there would exist an open set $A \supset F$ with $P(A) < 1$. But by compactness, A would contain some member of the system in question; hence we would have $P(A) = 1$, a contradiction. Furthermore, if F contained more than one point, the P-measure of each point of F would equal 0, hence we could find an open set A, $P(A) = 0$, such that $F - A \neq F$. Since $P(F - A) = 1$ and $F - A$ is closed, this would contradict the definition of F.

Thus, the probability measure $P(d\theta)$ is concentrated entirely on one coset $G_\theta = G + \theta$ and is invariant with respect to shifts by the elements of the subgroup G. It is well-known that such a measure is unique. Namely, if $P_0(d\theta)$ is the Haar measure on the subgroup G, then

$$P(\Gamma) = P_0(\Gamma - \theta) \tag{7.17}$$

for any neighborhood Γ in the coset G_θ ($\Gamma - \theta$ is a neighborhood in the subgroup G).

In particular, if the points of the spectrum of the stationary process $\boldsymbol{\xi}$ are not rationally related [i.e., if for no integers $m(\lambda)$, not all identically zero, can (7.15), in the case of discrete t, or (7.16), in the case of continuous t, hold], then the subgroup G coincides with the entire group K^{Λ} [its annihilator (M, G) consists of only the zero element], and the measure $P(d\theta)$ is Haar measure on the countable-dimensional torus K^{Λ}. This means that the random variables $\theta(\lambda_k)$, $k = 1, 2, \ldots$, are uniformly distributed on the interval $[-\pi, \pi]$ and are mutually independent.

We have considered one-dimensional stationary processes with discrete spectrum. In the case of a multi-dimensional stationary process $\boldsymbol{\xi} = \{\xi_k(t)\}_{k=\overline{1,n}}$ nothing new arises. Only, the random variables $\Phi_k(\lambda)$ corresponding to the different components $\xi_k(t)$ and the same λ, $\lambda \in \Lambda$, differ from one another by a constant factor.

8. The decomposition of a stationary process into metrically transitive components

Let $\boldsymbol{\xi} = \{\xi_k(t)\}_{k=\overline{1,n}}$ be a strictly stationary process, Ω the corresponding space of elementary events ω, and $P(d\omega)$ the probability measure on the σ-algebra $\mathfrak{A}_\xi$ [the smallest σ-algebra of ω-sets relative to which the values $\xi_k(t) = \xi_k(\omega, t)$ of $\boldsymbol{\xi}$ are measurable].

Suppose that there exists a family of probability measures $P(d\omega, \omega')$, $\omega' \in \Omega$, defined on $\mathfrak{A}_\xi$, with the following properties:

1. For any set $A \in \mathfrak{A}_\xi$, the function $P(A, \omega')$ of ω' is measurable relative to the σ-algebra $\mathfrak{J}$ of invariant sets, and

$$P(AB) = \int_B P(A, \omega')P(d\omega') \tag{8.1}$$

for every $B \in \mathfrak{J}$. In other words, $P(d\omega, \omega')$, $\omega' \in \Omega$, is a conditional probability distribution relative to the σ-algebra $\mathfrak{J}$.

2. For any ω', ω'', the measures $P(d\omega, \omega')$ and $P(d\omega, \omega'')$ either coincide or are mutually singular.

3. If $\xi_k(\omega, t)$ is considered as a random variable relative to the probability measure $P(d\omega, \omega')$, then for every ω' the $\xi_k(\omega, t)$ form a multi-dimensional strictly stationary random process. To distinguish it from the original process $\boldsymbol{\xi}$, we will denote such a process by $\boldsymbol{\xi}_{\omega'}$.

4. Each of the $\boldsymbol{\xi}_{\omega'}$ is metrically transitive.

Then we will say that *we have a decomposition*

$$\boldsymbol{\xi} = \langle \boldsymbol{\xi}_{\omega'} \rangle \tag{8.2}$$

of the stationary process $\boldsymbol{\xi}$ *into metrically transitive components* $\boldsymbol{\xi}_{\omega'}$, $\omega' \in \Omega$.

In order to formulate sufficient conditions for the existence of such a family, we need several definitions.

We will say that a σ-algebra $\mathfrak{A}$ has a countable number of generators if it is generated by a countable system of sets A_j, $j = 1, 2, \ldots$; i.e., $\mathfrak{A}$ is the smallest σ-algebra containing all the A_j.

Further, we will say that a σ-algebra $\mathfrak{A}'$, $\mathfrak{A}' \subseteq \mathfrak{A}$, coincides mod 0 with the σ-algebra $\mathfrak{A}$, if for any set $A \in \mathfrak{A}$ there is a set $A' \in \mathfrak{A}'$ which differs from A only by a set of probability zero: $P(A \circ A') = 0$.

Let us further define a perfect measure. A probability measure $P(d\omega)$ on a σ-algebra $\mathfrak{A}$ is said to be *perfect* if every real random variable η [that is, function $\eta(\omega)$, measurable relative to $\mathfrak{A}$] has the following property; for any set Γ on the real line such that the ω-set $\{\omega : \eta(\omega) \in \Gamma\}$ belongs to $\mathfrak{A}$, one has

$$P\{\omega : \eta(\omega) \in \Gamma\} = \inf P\{\eta(\omega) \in \Gamma'\} , \tag{8.3}$$

where the infimum is taken over all Borel sets Γ' containing Γ.

Theorem 8.1. *A measurable stationary process* $\boldsymbol{\xi} = \{\xi_k(t)\}_{k=\overline{1,n}}$ *such* *that the σ-algebra* $\mathfrak{A}_\xi$ *has a countable number of generators and the probability measure* $P(d\omega)$*, considered on* $\mathfrak{A}_\xi$*, is perfect, always admits a decomposition into metrically transitive components.*

Remark. It should be mentioned that the requirements placed upon the process $\boldsymbol{\xi}$ are automatically fulfilled when the parameter t is discrete and the process is directly defined. In the continuous parameter case these conditions can be fulfilled (for stochastically continuous and directly defined processes) by changing each of the values $\xi_k(t) = \xi_k(\omega, t)$ on at most an ω-set of probability zero.

Thus, Theorem 8.1 has the following corollary;

Theorem 8.2. *For every directly defined and stochastically continuous process* $\boldsymbol{\xi}$ *there exists a process* $\tilde{\boldsymbol{\xi}}$ *which is equivalent to it and which admits a decomposition into metrically transitive components.*

The proof of Theorem 8.1 rests upon a number of lemmas, whose validity will be established under the hypotheses of the theorem.

Lemma 8.1. *The conditional probability distribution* $P(d\omega, \omega')$ *exists relative to any σ-algebra* $\mathfrak{B}$, $\mathfrak{B} \subseteq \mathfrak{A}_\xi$.

Proof. We remark that any σ-algebra $\mathfrak{A}$ with a countable number of generators can be generated by some random variable η (that is, the smallest σ-algebra with respect to which η is measurable coincides with $\mathfrak{A}$). For example, we can take for η the so-called characteristic function of the sequence of sets A_j which generate $\mathfrak{A}$, defined by

$$\eta(\omega) = \sum_{j=1}^{\infty} \frac{2}{3^j} \chi_j(\omega) ,$$

where $\chi_j(\omega) = \chi_{A_j}(\omega)$ is the characteristic function of A_j. (This follows from the observation that each A_j is the inverse image of those points of the Cantor set such that the jth term in their ternary expansion equals 2.)

If $P(d\omega)$ is perfect, then there exists an ω-set Ω', with $P(\Omega') = 1$, such that the set of values which η takes on this set is a Borel set. This remark enables us to carry out the remainder of the proof in the same way as the proof of Theorem 9.5 on page 31 of Doob's book[*].

Lemma 8.2. *There exists a σ-algebra* $\mathfrak{J}'$ *of invariant sets, with a countable set of generators, which coincides* mod 0 *with the σ-algebra* $\mathfrak{J}$ *of all invariant sets.*†

† It should be observed that a σ-subalgebra of a countably generated σ-algebra need not be countably generated; consider the Borel sets of the real line and the σ-subalgebra consisting of all sets which are either countable or have countable complement.

Proof. Let us denote by $\boldsymbol{H}_0$ the subspace of invariant random variables in the Hilbert space $\boldsymbol{H}_\xi$. Since $\boldsymbol{H}_\xi$ is separable (see Section 4 of this Chapter), $\boldsymbol{H}_0$ is separable. Let η_k, $k = 1, 2, \ldots$ be an orthonormal basis in $\boldsymbol{H}_0$, and let $\mathfrak{J}'$ be the smallest σ-algebra relative to which all of the η_k are measurable. Obviously, $\mathfrak{J}'$ has a countable set of generators. Since every function in $\boldsymbol{H}_0$ is the limit in mean square of finite linear combinations of the η_k, it is clear that $\mathfrak{J}'$ coincides mod 0 with $\mathfrak{J}$. ▮

Obviously, a conditional probability distribution $P(d\omega, \omega')$ relative to $\mathfrak{J}'$ is at the same time a conditional probability distribution relative to $\mathfrak{J}$.

Lemma 8.3. *If $P(d\omega, \omega')$ is a conditional probability distribution relative to a σ-algebra $\mathfrak{J}'$ (with a countable number of generators), then there is a set N, $P(N) = 0$, such that if ω' is not in N, then*

$$P(B, \omega') = \begin{cases} 1 & \text{for } \omega' \in B, \\ 0 & \text{for } \omega' \notin B \end{cases} \tag{8.4}$$

for all $B \in \mathfrak{J}'$.

Proof. For any $B \in \mathfrak{J}'$ we have

$$\int_A P(B, \omega') P(d\omega') = P(A \cap B) = \int_A \chi_B(\omega') P(d\omega')$$

for any $A \in \mathfrak{J}'$, by the definition of a conditional probability distribution. Since $P(B, \omega')$ is measurable relative to $\mathfrak{J}'$, $P(B, \omega') = \chi_B(\omega')$ with probability 1, and so (8.4) holds for almost all ω', for each fixed $B \in \mathfrak{J}'$.

Let B_k, $k = 1, 2, \ldots$, be the generators of $\mathfrak{J}'$. For each B_k, (8.4) can be violated only for ω' in a set N_k of probability zero. We set $N = \bigcup_k N_k$. Obviously, (8.4) holds for any set B which is the intersection of finitely many of the B_k, for $\omega' \notin N$. In fact, if $B = \bigcap_j B_{k_j}$ and $\omega' \in B$, $\omega' \notin N$, then $P(B_{k_j}, \omega') = 1$ for each j, and therefore $P(B, \omega') = 1$. For $\omega' \notin B \cup N$, we have $P(B_{k_j}, \omega') = 0$ for some j; hence $P(B, \omega') = 0$. Further, if B is any set in $\mathfrak{J}'$, then, as is well-known,

$$P(B, \omega') = \inf_{B^{(j)}} \sum_j P(B^{(j)}, \omega'),$$

where the $B^{(j)}$ are finite intersections of the B_k, and the infimum is taken over all families $\{B^{(j)}\}$ such that $B \subseteq \bigcup_j B^{(j)}$. If $\omega' \notin N$ and $\omega' \in B$, then at least one $B^{(j)}$ always contains ω', and so $P(B^{(j)}, \omega') = 1$. Consequently, $P(B, \omega') = 1$. If $\omega' \notin B$, then $\omega' \in \Omega - B$, and, as we have just seen, $P(\Omega - B, \omega') = 1$. Therefore, $P(B, \omega') = 0$.

Lemma 8.4. *If $P(d\omega, \omega')$ is a conditional probability distribution* *relative to the σ-algebra $\mathfrak{F}'$ of Lemma* 8.2, *then the random processes $\xi_{\omega'}$ will be strictly stationary for almost all ω'.*

Proof. We may assume, without loss of generality, that the countable set of generators A_k, $k = 1, 2, \ldots$, of the σ-algebra $\mathfrak{A}_\xi$ has been selected from the cylinder sets of the form†

$$A = \{\omega : \xi(\omega, s) < x\} .$$

(We will consider the stationary process ξ one-dimensional.)

It is sufficient for us to prove that for any set A of the algebra $\mathscr{A}$ generated by the A_k we have

$$P(A_t, \omega') = P(A, \omega')$$

for all ω' outside some fixed set of probability zero, and for all t. For definiteness we will consider the more difficult continuous-parameter case, and to simplify the notation we take $A = \{\omega : \xi(\omega, 0) < x\}$.

Let us consider the direct product $\Omega \times R$, where R is the space of value of the parameter t (i.e., the real line), and the probability distribution $P \times Q$ on the σ-algebra $\mathfrak{A}_\xi \times \mathfrak{B}$, where $\mathfrak{B}$ is the family of Borel sets of the line, and Q is the measure $\exp(-x^2)\, dx/\sqrt{\pi}$.

For each t' let $Q(dt, t')$ be the probability measure concentrated at the point t'; i.e.,

$$Q(\Delta, t') = \begin{cases} 1 & \text{for } \Delta \ni t' , \\ 0 & \text{for } \Delta \not\ni t' . \end{cases}$$

It is easy to verify that the probability distributions

$$P \times Q\{\cdot, (\omega', t')\} = P(d\omega, \omega') \times Q(dt, t')$$

are the conditional probability distributions of $P \times Q$ relative to the σ-algebra $\mathfrak{F}' \times \mathfrak{B}$.

We put

$$\Gamma = \{(\omega, t) : \xi(\omega, t) < x\} .$$

Then Γ is measurable, and if

$$\Gamma_t = \{\omega : (\omega, t) \in \Gamma\} ,$$

then

$$P \times Q\{\Gamma, (\omega', t')\} = \int_{-\infty}^{\infty} P(\Gamma_t, \omega') Q(dt, t') = P(\Gamma_{t'}, \omega') .$$

† Indeed, in the discrete-parameter case the σ-algebra $\mathfrak{A}_\xi$ is generated by the countable family of cylinder sets of the indicated form, with x a rational number. In the continuous-parameter case, the validity of the assumption in the text follows from this remark, combined with the well-known fact that for any set A in $\sigma(\mathsf{M})$, the σ-algebra generated by an uncountable family M of sets, there exists a countable subfamily I of M such that $A \in \sigma(\mathsf{I})$.

Now it is obvious, as a matter of fact, that $\Gamma_0 = A_0$, and $P(\Gamma_{t'}, \omega') = P(A_{t'}, \omega')$. Let B be any invariant set (with $B \in \mathfrak{J}'$) and Δ any Borel set of the line. On the one hand,

$$P \times Q\{\Gamma \cap (B \times \Delta)\} = \int_{\Delta} P(\Gamma_t B) Q(dt)$$

$$= \int_{\Delta} P(A_t B) Q(dt) = P(AB) \cdot Q(\Delta) ,$$

and, on the other hand,

$$P \times Q\{\Gamma \cap (B \times \Delta)\} = \int_{B}\int_{\Delta} P \times Q\{\Gamma, (\omega', t')\} Q(dt') P(d\omega')$$

$$= \int_{B}\int_{\Delta} P(A_{t'}, \omega') Q(dt') P(d\omega') .$$

We see that

$$\int_{B}\int_{\Delta} [P(A_{t'}, \omega') - P(A, \omega')] Q(dt') P(d\omega') = 0$$

for all $B \in \mathfrak{J}'$ and $\Delta \in \mathfrak{B}$. It follows at once that for almost all ω' (excluding ω' from some set N_A of probability zero)

$$P(A_{t'}, \omega') = P(A, \omega')$$

for almost all t'.

Now the algebra $\mathscr{A}$, since it is generated by the countable family $\{A_k\}$, is itself countable. We set $N = \bigcup_{\mathscr{A}} N_A$. The relation which we have established for each fixed $A \in \mathscr{A}$ obviously extends to all $A \in \mathscr{A}$ for $\omega' \notin N$, and then to all the sets in $\mathfrak{A}_\xi$ (using, say, Theorem A, § 13 of Halmos[*]). Since this relation holds for almost all t', and for any t one can find t_1' and t_2' such that $t = t_1' + t_2'$, we have

$$P(A_t, \omega') = P((A_{t_2'})_{t_1'}, \omega') = P(A_{t_2'}, \omega') = P(A, \omega')$$

for $\omega' \notin N$. ▮

Lemma 8.5. *If a σ-algebra $\mathfrak{J}'$ with a countable number of generators coincides* mod 0 *with the σ-algebra $\mathfrak{J}$ of all invariant sets, then any conditional probability distribution, $P(d\omega, \omega')$, relative to $\mathfrak{J}'$, has the property that for almost every ω' the stationary process $\xi_{\omega'}$ is metrically transitive.*

Proof. As in the proof of the preceding lemma, we will assume, for simplicity, that the generators A_k, $k = 1, 2, \ldots$, of $\mathfrak{A}_\xi$ were chosen from the cylinder sets. Without restriction of generality, we may suppose that the set of all linear combinations of characteristic functions of these sets is everywhere dense in each of the Hilbert spaces $\boldsymbol{H}_{\xi_{\omega'}}$, since this can always be achieved by replacing the initial system A_k, $k = 1, 2, \ldots$, by the algebra generated by it. Let us take any set

A from this system, say $A = \{\omega : \xi(\omega, s) < x\}$ (to simplify the notation), and set $\eta(t) = \chi_{A_t}(\omega)$, where $A_t = \{\omega : \xi(\omega, s - t) < x\}$. We will establish the ergodicity of the stationary process $\boldsymbol{\eta}_{\omega'}$ by showing that

$$\lim_{T\to\infty} \frac{1}{T}\int_0^T \eta_{\omega'}(t)\,dt = \int_\Omega \eta_{\omega'}(\omega) P(d\omega, \omega')$$

almost everywhere relative to $P(d\omega, \omega')$. We draw attention to the fact that the random variable $\eta_{\omega'}(\omega)$, as a function of ω, is the same for all ω': $\eta_{\omega'}(\omega) = \eta(\omega)$. Setting $\tilde{\eta}(\omega) = \boldsymbol{E}\{\eta | \mathfrak{J}'\}$, we have

$$\begin{aligned} 0 &= \lim_{T\to\infty} \int_\Omega \left| \frac{1}{T}\int_0^T \eta(t)\,dt - \tilde{\eta}(\omega) \right|^2 P(d\omega) \\ &= \lim_{T\to\infty} \int_\Omega \left\{ \int_\Omega \left| \frac{1}{T}\int_0^T \eta_{\omega'}(t) - \tilde{\eta}_{\omega'}(\omega) \right|^2 P(d\omega, \omega') \right\} P(d\omega') \,. \end{aligned}$$

It is evident from this that the sequence of functions

$$\int_\Omega \left| \frac{1}{T}\int_0^T \eta_{\omega'}(t)\,dt - \tilde{\eta}_{\omega'} \right|^2 P(d\omega, \omega')$$

of ω' converges in probability to zero as $T \to \infty$. Consequently, there exists a sequence T_k, $k = 1, 2, \ldots$, for which

$$\lim_{T_k\to\infty} \int_\Omega \left| \frac{1}{T_k}\int_0^{T_k} \eta_{\omega'}(t)\,dt - \tilde{\eta}_{\omega'} \right|^2 P(d\omega, \omega') = 0$$

with probability 1. This relation shows that for almost all ω' one can take, for the random variable $\lim \int_0^T \eta_{\omega'}(t)\,dt/T$ (as a function of ω), $\tilde{\eta}(\omega) = \boldsymbol{E}\{\eta|\mathfrak{J}'\}$. But $\tilde{\eta}(\omega)$ is measurable relative to $\mathfrak{J}'$, and almost all of the measures $P(d\omega, \omega')$ assume only the values zero or 1 on the sets of $\mathfrak{J}'$. This means that for almost every ω' the random variable $\tilde{\eta}_{\omega'}(\omega)$ is constant almost everywhere relative to $P(d\omega, \omega')$. Thus, the "time average" $\int_0^T \eta_{\omega'}(t)\,dt/T$ for almost every stationary process $\boldsymbol{\eta}_{\omega'}$ has a constant limit (which depends upon ω'). By virtue of the arbitrariness of η, we conclude that for almost every ω' the stationary process $\boldsymbol{\xi}_{\omega'}$ is metrically transitive. ∎

Taken together, these lemmas prove the validity of Theorem 8.1.

Example 8.1. To illustrate the decomposition theorem, let us consider a stationary metrically transitive process $\boldsymbol{\eta}$ with zero mean, and a random variable η_0 which is independent of the process $\boldsymbol{\eta}$ [this means that $P(A_0 \cap A) = P(A_0)P(A)$ for any sets $A_0 \in \mathfrak{A}_{\eta_0}$ and $A \in \mathfrak{A}_\eta$]. The sums $\xi(t) = \eta_0 + \eta(t)$ constitute a stationary process, and the σ-algebra $\mathfrak{A}_{\eta_0}$ coincides mod 0 with the σ-algebra $\mathfrak{J}$ of invariant sets corresponding to the process $\boldsymbol{\xi}$.

We note that both $\mathfrak{A}_{\eta_0}$ and $\mathfrak{A}_\eta$ are contained in the σ-algebra $\mathfrak{A}_\xi$, because

$$\eta_0 = \lim_{T\to\infty} \frac{1}{T}\int_0^T \xi(t)\,dt\,.$$

Moreover, $\mathfrak{A}_\xi$ is the smallest σ-algebra containing $\mathfrak{A}_{\eta_0}$ and $\mathfrak{A}_\eta$. Therefore every probability measure on $\mathfrak{A}_\eta$ is uniquely defined by its values for all sets of the form $A_0 \cap A$, where $A_0 \in \mathfrak{A}_{\eta_0}$ and $A \in \mathfrak{A}_\eta$. The conditional probability distributions relative to $\mathfrak{J}$, $P(d\omega, \omega')$, relative to which the stationary processes $\xi_{\omega'}$ will be metrically transitive, are defined as follows:

$$P(A_0 \cap A, \omega') = \begin{cases} P(A) & \text{for } A_0 \ni \omega'\,, \\ 0 & \text{for } A_0 \not\ni \omega'\,, \end{cases}$$

for any $A_0 \in \mathfrak{A}_{\eta_0}$ and $A \in \mathfrak{A}_\eta$.

9. Regular stationary processes

Let $\boldsymbol{\xi} = \{\xi_k(t)\}_{k=\overline{1,n}}$ be a strictly stationary random process; we will say that it is *regular* if the σ-algebra $\mathfrak{A}^-$, defined by (6.2) as

$$\mathfrak{A}^- = \bigcap_t \mathfrak{A}^t_{-\infty}\,, \tag{9.1}$$

is trivial, that is, if it contains only ω-sets of probability either zero or 1.

As we have already seen in the previous section, as an example of a regular process one can take a sequence of independent identically distributed random variables.

The condition of regularity has a very simple meaning. Namely, denote by $\boldsymbol{H}^t_s$ the subspace in $\boldsymbol{H}_\xi$ formed by all random variables in $\boldsymbol{H}_\xi$ which have zero means and are measurable relative to the σ-algebra $\mathfrak{A}^t_s$. Then the regularity of $\boldsymbol{\xi}$ is obviously equivalent to the condition

$$\bigcap_t \boldsymbol{H}^t_{-\infty} = 0\,. \tag{9.2}$$

Relation (9.2) recalls the condition of linear regularity for wide-sense stationary processes (see Chapter II, Section 2) and is in fact substantially by stronger than the former. In particular, every process $\boldsymbol{\eta}$, $\eta(t) = U_t\eta_0$, where η_0 lies in any subspace $\boldsymbol{H}^s_{-\infty}$, $s < \infty$, must be linearly regular if (9.2) holds.

For Gaussian processes the concepts of regularity and linear regularity are equivalent. In fact, if the Gaussian process $\boldsymbol{\xi} = \{\xi_k(t)\}_{k=\overline{1,n}}$ (discrete parameter) is linearly regular, then the values of the process $\boldsymbol{\zeta} = \{\zeta_j(t)\}_{j=\overline{1,m}}$, which is fundamental for $\boldsymbol{\xi}$, being Gaussian and mutually uncorrelated, will be mutually independent.

On the basis of (3.8) of Chapter II, we can conclude that $\mathfrak{A}_{-\infty}^{t}$ is the smallest σ-algebra relative to which all the $\zeta_j(s)$, $s \leq t$, $j = \overline{1, m}$, are measurable, and therefore $\mathfrak{A}^{-}$ is trivial (see Example 6.1 earlier in this Chapter).

In the continuous-parameter case, the σ-algebra $\mathfrak{A}_{-\infty}^{t}$ corresponding to $\boldsymbol{\xi}$ is the smallest σ-algebra relative to which all values $\zeta_j(\Delta_j)$ of the random measure $\boldsymbol{\zeta}$ (which is fundamental for $\boldsymbol{\xi}$), $j = \overline{1, m}$, and $\Delta_j \subseteq (-\infty, t]$ are measurable. The values $\zeta_j(\Delta)$ of $\boldsymbol{\zeta}$ are independent for different j and also for nonintersecting sets Δ. The arguments in Example 6.1, which are also applicable to this case, again lead to the triviality of $\mathfrak{A}^{-}$.

Let us now consider an arbitrary regular process $\boldsymbol{\xi}$. The projection $\eta_{-\infty}^{t}$ of any $\eta \in \boldsymbol{H}_\xi$ on the subspace $\boldsymbol{H}_{-\infty}^{t}$ has the property that

$$\lim_{t \to -\infty} \eta_{-\infty}^{t} = 0 . \tag{9.3}$$

(See Lemma 2.1, Chapter II.)

For any $\zeta \in \boldsymbol{H}_{-\infty}^{t}$ we have

$$(\eta, \zeta) = (\eta_{-\infty}^{t}, \zeta) , \qquad |(\eta, \zeta)| \leq ||\eta_{-\infty}^{t}|| \, ||\zeta|| . \tag{9.4}$$

Let A be an arbitrary ω-set from $\mathfrak{A}_\xi$, and set

$$\eta = \chi_A - P(A) , \qquad \zeta = \chi_B - P(B) ,$$

where $B \in \mathfrak{A}_{-\infty}^{t}$. Applying the inequality in (9.4) to η and ζ, we obtain

$$|P(AB) - P(A)P(B)| \leq ||\eta_{-\infty}^{t}|| .$$

It follows that a regular process $\boldsymbol{\xi}$ has the following property:

$$\lim_{t \to -\infty} \sup_{B \in \mathfrak{A}_{-\infty}^{t}} |P(AB) - P(A)P(B)| = 0 \tag{9.5}$$

for any $A \in \mathfrak{A}_\xi$.

It is not difficult to see that condition (9.5) is actually equivalent to regularity. In fact, let B be any ω-set from the σ-algebra $\mathfrak{A}^{-}$ (B therefore belongs to every σ-algebra $\mathfrak{A}_{-\infty}^{t}$). Condition (9.5), for the sets $A = B$ and B, reduces to

$$P(B) = P(B)P(B) ,$$

which can only hold if either $P(B) = 0$ or $P(B) = 1$; this is, if the σ-algebra $\mathfrak{A}^{-}$ is trivial.

Consequently, we have proven the following result.

Theorem 9.1. *Condition* (9.5) *is a necessary and sufficient condition for the regularity of a stationary process* $\boldsymbol{\xi}$.

Further, we will call a stationary process $\boldsymbol{\xi}$ *completely regular*, if†

$$\alpha(\tau) = \sup_{\substack{A \in \mathfrak{A}_{-\infty}^{t} \\ B \in \mathfrak{A}_{t+\tau}^{\infty}}} |P(AB) - P(A)P(B)| \to 0 \tag{9.6}$$

as $\tau \to \infty$. Here, as before, $\mathfrak{A}_u^v$ denotes the σ-algebra of ω-sets generated by the variables $\xi_j(t)$, $u \leq t \leq v$.

Condition (9.6) in the definition of the complete regularity of the stationary process $\boldsymbol{\xi}$ means that, in the course of time, events concerning the "future" of the process become almost independent of events in the "past." We will use this condition in the proof of the central limit theorem.

10. Conditions for the complete regularity of Gaussian stationary processes

For any two systems $\{\xi'\} = \mathfrak{M}'$ and $\{\xi''\} = \mathfrak{M}''$ of real random variables ξ' and ξ'', having second moments, we introduce the index

$$\rho(\mathfrak{M}', \mathfrak{M}'') = \sup_{\substack{\xi' \in \mathfrak{M}' \\ \xi'' \in \mathfrak{M}''}} \frac{\boldsymbol{E}(\xi' - \boldsymbol{E}\xi')(\xi'' - \boldsymbol{E}\xi'')}{[\boldsymbol{E}(\xi' - \boldsymbol{E}\xi')^2 \boldsymbol{E}(\xi'' - \boldsymbol{E}\xi'')^2]^{1/2}} \,. \tag{10.1}$$

If $\mathfrak{M}'$ and $\mathfrak{M}''$ are the families of all random variables with finite second moments which are measurable relative to σ-algebras $\mathfrak{A}'$ and $\mathfrak{A}''$, respectively, then we call

$$\rho(\mathfrak{A}', \mathfrak{A}'') = \rho(\mathfrak{M}', \mathfrak{M}'') \tag{10.2}$$

the *maximal correlation coefficient* between $\mathfrak{A}'$ and $\mathfrak{A}''$. If we put

$$\alpha(\mathfrak{A}, \mathfrak{A}'') = \sup_{\substack{A' \in \mathfrak{A}' \\ A'' \in \mathfrak{A}''}} |P(A'A'') - P(A')P(A'')| \tag{10.3}$$

then, obviously, we always have

$$\alpha(\mathfrak{A}', \mathfrak{A}'') \leq \rho(\mathfrak{A}', \mathfrak{A}'') \,. \tag{10.4}$$

Now suppose that $\{\xi'\}$ and $\{\xi''\}$ are two collections of random variables such that any finite set $\xi_1', \ldots, \xi_m', \xi_1'', \ldots, \xi_n''$ has a Gaussian joint distribution; $\mathfrak{A}_{\xi'}$ and $\mathfrak{A}_{\xi''}$ are the smallest σ-algebras with respect to which all of the ξ' and ξ'', respectively, are measurable, and, finally, $H_{\xi'}$ and $H_{\xi''}$ are the closed (in mean square) linear manifolds generated by $\{\xi'\}$ and $\{\xi''\}$, respectively.

† By virtue of the stationarity of $\boldsymbol{\xi}$, the expression in the left side of (9.6) does not change under a simultaneous "shift" of the σ-algebras $\mathfrak{A}_{-\infty}^{t}$ and $\mathfrak{A}_{t+\tau}^{\infty}$, and therefore depends only upon τ.

Theorem 10.1. *The following equality holds:*

$$\rho(\mathfrak{A}_{\xi'}, \mathfrak{A}_{\xi''}) = \rho(H_{\xi'}, H_{\xi''}) . \tag{10.5}$$

Theorem 10.2. *The maximal correlation coefficient satisfies the following inequalities:*

$$\alpha(\mathfrak{A}_{\xi'}, \mathfrak{A}_{\xi''}) \leq \rho(\mathfrak{A}_{\xi'}, \mathfrak{A}_{\xi''}) \leq 2\pi\alpha(\mathfrak{A}_{\xi'}, \mathfrak{A}_{\xi''}) . \tag{10.6}$$

The proof of these theorems rests upon a number of lemmas.

Lemma 10.1. *Let $\{\xi'\}$ and $\{\xi''\}$ be two collections of finite numbers of real random variables having finite second moments. One can then choose a basis $\zeta_1', \ldots, \zeta_m'$ in $H_{\xi'}$ and a basis $\zeta_1'', \ldots, \zeta_n''$ in $H_{\xi''}$ such that all pairs from among these basis elements are uncorrelated with the possible exception of the pairs (ζ_k', ζ_k''), $k = 1, \ldots, \min(m, n)$.*

Proof. Let H be the (real) linear span of all of the ξ' and ξ''. As usual, we introduce a scalar product in H by $(h_1, h_2) = \boldsymbol{E}h_1h_2$, making it a unitary space (finite-dimensional Hilbert space). Let P' and P'' be the projections onto the subspaces $H_{\xi'}$ and $H_{\xi''}$, respectively, and set

$$P = P'P''P' .$$

The operator P is symmetric, and therefore there exists an orthogonal basis B in H consisting of its eigenvectors. Let η' be one of these, corresponding to the eigenvalue $\lambda \neq 0$, and let $\eta'' = P''\eta'$. We have

$$P'\eta' = \frac{1}{\lambda}P'P\eta' = \frac{1}{\lambda}P\eta' = \eta' ,$$
$$P'\eta'' = P'P''\eta' = P'P''P'\eta' = \lambda\eta' .$$

Let $\eta_1', \ldots, \eta_r'$ be the orthogonal system consisting of those elements of B corresponding to nonzero eigenvalues $\lambda_1, \ldots, \lambda_r$. We set

$$\eta_k'' = P''\eta_k', \qquad k = \overline{1, r} .$$

Then we have

$$(\eta_k'', \eta_j') = (\eta_k'', P'\eta_k') = (P'\eta_k'', \eta_j') = \lambda_k(\eta_k', \eta_j') = 0 ,$$
$$(\eta_k'', \eta_j'') = (\eta_k'', P''\eta_j') = (P''\eta_k'', \eta_j') = (\eta_k'', \eta_j') = 0 ,$$

for all $k \neq j$. Suppose further that $\eta' \in H_{\xi'}$ is an arbitrary element, orthogonal to $\eta_1', \ldots, \eta_r'$. Then η' is orthogonal to $H_{\xi''}$. Indeed,

$$\begin{aligned}(P''\eta', P''\eta') &= (\eta', P''\eta') = (P'\eta', P''P'\eta') \\ &= (\eta', P'P''P'\eta') = (\eta', P\eta') = 0 ,\end{aligned}$$

since, obviously, $P\eta' = 0$. In the same way, if $\eta'' \in H_{\xi''}$ is orthogonal to $\eta_1'', \ldots, \eta_r''$, then it is orthogonal to $H_{\xi'}$. In fact, $P'\eta''$ is orthogonal to $\eta_1', \ldots, \eta_r'$:

$$\begin{aligned}(P'\eta'', \eta_k') &= (\eta'', \eta_k') = (P''\eta'', \eta_k') \\ &= (\eta'', P''\eta_k') = (\eta'', \eta_k'') = 0\,, \qquad k = \overline{1, r}\,.\end{aligned}$$

Consequently, as was just proved, the element $\eta' = P'\eta''$ is orthogonal to $H_{\xi''}$, and, therefore,

$$(P'\eta'', P'\eta'') = (\eta'', P'\eta'') = 0\,.$$

Obviously, any complete orthogonal systems $\zeta_1', \ldots, \zeta_m'$ and $\zeta_1'', \ldots, \zeta_n''$ in $H_{\xi'}$ and $H_{\xi''}$, whose first r elements are $\eta_1', \ldots, \eta_r'$ and $\eta_1'', \ldots, \eta_r''$, respectively, have the properties stated in the lemma. ▮

Lemma 10.2. *Suppose that the random variables ξ' and ξ'' have a joint Gaussian distribution, and let ρ be their correlation coefficient. Then*

$$\sup_{f,g} \boldsymbol{E} f(\xi')\, g(\xi'') = |\rho| \tag{10.7}$$

where the supremum is taken over all functions f and g for which

$$\begin{aligned}\boldsymbol{E} f(\xi') &= \boldsymbol{E} g(\xi'') = 0\,, \\ \boldsymbol{E}[f(\xi')]^2 &= \boldsymbol{E}[g(\xi'')]^2 = 1\,.\end{aligned}$$

Proof. We have

$$\boldsymbol{E} f(\xi') g(\xi'') = \int_{-\infty}^{\infty}\int_{-\infty}^{\infty} f(x) g(y) p(x, y)\, dx\, dy\,,$$

where

$$p(x, y) = \frac{1}{2\pi\sqrt{1-\rho^2}} \exp\left\{-\frac{x^2 + y^2 - 2\rho x y}{2(1-\rho^2)}\right\}.$$

We will make use of the expansion of the probability density $p(x, y)$ in a series of Hermite polynomials:

$$p(x, y) = \frac{1}{2\pi} \exp\left\{-\frac{x^2+y^2}{2}\right\} \sum_{\nu=0}^{\infty} \frac{\rho^\nu}{\nu!} H_\nu(x) H_\nu(y)\,,$$

$$H_\nu(x) = (-1)^n e^{x^2/2} \frac{d^\nu}{dx^\nu} e^{-x^2/2}\,, \qquad \nu = 0, 1, \ldots\,.$$

As is well-known, these polynomials form a complete orthogonal system in the space of functions which are square integrable over the real line with respect to the weight $e^{-x^2/2}$:

$$\frac{1}{\sqrt{2\pi}} \int_{-\infty}^{\infty} H_\nu(x) H_\mu(x)\, e^{-x^2/2}\, dx = \begin{cases} \nu! & \text{for } \nu = \mu\,, \\ 0 & \text{for } \nu \neq \mu\,. \end{cases}$$

Since

$$\boldsymbol{E}[f(\xi')]^2 = \frac{1}{\sqrt{2\pi}}\int_{-\infty}^{\infty} [f(x)]^2 e^{-x^2/2}\, dx = 1 ,$$

$$\boldsymbol{E}[g(\xi'')]^2 = \frac{1}{\sqrt{2\pi}}\int_{-\infty}^{\infty} [g(x)]^2 e^{-x^2/2}\, dx = 1 ,$$

the functions f and g can also be expanded in a series of Hermite polynomials:

$$f(x) = \sum_{\nu=0}^{\infty} \frac{\alpha_\nu H_\nu(x)}{\nu!} ,$$

$$g(x) = \sum_{\nu=0}^{\infty} \frac{\beta_\nu H_\nu(x)}{\nu!} ,$$

where

$$\alpha_\nu = \frac{1}{\sqrt{2\pi}}\int_{-\infty}^{\infty} f(x)H_\nu(x)\, e^{-x^2/2}\, dx ;$$

$$\beta_\nu = \frac{1}{\sqrt{2\pi}}\int_{-\infty}^{\infty} g(x)H_\nu(x)\, e^{-x^2/2}\, dx ; \qquad \nu = 0, 1, \ldots .$$

It is not difficult to ascertain from these expansions that

$$\boldsymbol{E}f(\xi')g(\xi'') = \sum_{0}^{\infty} \frac{\rho^\nu}{\nu!}\alpha_\nu\beta_\nu .$$

The normalization condition on $f(\xi')$ and $g(\xi'')$ means that

$$\alpha_0 = \beta_0 = 0 ,$$

$$\sum_{1}^{\infty} \frac{\alpha_\nu^2}{\nu!} = \sum_{1}^{\infty} \frac{\beta_\nu^2}{\nu!} = 1 .$$

Using the Cauchy-Bunyakovskii inequality, we have

$$\boldsymbol{E}f(\xi')g(\xi'') = \left|\sum_{1}^{\infty} \frac{\rho^\nu}{\nu!}\alpha_\nu\beta_\nu\right| \le |\rho| \sum_{1}^{\infty} \left|\frac{1}{\nu!}|\alpha_\nu|\,|\beta_\nu|\right|$$

$$\le |\rho| \left[\sum_{1}^{\infty} \frac{|\alpha_\nu|^2}{\nu!}\right]^{1/2} \left[\sum_{1}^{\infty} \frac{|\beta_\nu|^2}{\nu!}\right]^{1/2} \le |\rho| .$$

The equality holds for

$$f(\xi') = \frac{\xi' - \boldsymbol{E}\xi'}{[\boldsymbol{D}\xi']^{1/2}} ; \qquad g(\xi'') = \frac{\xi'' - \boldsymbol{E}\xi''}{[\boldsymbol{D}\xi'']^{1/2}} . \quad \blacksquare$$

Lemma 10.3. *Suppose that the space Ω with probability measure $P(d\omega)$ is the direct product of the spaces Ω_1 and Ω_2 with probability measures $P_1(d\omega_1)$ and $P(d\omega_2)$:*

$$\Omega = \Omega_1 \times \Omega_2, \qquad P(d\omega) = P_1(d\omega_1) \times P_2(d\omega_2) . \tag{10.8}$$

Suppose that $\mathfrak{A}_1' \supseteq \mathfrak{A}_1''$ and $\mathfrak{A}_2'$ are σ-algebras of measurable sets in Ω_1

and Ω_2, respectively. Then for any random variable η on Ω the following equality holds with probability 1:

$$\boldsymbol{E}[\boldsymbol{E}(\eta|\mathfrak{A}_1' \times \mathfrak{A}_2')|\mathfrak{A}_1'' \times \mathfrak{J}_2] = \boldsymbol{E}[\boldsymbol{E}(\eta|\mathfrak{A}_1' \times \mathfrak{J}_2)|\mathfrak{A}_1'' \times \mathfrak{J}_2], \tag{10.9}$$

where $\mathfrak{J}_2$ is the trivial σ-algebra in Ω_2.

Proof. Using the simple properties of conditional expectations (see, for example, Doob[*], page 18), for any $A \in \mathfrak{A}_1''$ one can write the following relations:

$$\begin{aligned}
&\int_A \int_{\Omega_2} \boldsymbol{E}[\boldsymbol{E}(\eta|\mathfrak{A}_1' \times \mathfrak{A}_2')|\mathfrak{A}_1'' \times \mathfrak{J}_2] P(d\omega) \\
&= \int_A \left[\int_{\Omega_2} \boldsymbol{E}(\eta|\mathfrak{A}_1' \times \mathfrak{A}_2') P_2(d\omega_2)\right] P_1(d\omega_1) = \int_A \int_{\Omega_2} \eta(\omega) P(d\omega) \\
&= \int_A \left[\int_{\Omega_2} \boldsymbol{E}(\eta|\mathfrak{A}_1' \times \mathfrak{J}_2) P_2(d\omega_2)\right] P_1(d\omega_1) \\
&= \int_A \int_{\Omega_2} \boldsymbol{E}[\boldsymbol{E}(\eta|\mathfrak{A}_1' \times \mathfrak{J}_2)|\mathfrak{A}_1'' \times \mathfrak{J}_2] P(d\omega),
\end{aligned}$$

from which (9.9) easily follows. ∎

Proof of Theorem 10.1. Obviously, $\rho(\mathfrak{A}_{\xi'}, \mathfrak{A}_{\xi''}) \geq \rho(H_{\xi'}, H_{\xi''})$. Let us prove the reverse inequality. Since any random variables, measurable relative to the σ-algebras $\mathfrak{A}_{\xi'}$ or $\mathfrak{A}_{\xi''}$, can be approximated by functions of a finite number of the elements of $\{\xi'\}$ and $\{\xi''\}$, respectively, we may suppose that $\{\xi'\}$ and $\{\xi''\}$ consist of only finitely many elements.

In accordance with Lemma 10.1 we choose basis elements $\xi_1', \ldots, \xi_m'$ and $\xi_1'', \ldots, \xi_n''$ in the spaces $H_{\xi'}$ and $H_{\xi''}$, respectively, (the ξ_i' and ξ_j'' are not necessarily members of $\{\xi'\}$ and $\{\xi''\}$) such that any two are independent with the possible exception of pairs (ξ_k', ξ_k''), $k = 1, \ldots, \min(m, n)$ (recall that the joint probability distribution of all the elements in $\{\xi'\}$ and $\{\xi''\}$ was assumed Gaussian, and therefore the same will be true of the joint distribution of all the basis elements), and

$$\boldsymbol{E}\xi_k' = \boldsymbol{E}\xi_j'' = 0, \qquad \boldsymbol{D}\xi_k' = \boldsymbol{D}\xi_j'' = 1; \qquad k = \overline{1, m}, \quad j = \overline{1, n}.$$

Any random variables $f = f(\xi_1', \ldots, \xi_m')$ and $g = g(\xi_1'', \ldots, \xi_n'')$ ($\boldsymbol{E}f = \boldsymbol{E}g = 0$, $\boldsymbol{D}f = \boldsymbol{D}g = 1$) can be represented in the form

$$f = \sum_{k=1}^{m} f_k(\xi_1', \ldots, \xi_k'), \qquad g = \sum_{j=1}^{n} g_j(\xi_1'', \ldots, \xi_j''), \tag{10.10}$$

where

$$\begin{aligned}
f_k &= \boldsymbol{E}(f|\xi_1', \ldots, \xi_k') - \boldsymbol{E}(f|\xi_1', \ldots, \xi_{k-1}'), \\
g_j &= \boldsymbol{E}(g|\xi_1'', \ldots, \xi_j'') - \boldsymbol{E}(g|\xi_1'', \ldots, \xi_{j-1}'').
\end{aligned}$$

On the basis of Lemma 10.3 we conclude that

$$E[E(f|\xi_1', \ldots, \xi_k')|\xi_1'', \ldots, \xi_j''] = E[E(f|\xi_1', \ldots, \xi_j')|\xi_1'', \ldots, \xi_j''] \quad (10.11)$$

for $k \geq j$, and

$$E[E(g|\xi_1'', \ldots, \xi_j'')|\xi_1', \ldots, \xi_k'] = E[E(g|\xi_1'', \ldots, \xi_k'')|\xi_1', \ldots, \xi_k'] \quad (10.12)$$

for $k \leq j$. From these relations it follows that

$$Ef_k g_j = 0 \quad (10.13)$$

for $k \neq j$. In fact,

$$\begin{aligned} Ef_k g_j &= E[E(f_k g_j|\xi_1'', \ldots, \xi_j'')] = Eg_j[E(f_k|\xi_1'', \ldots, \xi_j'')| \\ &= Eg_j\{E[E(f|\xi_1', \ldots, \xi_k')|\xi_1'', \ldots, \xi_j''] \\ &\quad - E[E(f|\xi_1', \ldots, \xi_{k-1}')|\xi_1'', \ldots, \xi_j'']\} = 0 \end{aligned} \quad (10.14)$$

for $k > j$; the same way we can deduce (10.13) for $k < j$ from (10.12).

Assuming, for definiteness, that $m \leq n$, we have

$$Efg = \sum_{k=1}^{m} Ef_k g_k = \sum_{j=1}^{m} E\left[E\left(f_k g_k \middle| \begin{matrix} \xi_1', \ldots, \xi_{k-1}' \\ \xi_1'', \ldots, \xi_{k-1}'' \end{matrix}\right)\right]. \quad (10.15)$$

Further, we easily deduce from Lemma 10.3 that

$$E(f_k|\xi_1', \ldots, \xi_{k-1}', \xi_1'', \ldots, \xi_{k-1}'') = E(g_k|\xi_1'', \ldots, \xi_{k-1}', \xi_1'', \ldots, \xi_{k-1}'') = 0 \quad (10.16)$$

for all k.

For fixed $\xi_1', \ldots, \xi_{k-1}', \xi_1'', \ldots, \xi_{k-1}''$ the random variables f_k and g_k are functions only of ξ_k' and ξ_k'', and, applying Lemma 10.2 to them, we obtain

$$|E(f_k g_k|\xi_1', \ldots, \xi_{k-1}', \xi_1'', \ldots, \xi_{k-1}'')| \leq \rho a_k b_k, \quad (10.17)$$

where

$$a_k^2 = E(f_k^2|\xi_1', \ldots, \xi_{k-1}', \xi_1'', \ldots, \xi_{k-1}''),$$
$$b_k^2 = E(g_k^2|\xi_1', \ldots, \xi_{k-1}', \xi_1'', \ldots, \xi_{k-1}''),$$

and

$$\rho = \rho(H_{\xi'}, H_{\xi''}).$$

By the Cauchy-Bunyakovskii inequality,

$$\begin{aligned} |Efg| &\leq \rho \sum_1^m Ea_k b_k \leq \rho \sum_1^m (Ea_k^2)^{1/2}(Eb_k^2)^{1/2} \\ &\leq \rho\left[\sum_1^m Ea_k^2\right]^{1/2}\left[\sum_1^m Eb_k^2\right]^{1/2} \leq \rho, \end{aligned} \quad (10.18)$$

since

$$\sum_1^m \boldsymbol{E}a_k^2 = \sum_1^m \boldsymbol{E}f_k^2 \leq \boldsymbol{E}f^2 = 1 ,$$

$$\sum_1^m \boldsymbol{E}b_k^2 = \sum_1^m \boldsymbol{E}g_k^2 \leq \boldsymbol{E}g^2 = 1 . \tag{10.19}$$

Thus, Theorem 10.1 is proved.

Proof of Theorem 10.2. Let us choose $\varepsilon > 0$ and random variables $\xi'_\varepsilon \in H_{\xi'}$, $\xi''_\varepsilon \in H_{\xi''}$, such that

$$\boldsymbol{E}\xi'_\varepsilon = \boldsymbol{E}\xi''_\varepsilon = 0 , \qquad \boldsymbol{D}\xi'_\varepsilon = \boldsymbol{D}\xi''_\varepsilon = 1 , \qquad r = \boldsymbol{E}\xi'_\varepsilon\xi''_\varepsilon \geq \rho - \varepsilon .$$

We consider the events

$$A'_\varepsilon = \{\xi'_\varepsilon > 0\} \quad A''_\varepsilon = \{\xi''_\varepsilon > 0\} .$$

For ξ'_ε and ξ''_ε Gaussian it is not hard to calculate† that

$$\begin{aligned} P(A'_\varepsilon A''_\varepsilon) &= \frac{1}{4} + \frac{1}{2\pi} \operatorname{arc\,sin} r , \\ P(A'_\varepsilon)P(A''_\varepsilon) &= \frac{1}{4} \end{aligned} \tag{10.20}$$

and

$$\frac{1}{2\pi} \operatorname{arc\,sin} r = P(A'_\varepsilon A''_\varepsilon) - P(A'_\varepsilon)P(A''_\varepsilon) \leq \alpha(\mathfrak{A}_{\xi'}, \mathfrak{A}_{\xi''}) ,$$

If $\alpha > \frac{1}{4}$, then the inequality $\rho \leq 2\pi\alpha$ is trivial; if $\alpha \leq \frac{1}{4}$, then

$$\rho - \varepsilon \leq r \leq \sin 2\pi\alpha , \qquad \rho \leq 2\pi\alpha + \varepsilon \tag{10.21}$$

and, since ε is arbitrary,

$$\rho \leq 2\pi\alpha , \tag{10.22}$$

which was to be proved.

It follows from Theorems 10.1 and 10.2 that *a Gaussian stationary process* $\boldsymbol{\xi} = \{\xi_k(t)\}_{k=\overline{1,n}}$ *has the property* (9.6) *of complete regularity if and only if*

$$\rho(\tau) = \rho[H_\xi^-(t), H_\xi^+(t + \tau)] \to 0 \tag{10.23}$$

as $\tau \to \infty$ [where $H_\xi^-(t)$ and $H_\xi^+(t + \tau)$ are the closed, in mean square, linear manifolds generated by the values $\xi_k(s)$, $k = \overline{1, n}$, of $\boldsymbol{\xi}$ for $s \leq t$ and $s \geq t + \tau$, respectivly].

We will investigate below the dependence of property (10.23) of the index $\rho(\tau)$ for a one-dimensional wide-sense stationary process upon properties of its spectral measure $F(d\lambda)$.

† See, for example, Cramer[*], p. 290.

If property (10.23) is fulfilled, then, of course, ξ is linearly regular and, in particular, has a spectral density $f(\lambda)$.

We shall need some general facts from functional analysis.

Lemma 10.4. *Let L be some Banach space, and L^* its adjoint space. Let H be a subspace in L, and L_0^* the family of linear functionals on L which vanish on H.*

For any linear functional $l^* \in L^*$ the following relation holds:

$$\sup_{\substack{h \in H \\ \|h\|=1}} l^*(h) = \inf_{l_0^* \in L_0^*} \|l^* - l_0^*\| . \tag{10.24}$$

Proof. Since for any $l_0^* \in L_0^*$

$$l^*(h) - l_0^*(h) = l^*(h)$$

for $h \in H$, then

$$\|l^*(h)\| \leq \|l^* - l_0^*\| \, \|h\| ,$$

and, therefore,

$$\sup_{\substack{h \in H \\ \|h\|=1}} \|l^*(h)\| \leq \inf_{l_0^* \in L_0^*} \|l^* - l_0^*\| . \tag{10.25}$$

Further, by the well-known Hahn-Banach theorem on the extension of a linear functional, there exists a functional $l_1^* \in L^*$ which coincides on H with the given functional l^*, and such that

$$\|l_1^*\| = \sup_{\substack{h \in H \\ \|h\|=1}} \|l^*(h)\| .$$

The difference $l^* - l_1^*$ belongs to L_0^*, and

$$\|l^* - (l^* - l_1^*)\| = \|l_1^*\| = \sup_{\substack{h \in H \\ \|h\|=1}} \|l^*(h)\| . \tag{10.26}$$

Comparing (10.25) and (10.26) leads to (10.24).

Lemma 10.5. *Suppose that ξ is a wide-sense stationary (one-dimensional) process with spectral density $f(\lambda)$. The index*

$$\rho(\tau) = \rho[H_\xi^-(t), H_\xi^+(t+\tau)]$$

can be found from the formula

$$\rho(\tau) = \inf \operatorname{ess\,sup}_{\lambda} [|f(\lambda) - e^{i\lambda\tau}\varphi(\lambda)| f^{-1}(\lambda)] , \tag{10.27}$$

where the essential supremum is with respect to the measure $f(\lambda)\,d\lambda$, and the infimum is taken over all integrable functions $\varphi(\lambda)$ satisfying the following requirement:†

† The limits of integration in (10.28) are $-\pi, \pi$ in the discrete-parameter case, and $-\infty, \infty$ in the continuous-parameter case.

$$\int e^{-i\lambda t}\varphi(\lambda)\,d\lambda = 0\,, \qquad t \geq 0\,. \tag{10.28}$$

Proof. We will only consider the discrete-parameter case, since the continuous-parameter case is completely analogous.

Obviously,

$$\rho(\tau) = \sup_{P_1, P_2} \int_{-\pi}^{\pi} e^{-i\lambda\tau} P_1(e^{-i\lambda}) P_2(e^{-i\lambda}) f(\lambda)\,d\lambda\,, \tag{10.29}$$

where the supremum is taken over all polynomials $P_1(z)$, $P_2(z)$, such that

$$\int_{-\pi}^{\pi} |P_k(e^{-i\lambda})|^2 f(\lambda)\,d\lambda \leq 1\,, \qquad k = 1, 2\,.$$

Of course, one can take for $P_1(e^{-i\lambda})$ and $P_2(e^{-i\lambda})$ in (10.29) not only polynomials, but also any functions which are the boundary values of functions $P_1(z)$ and $P_2(z)$ which are analytic in the unit disc and bounded for all z, $|z| \leq 1$.

Let us take an arbitrary polynomial $P(z)$ satisfying the condition

$$\int_{-\pi}^{\pi} |P(e^{-i\lambda})|\, f(\lambda)\,d\lambda \leq 1\,. \tag{10.30}$$

As we have seen in Sections 5 and 8 of Chapter II, $P(z)$ can be represented in the form

$$P(z) = b(z) \exp\left\{\frac{1}{2\pi}\int_{-\pi}^{\pi} \log|P(e^{-i\lambda})| \frac{e^{-i\lambda} + z}{e^{-i\lambda} - z}\,d\lambda\right\},$$

where $b(z)$ is a rational analytic function of z such that $|b(e^{-i\lambda})| = 1$. The functions

$$\begin{aligned} P_1(z) &= b(z) \exp\left\{\frac{1}{4\pi}\int_{-\pi}^{\pi} \log|P(e^{-i\lambda})| \frac{e^{-i\lambda} + z}{e^{-i\lambda} - z}\,d\lambda\right\}, \\ P_2(z) &= \exp\left\{\frac{1}{4\pi}\int_{-\pi}^{\pi} \log|P(e^{-i\lambda})| \frac{e^{-i\lambda} + z}{e^{-i\lambda} - z}\,d\lambda\right\} \end{aligned} \tag{10.31}$$

are analytic and bounded inside the unit disc, and the values $P_1(e^{-i\lambda})$ and $P_2(e^{-i\lambda})$ are such that

$$|P_1(e^{-i\lambda})|^2 = |P_2(e^{-i\lambda})|^2 = |P(e^{-i\lambda})|$$

for almost all λ.

Obviously, if one takes the supremum in (10.29) only over functions P_1 and P_2 of the form (10.31), then the supremum can only be decreased, and, therefore, in fact

$$\rho(\tau) = \sup_{P} \int_{-\pi}^{\pi} e^{-i\lambda\tau} P(e^{-i\lambda}) f(\lambda)\,d\lambda\,, \tag{10.32}$$

where the supremum is taken over all polynomials $P(z)$ satisfying condition (10.30).

Further, let L be the space of all functions $l(\lambda)$ which are integrable with respect to the weight $f(\lambda)$, and put

$$||l|| = \int_{-\pi}^{\pi} |l(\lambda)| f(\lambda)\, d\lambda \,.$$

We shall consider in L the subspace H, the closed linear span of the functions $P(e^{-i\lambda}) = e^{-i\lambda k}$, $k \geq 0$.

Every linear functional l^* on L has the form

$$l^*(l) = \int_{-\pi}^{\pi} l^*(\lambda) l(\lambda) f(\lambda)\, d\lambda \,, \tag{10.33}$$

and

$$||l^*|| = \operatorname{ess\,sup}_{\lambda} |l^*(\lambda)| \,, \tag{10.34}$$

where ess sup is with respect to $f(\lambda)\, d\lambda$ (in this connection, see Riesz-Nagy[*], p.78).

If a linear functional l_0^* vanishes on H, then the function $l_0^*(\lambda)$ corresponding to l_0^* in the representation (10.33) must satisfy the following requirement:

$$\int_{-\pi}^{\pi} e^{-i\lambda k} l_0^*(\lambda) f(\lambda)\, d\lambda = 0 \tag{10.35}$$

for all $k \geq 0$.

We set $l_0^*(\lambda) f(\lambda) = \varphi(\lambda)$. Let us consider the functional l^* defined by the function $l^*(\lambda) = e^{-i\lambda\tau}$. From relation (10.24) of Lemma 10.4 we obtain

$$\begin{aligned}\sup_P \int_{-\pi}^{\pi} e^{-i\lambda\tau} P(e^{-i\lambda}) f(\lambda)\, d\lambda &= \inf_{l_0^*} \operatorname{ess\,sup}_{\lambda} |e^{-i\lambda\tau} - l_0^*(\lambda)| \\ &= \inf_{\varphi} \operatorname{ess\,sup}_{\lambda} [|f(\lambda) - e^{i\lambda\tau}\varphi(\lambda)| f^{-1}(\lambda)] \,, \end{aligned} \tag{10.36}$$

where the infimum is taken over all functions φ satisfying condition (10.28), and for which the ratio φ/f is bounded almost everywhere. Obviously, this last requirement can be omitted. ∎

Lemma 10.6. *If there exists a function $\varphi_0(\lambda)$, satisfying condition (10.28), and such that the ratio f/φ_0 is a uniformly continuous function of λ, and for some ε, $|f/\varphi_0| \geq \varepsilon > 0$ for almost all λ, then*

$$\lim_{\tau\to\infty} \rho(\tau) = 0 \,. \tag{10.37}$$

If there exists φ_0 such that $|f/\varphi_0| \geq \varepsilon$ and the derivative $(f/\varphi_0)^{(k)}$ is bounded, then

$$\rho(\tau) = c\tau^{-k}. \tag{10.38}$$

Proof. Let $\psi(z)$ be a polynomial of degree not greater than $[\tau/2]$ in the discrete-parameter case (or an analytic function of exponential type, with exponent not greater than $\tau/2$, and bounded on the real axis, in the continuous-parameter case), satisfying condition (10.28). Then the product $\varphi(\lambda) = \varphi_0(\lambda)\psi(e^{-i\lambda})$ [respectively, $\varphi(\lambda) = \varphi_0(\lambda)\psi(\lambda)$] also satisfies this condition.

We have

$$\inf_{\varphi} \operatorname{ess\,sup}_{\lambda} [|f(\lambda) - e^{i\lambda\tau}\varphi| f^{-1}(\lambda)] \le \inf_{\psi} \operatorname{ess\,sup}_{\lambda} [|f/\varphi_0 - e^{i\lambda\tau}\psi|\, |\varphi_0|/f]$$
$$\le \frac{1}{\varepsilon} \inf_{\psi} \sup_{\lambda} |f/\varphi_0 - e^{i\lambda\tau}\psi| \to 0$$

as $\tau \to \infty$, since the ratio f/φ_0 can be uniformly approximated by trigonometric polynomials in the discrete-parameter case (or by analytic functions of exponential type in the continuous-parameter case†). ∎

Let us mention that property (10.37) is fulfilled if the spectral density $f(\lambda)$ is continuous and does not vanish (in the discrete-parameter case), or if $f(\lambda)$ is uniformly continuous on the entire line, does not vanish, and satisfies the inequality

$$\frac{m}{\lambda^k} \le f(\lambda) \le \frac{M}{\lambda^{k-1}} \tag{10.39}$$

for sufficiently large λ, for some positive m and M and integer k (in the continuous-parameter case).

This results directly from Lemma 10.6; in the continuous-parameter case the function $\varphi_0(\lambda) = (1 + i\lambda)^{-k}$ satisfies the hypothesis of the lemma.

11. The central limit theorem

We have already repeatedly considered the question of the asymptotic behavior, as $t - s \to \infty$, of the "time averages" $H(s, t)/(t - s)$ of a stationary process $\boldsymbol{\xi} = \{\xi_k(t)\}_{k=\overline{1,n}}$, where

$$H(s, t) = \sum_{s \le u < t} \xi(u)$$

in the discrete-parameter case, and

$$H(s, t) = \int_s^t \xi(u)\, du$$

in the continuous-parameter case, and we have seen, in particular, that for ergodic processes

† In this connection, see Akhiezer[*], Chapter 5.

$$\lim_{t-s\to\infty} \frac{1}{t-s}[H(s, t) - \boldsymbol{E}H(s, t)] = 0 .$$

In this section we will be interested in the behavior of the quantity

$$\eta(s, t) = \frac{1}{(t-s)^{1/2}}[H(s, t) - \boldsymbol{E}H(s, t)] . \tag{11.1}$$

We will say that *the central limit theorem is applicable to the multi-dimensional stationary process* $\boldsymbol{\xi} = \{\xi_k(t)\}_{k=\overline{1,n}}$ if the limit

$$\lim_{t-s\to\infty} \boldsymbol{E}\eta(s, t)\eta^*(s, t) = b \tag{11.2}$$

exists and the distribution function $F_{\eta(s,t)}(x)$, $x = \{x_k\}_{k=\overline{1,n}}$, of the random variable $\eta(s, t)$ is such that

$$\lim_{t-s\to\infty} F_{\eta(s,t)}(x) = \Phi(x) , \tag{11.3}$$

where $\Phi(x)$ is the multi-dimensional Gaussian distribution function with zero means and with the matrix $b = \{b_{kl}\}_{k=\overline{1,n}}^{l=\overline{1,n}}$ of second moments.

Theorem 11.1. *Suppose that the stationary process* $\boldsymbol{\xi} = \{\xi_k(t)\}_{k=\overline{1,n}}$ *is completely regular and has a bounded spectral density* $f = \{f_{kl}(\lambda)\}_{k=\overline{1,n}}^{l=\overline{1,n}}$ *which is continuous at* $\lambda = 0$ *and whose value* $f(0)$ *at* $\lambda = 0$ *is a non-degenerate matrix.*

In order that the central limit theorem be applicable to $\boldsymbol{\xi}$, *the following condition is necessary and sufficient: For any* $\varepsilon > 0$ *one can find* N_ε *and* T_ε *such that*

$$\int_{\|x\|>N_\varepsilon} \|x\|^2\, dF_{\eta(s,t)}(x) \le \varepsilon , \tag{11.4}$$

when $t - s > T_\varepsilon$. *In this case the matrix* b *of second moments in relation* (11.2) *is given by*

$$b = 2\pi f(0) . \tag{11.5}$$

Theorem 11.2. *Suppose that the index* $\alpha(\tau)$ *in condition* (9.6) *for complete regularity of the process* $\boldsymbol{\xi}$ *decreases sufficiently fast, and the process* $\boldsymbol{\xi}$ *has moments of sufficiently high order, namely*

$$\alpha(\tau) = O(\tau^{-1-\varepsilon}) , \qquad \boldsymbol{E}\|\xi(t)\|^{2+\delta} < \infty \tag{11.6}$$

for some $\varepsilon > 0$ *and* $\delta > 4/\varepsilon$.

Suppose also that the spectral density $f = \{f_{kl}(\lambda)\}_{k=\overline{1,n}}^{l=\overline{1,n}}$ *of* $\boldsymbol{\xi}$ *is bounded, and also continuous and nondegenerate at zero.*

Then the central limit theorem is applicable to $\boldsymbol{\xi}$, *and, moreover, relation* (11.5) *is fulfilled.*

Let us turn to the proof of these theorems.

Lemma 11.1. *Set*

$$\alpha'(\tau) = \sup_{\eta,\zeta} |\boldsymbol{E}\eta\zeta - \boldsymbol{E}\eta\boldsymbol{E}\zeta| , \tag{11.7}$$

where the supremum is taken over all random variables η, $|\eta| \leq 1$, *which are measurable relative to the* σ*-algebra* $\mathfrak{A}_{-\infty}^{t}$, *and over all random variables* ζ, $|\zeta| \leq 1$, *which are measurable relative to the* σ*-algebra* $\mathfrak{A}_{t+\tau}^{\infty}$.

The following inequality holds:

$$\alpha(\tau) \leq \alpha'(\tau) \leq 16\alpha(\tau) . \tag{11.8}$$

Proof. The first inequality in (11.8) is obvious. Let us consider real η and ζ. We have

$$\begin{aligned} \boldsymbol{E}\eta\zeta - \boldsymbol{E}\eta\boldsymbol{E}\zeta &= \boldsymbol{E}[\boldsymbol{E}(\eta\zeta|\mathfrak{A}_{-\infty}^{t}) - \eta\boldsymbol{E}\zeta] \\ &= \boldsymbol{E}[\eta\boldsymbol{E}(\zeta|\mathfrak{A}_{-\infty}^{t}) - \eta\boldsymbol{E}\zeta] = \boldsymbol{E}\eta[\boldsymbol{E}(\zeta|\mathfrak{A}_{-\infty}^{t}) - \boldsymbol{E}\zeta] , \\ |\boldsymbol{E}\eta\zeta - \boldsymbol{E}\eta\boldsymbol{E}\zeta| &\leq |\boldsymbol{E}\eta'[\boldsymbol{E}(\zeta|\mathfrak{A}_{-\infty}^{t}) - \boldsymbol{E}\zeta]| = |\boldsymbol{E}\eta'\zeta - \boldsymbol{E}\eta'\boldsymbol{E}\zeta| , \end{aligned}$$

where

$$\eta' = \begin{cases} 1, & \text{if } \boldsymbol{E}(\zeta|\mathfrak{A}_{-\infty}^{t}) - \boldsymbol{E}\zeta > 0 , \\ -1, & \text{if } \boldsymbol{E}(\zeta|\mathfrak{A}_{-\infty}^{t}) - \boldsymbol{E}\zeta \leq 0 . \end{cases}$$

Completely analogously,

$$|\boldsymbol{E}\eta'\zeta - \boldsymbol{E}\eta'\boldsymbol{E}\zeta| \leq |\boldsymbol{E}\eta'\zeta' - \boldsymbol{E}\eta'\boldsymbol{E}\zeta'| ,$$

where

$$\zeta' = \begin{cases} 1, & \text{if } \boldsymbol{E}(\eta'|\mathfrak{A}_{t+\tau}^{\infty}) - \boldsymbol{E}\eta' > 0 , \\ -1, & \text{if } \boldsymbol{E}(\eta'|\mathfrak{A}_{t+\tau}^{\infty}) - \boldsymbol{E}\eta' \leq 0 . \end{cases}$$

It is evident from this that the supremum in (11.7) can be taken over only random variables of the form

$$\eta = 2\chi_A - 1 , \qquad \zeta = 2\chi_B - 1 ,$$

where χ_A and χ_B are the characteristic functions of sets $A \in \mathfrak{A}_{-\infty}^{t}$ and $B \in \mathfrak{A}_{t+\tau}^{\infty}$, and for such r.v.'s

$$\boldsymbol{E}\eta\zeta - \boldsymbol{E}\eta\boldsymbol{E}\zeta = 4[P(AB) - P(A)P(B)] .$$

To prove the inequality

$$\alpha'(\tau) \leq 16\alpha(\tau) ,$$

it now remains only to note that for arbitrary complex r.v.'s η, $|\eta| \leq 1$, and ζ, $|\zeta| \leq 1$,

$$|\boldsymbol{E}\eta\zeta - \boldsymbol{E}\eta\boldsymbol{E}\zeta| \leq \sup 4|\boldsymbol{E}\eta'\zeta' - \boldsymbol{E}\eta'\boldsymbol{E}\zeta'| ,$$

where here the supremum is taken over only real r.v.'s η' and ζ', $|\eta'| \leq 1$, $|\zeta'| \leq 1$.

Lemma 11.2. *Suppose that the r.v.'s* η_k, $|\eta_k| \le 1$, $(k = \overline{1, N})$, *are measurable relative to the σ-algebras* $\mathfrak{A}_{s_k}^{t_k}$, *respectively, and* $s_1 \le t_1 < \cdots < s_n \le t_n$, $s_{k+1} - t_k \ge \tau$ *for all* k.

Then

$$|E(\eta_1 \cdots \eta_N) - E\eta_1 \cdots E\eta_N| \le (N-1)\alpha'(\tau) . \tag{11.9}$$

Proof. For $N = 2$ relation (11.9) is fulfilled. We shall suppose that it holds for $(N-1)$ r.v.'s, and will prove it for N r.v.'s.

We have

$$\begin{aligned} |E(\eta_1 \cdots \eta_N) - E\eta_1 \cdots E\eta_N| &\le |E(\eta_1 \cdots \eta_N) - E(\eta_1 \cdots \eta_{N-1})E\eta_N| \\ &\quad + |E(\eta_1 \cdots \eta_{N-1}) - E\eta_1 \cdots E\eta_{N-1}| \\ &\le \alpha'(\tau) + (N-2)\alpha'(\tau) = (N-1)\alpha'(\tau) , \end{aligned}$$

which was to be proved.

Lemma 11.3. *Suppose that the r.v.'s* η *and* ζ *are measurable relative to the σ-algebras* $\mathfrak{A}_{-\infty}^{t}$ *and* $\mathfrak{A}_{t+\tau}^{\infty}$, *respectively, and have second momemts. Then*

$$|E\eta\zeta - E\eta E\zeta| \le N^2\alpha'(\tau) + 6\sigma\varepsilon , \tag{11.10}$$

where

$$\sigma^2 = \max(E|\eta|^2, E|\zeta|^2) ,$$

$$\varepsilon^2 = \max\left(\int_{|x|>N} x^2\, dF_\eta(x), \int_{|x|>N} x^2\, dF_\zeta(x)\right) .$$

Proof. We set

$$\eta_1 = \begin{cases} \eta & \text{for} \quad |\eta| \le N , \\ 0 & \text{for} \quad |\eta| > N , \end{cases} \qquad \eta_2 = \eta - \eta_1 ,$$

and similarly

$$\zeta_1 = \begin{cases} \zeta & \text{if} \quad |\zeta| \le N , \\ 0 & \text{if} \quad |\zeta| > N , \end{cases} \qquad \zeta_2 = \zeta - \zeta_1 .$$

Using the Cauchy-Bunyakovskii inequality, we obtain

$$\begin{aligned} |E\eta\zeta - E\eta E\zeta| &\le |E\eta_1\zeta_1 - E\eta_1 E\zeta_1| + |E\eta_1\zeta_2| + |E\eta_1 E\zeta_2| + |E\eta_2\zeta_1| \\ &\quad + |E\eta_2 E\zeta_1| + |E\eta_2\zeta_2| + |E\eta_2 E\zeta_2| \le N^2\alpha'(\tau) + 6\sigma\varepsilon , \end{aligned}$$

which was to be proved.

Lemma 11.4. *Suppose that the index* $\alpha(\tau)$ *in the condition* (9.6) *for complete regularity decreases sufficiently fast:*

$$\alpha(\tau) = O[\tau^{-1-\varepsilon}] , \qquad \varepsilon > 0 . \tag{11.11}$$

Then for any r.v.'s η and ζ, having bounded moments of order $2+\delta$, $\delta > 4/\varepsilon$, and measurable relative to $\mathfrak{A}_{-\infty}^{t}$ and $\mathfrak{A}_{t+\tau}^{\infty}$, respectively, the following inequality holds:

$$|\boldsymbol{E}\eta\zeta - \boldsymbol{E}\eta\boldsymbol{E}\zeta| \le C[\tau^{-1-\varepsilon'}] , \tag{11.12}$$

where ε', $\varepsilon' > 0$ and C, $C < \infty$, are certain constants.

Proof. Since

$$\int_{|x|>N} x^2 \, dF(x) \le N^{-\delta} \int_{-\infty}^{\infty} |x|^{2+\delta} \, dF(x) ,$$

inequality (11.10) of the previous lemma allows us to conclude that

$$|\boldsymbol{E}\eta\zeta - \boldsymbol{E}\eta\boldsymbol{E}\zeta| \le N^2\alpha(\tau) + C'N^{-\delta/2} .$$

Choosing $N=\tau^a$, $a = 2(1+\varepsilon)/(4+\delta)$, and taking (11.8) into account, we obtain inequality (11.12) of the present lemma, in which

$$\varepsilon' = \frac{\varepsilon\delta - 4}{4+\delta} > 0 \qquad \text{for } \delta > \frac{4}{\varepsilon} .$$

Lemma 11.5. *Let ξ_k, $k=\overline{1, N}$, be r.v.'s such that $\boldsymbol{E}|\xi_k|^r \le M_0$ for all $k = \overline{1, N}$. Then*

$$\boldsymbol{E}|\xi_1 + \cdots + \xi_N|^r \le M_0 N^r . \tag{11.13}$$

Proof. Using Hölder's inequality, we easily obtain

$$\boldsymbol{E}|\xi_{k_1}\cdots\xi_{k_r}| \le [\boldsymbol{E}|\xi_{k_1}|^r]^{1/r}\cdots[\boldsymbol{E}|\xi_{k_r}|^r]^{1/r} \le M_0 ,$$

from which

$$\boldsymbol{E}|\xi_1 + \cdots + \xi_N|^r \le \sum_{k_1\ldots k_r} \boldsymbol{E}|\xi_{k_1}\cdots\xi_{k_r}| \le M_0 N^r .$$

Proof of Theorem 11.1. Suppose $\boldsymbol{E}\xi(t) = 0$. If the process $\boldsymbol{\xi} = \{\xi_k(t)\}_{k=\overline{1,n}}$ has a spectral density $f = \{f_{kl}(\lambda)\}_{k=\overline{1,n}}^{l=\overline{1,n}}$, then

$$\boldsymbol{E}\eta(s,t)\eta^*(s,t) = \frac{1}{t-s}\int_{-\pi}^{\pi} \frac{\sin^2(\lambda/2)(t-s)}{\sin^2 \lambda/2} f(\lambda)\, d\lambda$$

in the discrete-parameter case, and

$$\boldsymbol{E}\eta(s,t)\eta^*(s,t) = \frac{1}{t-s}\int_{-\infty}^{\infty} \frac{4\sin^2(\lambda/2)(t-s)}{\lambda^2} f(\lambda)\, d\lambda$$

in the continuous-parameter case. Since

$$\frac{1}{t-s}\int_{-\pi}^{\pi} \frac{\sin^2(\lambda/2)(t-s)}{\sin^2\lambda/2}\, d\lambda = \frac{1}{t-s}\int_{-\infty}^{\infty} \frac{4\sin^2(\lambda/2)(t-s)}{\lambda^2}\, d\lambda = 2\pi ,$$

and for any $\varepsilon > 0$

$$\lim_{t-s\to\infty}\frac{1}{t-s}\int_{|\lambda|>\varepsilon}\frac{\sin^2(\lambda/2)(t-s)}{\sin^2\lambda/2}d\lambda=\lim_{t-s\to\infty}\frac{1}{t-s}\int_{|\lambda|>\varepsilon}\frac{4\sin^2(\lambda/2)(t-s)}{\lambda^2}=0\,,$$

then, as is easily seen, for a spectral density f which is bounded and continuous at zero

$$\lim_{t-s\to\infty}\boldsymbol{E}\eta(s,t)\eta^*(s,t)=2\pi f(0)\,. \tag{11.14}$$

We now show that condition (11.4) is necessary. Let $\Gamma_N=\{x:|x_k|\le N, k=\overline{1,n}\}$. From the weak convergence of the distributions $F_{\eta(s,t)}(x)$ and the continuity of the limit distribution $\Phi(x)$ (which is Gaussian) it follows that

$$\lim_{t-s\to\infty}\int_{\Gamma_N}||x||^2\,dF_{\eta(s,t)}(x)=\int_{\Gamma_N}||x||^2\,d\Phi(x)\,.$$

Further, as relation (11.14) shows,

$$\lim_{t-s\to\infty}\int_{R^n}||x||^2\,dF_{\eta(s,t)}(x)=\int_{R^n}||x||^2\,d\Phi(x)\,.$$

Hence, if $\bar\Gamma_N$ denotes the exterior of the "rectangle" Γ_N, we have

$$\lim_{t-s\to\infty}\int_{\bar\Gamma_N}||x||^2\,dF_{\eta(s,t)}(x)=\int_{\bar\Gamma_N}||x||^2\,d\Phi(x)\,.$$

The integral on the right side of this equality can be made arbitrarily small for sufficiently large N, which guarantees the fulfillment of condition (11.4).

In order not to burden the rest of the proof with secondary details and the related notation, we will present it only for the one-dimensional case; the proof in the multi-dimensional case is, in principle, not at all more difficult.

Suppose that condition (11.4) is fulfilled. We subdivide the interval $[s,t)$ by means of points s_k, t_k $(k=\overline{1,N-1})$ into intervals

$$\Delta_k=[s_k,t_k)\,,\qquad k=\overline{1,N}$$

and

$$\Delta'_k=[t_k,s_{k+1})\,,\qquad t_k-s_k=\tau\,,\qquad s_{k+1}-t_k=\tau'\,,$$

in such a way that

$$\begin{gathered}N=\frac{t-s-\tau}{\tau+\tau'}\to\infty\,,\qquad \tau'\to\infty\,,\qquad \frac{\tau'}{\tau}\to0\,,\qquad N\alpha(\tau')\to0\,,\\ N\sup_{k\ne j}|\boldsymbol{E}\eta(\Delta_k)\eta(\Delta_j)|\to0\,,\qquad N\sup_{k\ne j}|\boldsymbol{E}\eta(\Delta'_k)\eta(\Delta'_j)|\to0\end{gathered} \tag{11.15}$$

as $t-s\to\infty$ (where $\eta(\Delta_k)=\eta(s_k,t_k)$ and $\eta(\Delta'_k)=\eta(t_k,s_{k+1})$). This can be done because, for any τ and τ' tending to infinity, it follows from condition (11.4) and Lemma 11.3 that

$$\sup_{k\neq j} |\boldsymbol{E}\eta(\Delta_k)\eta(\Delta_j)| \to 0 , \qquad \sup_{k\neq j} |\boldsymbol{E}\eta(\Delta'_j)\eta(\Delta'_j)| \to 0$$

and, choosing the partition sufficiently coarse, i.e., choosing τ and τ' not too small in comparison with $t-s$ [as a result of which an estimate of the type (11.10) of the quantities $|\boldsymbol{E}\eta(\Delta_k)\eta(\Delta_j)|$ and $|\boldsymbol{E}\eta(\Delta'_k)\eta(\Delta'_j)|$ can only be decreased], we obtain the required relation (11.15).

Let us represent $\eta(s, t)$ in the form

$$\eta(s, t) = \sum_{k=1}^{N} \eta_k + \sum_{k=1}^{N-1} \eta'_k ,$$

where

$$\eta_k = \left(\frac{\tau}{t-s}\right)^{1/2} \eta(\Delta_k) , \qquad \eta'_k = \left(\frac{\tau'}{t-s}\right)^{1/2} \eta(\Delta'_k) .$$

From relations (11.15) we have

$$\begin{aligned} \boldsymbol{E}\left[\sum_{k=1}^{N-1} \eta'_k\right]^2 &\leq \sum_{k=1}^{N-1} \boldsymbol{E}(\eta'_k)^2 + N^2 \sup_{k\neq j} |\boldsymbol{E}\eta'_k\eta'_j| \\ &\leq C\left[\frac{N\tau'}{t-s} + N \sup_{k\neq j} |\boldsymbol{E}\eta(\Delta'_k)\eta(\Delta'_j)|\right] \to 0 \end{aligned} \tag{11.16}$$

as $t - s \to \infty$. Therefore, the asymptotic behavior of the distribution of $\eta(s, t)$ is the same as that of the distribution of $\zeta_N = \sum_{k=1}^{N} \eta_k$.

Further, from Lemmas 11.1, 11.2, and relations (11.15) we obtain

$$\left|\boldsymbol{E}e^{iu\zeta_N} - \prod_{k=1}^{N} \boldsymbol{E}e^{iu\eta_k}\right| \leq 16N\alpha(\tau') \to 0$$

as $t - s \to \infty$, and, consequently, due to the correspondence between characteristic functions and distributions, the asymptotic behavior of the distrbution of the sum ζ_N is the same as if the random variables η_k were mutually independent.

Further,

$$\sum_{k=1}^{N} \boldsymbol{E}\eta_k^2 = \boldsymbol{E}\left[\sum_{k=1}^{N} \eta_k\right]^2 - \sum_{k\neq j} M\eta_k\eta_j \to 2\pi f(0)$$

as $t - s \to \infty$, since, by virtue of (11.15) and (11.16),

$$\lim_{t-s\to\infty} \boldsymbol{E}\left[\sum_{k=1}^{N} \eta_k\right]^2 = \lim_{t-s\to\infty} \boldsymbol{E}\eta^2(s, t) = 2\pi f(0) ,$$

$$\left|\sum_{k\neq j} \boldsymbol{E}\eta_k\eta_j\right| \leq N^2 \frac{\tau}{t-s} \sup_{k\neq j} |\boldsymbol{E}\eta(\Delta_k)\eta(\Delta_j)| \to 0 .$$

Therefore, for the applicability to the process ξ of the central limit theorem it is sufficient that the terms η_k satisfy the well-known Lindeberg condition (see, for example, Loève[*]): for any $\varepsilon > 0$

$$\lim_{N\to\infty}\sum_{k=1}^{N}\int_{|x|>\varepsilon} x^2\,dF_{\eta_k}(x) = 0\,.$$

This condition is fulfilled:

$$\sum_{k=1}^{N}\int_{|x|>\varepsilon} x^2\,dF_{\eta_k}(x) = \sum_{k=1}^{N}\frac{\tau}{t-s}\int_{|x|>\varepsilon\left(\frac{t-s}{\tau}\right)^{1/2}} x^2\,dF_{\eta(\Delta_k)}(x)$$

$$\leq \int_{|x|>\varepsilon\left(\frac{t-s}{\tau}\right)^{1/2}} x^2\,dF_{\eta(0,\tau)}(x) \to 0$$

as $t-s\to\infty$, due to the requirement (11.4). Thus, Theorem 11.1 is proved.

Proof of Theorem 11.2. We will suppose that $\boldsymbol{E}\xi(t)=0$. As before, we subdivide the interval $[s,t)$ by means of points s_k, t_k into intervals $\Delta_k=[s_k,t_k)$ and $\Delta_k'=[t_k,s_{k+l})$ of lengths $\tau=t_k-s_k$ and $\tau'=s_{k+1}-t_k$.

By Lemma 11.4

$$|\boldsymbol{E}\xi(u)\xi(v)|\leq C\,|u-v|^{-1-\varepsilon'}\,,$$

from which

$$|\boldsymbol{E}H(\Delta_k)H(\Delta_{k+l})|\leq C\tau^2(\tau')^{-1-\varepsilon'}l^{-1-\varepsilon'}\,,$$
$$|\boldsymbol{E}H(\Delta_k')H(\Delta_{k+l}')|\leq C(\tau')^2\tau^{-1-\varepsilon'}l^{-1-\varepsilon'}\,.$$

We have

$$\frac{1}{t-s}\left|\sum_{k\neq j}\boldsymbol{E}H(\Delta_k)H(\Delta_j)\right| = \frac{2}{t-s}\left|\sum_{k=1}^{N}\sum_{l=1}^{N-k}\boldsymbol{E}H(\Delta_k)H(\Delta_{k+l})\right|$$

$$\leq C\frac{N}{t-s}\tau^2(\tau')^{-1-\varepsilon'}\sum_{l=1}^{\infty}l^{-1-\varepsilon'}\leq C\tau(\tau')^{-1-\varepsilon'}\to 0$$

as $t-s\to\infty$, if τ and τ' are chosen so that

$$\tau(\tau')^{-1-\varepsilon'}\to 0\,. \tag{11.17}$$

Similarly,

$$\frac{1}{t-s}\left|\sum_{k\neq j}\boldsymbol{E}H(\Delta_k')\,H(\Delta_j')\right|\leq C\tau'\tau^{-1-\varepsilon'}\to 0\,,$$

if

$$\frac{\tau'}{\tau}\to 0 \tag{11.18}$$

as $t-s\to\infty$. Therefore,

$$\frac{1}{t-s}\sum_{k=1}^{N-1}\boldsymbol{E}[H(\Delta_k')]^2\leq C\frac{\tau'}{\tau}\to 0$$

and, consequently,

$$\frac{1}{t-s}\boldsymbol{E}\left[\sum_{k=1}^{N-1} H(\Delta_k')\right]^2 \to 0$$

as $t - s \to \infty$. From this we conclude that the asymptotic distribution of $\eta(s, t)$ is the same as that of the random variable

$$\zeta_N = \sum_{k=1}^{N} \eta_k , \qquad \eta_k = \left(\frac{\tau}{t-s}\right)^{1/2} \eta(\Delta_k) .$$

Choosing the subdivision of the interval $[s, t)$ so that, in addition to relations (11.17) and (11.18),

$$N \to \infty , \qquad N\alpha(\tau') \to 0 \tag{11.19}$$

as $t - s \to \infty$, we can suppose that the terms η_k in the sum ζ_N are mutually independent, since, by Lemma 11.2,

$$\left| \boldsymbol{E}e^{iu\zeta_N} - \prod_{k=1}^{N} \boldsymbol{E}e^{iu\eta_k} \right| \le N\alpha(\tau') \to 0 .$$

But the sum ζ_N satisfies the well-known Lyapunov condition:

$$(t-s)^{-(2+\delta)/2} \sum_{k=1}^{N} \boldsymbol{E}|H(\Delta_k)|^{2+\delta} \le C(t-s)^{-(2+\delta)/2} N\tau^{2+\delta} \le C\tau^{1+\delta}(t-s)^{-\delta/2} \to 0$$

as $t - s \to \infty$, if we choose $\tau = (t-s)^a$, $a < \delta/2(1+\delta)$. [It is easy to see that such a choice of τ, for $\delta > 4/\varepsilon$, is compatible with the requirements (11.17)-(11.19).]

The theorem is proved.

HISTORICAL AND BIBLIOGRAPHIC REFERENCES

Chapter I

Section 1: The concept of a stationary process was introduced by Khinchin [2].

A very complete discussion of the theory of one-dimensional stationary processes can be found in the book by Doob[*].

Sections 2, 3: The stochastic integrals described in Section 2 were apparently first considered by Wiener; they are encountered, in an implicit form, in his paper [1].

Stochastic integrals of this type are a special case of integrals with respect to measures having values in a Hilbert space, which are conventional in the spectral theorem for operators (see, for example, the book by Riesz and Nagy[*]). Chapter IX of Doob[*] is entirely devoted to such integrals.

Integrals of random functions with respect to an ordinary measure, considered in Section 2, are a generalization of the Lebesgue integral of abstract functions, given by Bochner [1].

Section 4: The spectral representation of a stationary process apparently first appeared in papers of Kolmogorov [1–3]; the proof given, in this section, of Theorem 4.1 concerning the spectral representation, was given by Kolmogorov [2].

Theorem 4.1 can also be obtained directly, without using results on the spectral decomposition of one-parameter groups of unitary operators (see Karhunen [1]).

Section 5: The properties of the correlation functions of stationary processes, described in this section, were first studied by Khinchin [2] for the continuous-parameter case His results were carried over to the discrete-parameter case by Wold [1] and to the multi-dimensional case by Cramér [1]. The general properties of positive definite functions had already been studied by Bochner [2].

Section 6: The results of this section are due to Khinchin [2].

An interesting strengthening of these results was given by Loève [1].

A decomposition of the type (6.22) for a stationary process with a bounded spectrum is frequently used in radiotechnical literature.

Sections 7–9: The results of Sections 7–9 are generalizations to the multi-dimensional case, and also to the continuous-parameter case, of certain facts which are contained in Kolmogorov's work [2].

Section 10: Stationary processes with rational spectral density were treated in detail by Doob [1].

Theorem 10.1 on the factorization of a positive-definite matrix function with rational elements, in which the maximal matrix appears explicitly, is apparently new.

Chapter II

Section 1: The problem of linear extrapolation was posed and completely solved for one-dimensional discrete-parameter stationary processes by Kolmogorov [1–3].

Section 2: The results of this section are the multi-dimensional generalizations of corresponding results contained in Kolmogorov's paper [1].

Section 3: The decomposition (3.7) was introduced by Wold [1] for one-dimensional processes (see also Kolmogorov [2] and Zasukhin [1]).

Section 4: Theorem 4.1 on factorization was stated briefly in Doob's book[*].

The connection between problems of linear extrapolation and boundary problems for analytic matrices was noted by Krein; in particular, the connection between a maximal matrix and a fundamental process was discussed by him in lectures given at the Moscow State University in 1958, in which a detailed proof of Zasukhin's theorem (see Section 6 below) was given. A detailed discussion of this circle of topics can be found in Rozanov [2, 8].

The boundary properties of analytic matrices have been elucidated in some detail in a number of papers (see, for example, Potapov [1]); in particular, it is known that a maximal matrix function can be represented in the form of a multiplicative integral (Potapov [1] and Masani [4]).

The general form of a maximal matrix in the case of a rational spectral density was found by Rozanov [8].

Section 5: Theorems 5.1, 5.3, and 5.4 are due to Kolmogorov [2].

The basic relation (5.11) is a consequence of a theorem of Szegö [1].

The proof of Theorem 5.2 is taken, with slight changes, from the paper by Helson and Lowdenslager [1].

Section 6: The criterion for the linear regularity of stationary processes with maximal rank, given by Theorem 6.1, first appeared in a note by Zasukhin [1].

The basic relation (6.9) was first obtained, apparently, by Wiener and Masani [1].

Section 7: The question of stationary processes which form a basis is considered in detail in Rozanov [6]; in particular, it is proven in this paper that condition (7.2) of Theorem 7.1 is not only sufficient, but also necessary for the values of the corresponding stationary process to form a basis.

Formula (7.22) for a maximal matrix is due to Wiener and Masani [1]. Various generalizations of this formula have been obtained by Masani [2].

Section 8: A criterion for the regularity of stationary processes with degenerate spectral densities was first obtained for two-dimensional processes by Wiener and Masani [2], and for arbitrary processes of rank 1, by Rozanov [3]. A generalization of this criterion to the case of any rank was given by Matveev [1]. Similar criteria, but having an outwardly different form, were given by Helson and Lowdenslager [2].

The solution of the problem of linear extrapolation and other questions of the spectral theory of stationary processes of rank 1 was given by Rozanov [3].

Section 9: The general solution of the filtering problem, contained in this section, is apparently discussed here for the first time.

Sections 10, 11: The problem of linear interpolation has been considered in papers by Kolmogorov [3], Yaglom [1], Rozanov [1, 7], and others.

The interpolation formulas of this section were presented by Rozanov [7].

Condition (10.13) for the minimality of a stationary process was obtained in the one-dimensional case by Kolmogorov [2], and in the multi-dimensional case by Rozanov [1] and Masani [1].

Condition (10.28) for the error-free interpolation of a stationary process is due to Yaglom [1].

Chapter III

Section 1: The problem of the linear extrapolation of continuous-parameter stationary processes was considered in Wiener's book[*] (see also Krein [1] and Karhunen [2]).

Extremely interesting results, revealing a connection between the problem of linear filtering and problems concerning differential equations, were obtained by Krein [2].

Section 2: The analytic method enabling one to reduce the continuous-parameter case to the discrete-parameter case is described in Doob[*]. This method was first used for the same purpose by Krein [1]; it was extended to the multi-dimensional case by Gladyshev [1].

Section 3: Wold's decomposition for continuous-parameter stationary processes was first obtained by Hanner [1], who obtained it without using the spectral representation of a process.

Karhunen [2] arrived at the same result, starting from the spectral representation.

Section 4, 5: Formula (4.14), determining a maximal function, is due to Krein [1].

The solution presented of the problems of the linear extrapolation and filtering of stationary processes with rational spectral densities is a slight modification of the solution presented by Yaglom[*], [2, 3].

Section 6: The problem of the linear interpolation of continuous-parameter stationary processes was first considered by Karhunen [3]; in particular, condition (6.13) for the error-free interpolation of stationary processes is due to him.

The solution of the problem of the linear interpolation of multi-dimensional processes with rational spectral densities was given by Yaglom [3].

Section 7: The problem of linear forecasting by means of the values on a finite interval was considered in the general case by Krein [2]. The special case of a rational spectrum was considered by Yaglom [3].

The method presented in this section of solving integral equations of the type (7.5), together with its various applications, is discussed in a paper by Pisarenko and Rozanov [1]. This paper describes a wide class of problems which lead to equations of the type (7.5) and which are considered in detail in numerous works (see, for example, Zadeh and Ragazzini [1], Grenander [1], Grenander and Rosenblatt [1],

Dolph and Woodbury [1]).

Chapter IV

Section 1: The concept of a strictly stationary random process was introduced by Khinchin [2].

Section 2: The possibility of defining a random process by means of a compatible family of finite-dimensional distributions is given by a well-known theorem of Kolmogorov.

Section 3: The relation of the theory of strictly stationary processes with the general theory of measure preserving transformations was long known to specialists.

Section 4: Concerning the measurability of random processes, see, for example, Doob's book[*].

Section 5: The ergodic theorem was first proved by Birkhoff [1] for a certain special class of measure preserving transformations. The general case was considered by Khinchin [1].

The proof of the ergodic theorem presented in this section is a paraphrase of Kolmogorov's proof [4].

Section 6: The condition for the metric transitivity of Gaussian processes was first obtained by Maruyama [1]; see also Grenander [1].

Section 7: The description of metrically transitive stationary processes, given in this section, is rather closely related to a theorem of von Neumann [1] on dynamical systems with discrete spectra; see also the book by Blanc-Lapierre and Fortet [1].

Section 8: The decomposition of a dynamical system of classical type into metrically transitive components was indicated by von Neumann [1]. In a somewhat wider context, this question was studied by Kryloff and Bogoliouboff [1].

The general case was considered by Rokhlin [1].

Section 9: The property of regularity for stationary processes was considered in a paper by Vinokurov [1].

Condition (9.6) was introduced in a paper by Rosenblatt [1] for the case of a stationary sequence.

Section 10: The property of complete regularity for a Gaussian stationary process was studied by Kolmogorov and Rozanov [1]. The assertion of Lemma 10.1, which plays an important role in many questions, is contained in a paper by Obukhov [1].

Another type of property of the spectral density of a completely regular Gaussian stationary process was established by Ibragimov [2].

The notion of the maximal correlation coefficient of two random variables was introduced by Gebelein [1]; Lemma 8.2 follows from his results (see also Sarmanov [1]).

The index $\rho(1) = \rho[H_\xi^-(t), H_\xi^+(t+1)]$ was computed in a paper by Helson and Szegö [1].

Section 11: The central limit theorem for weakly dependent variables of a general type was already obtained by Bernstein [1].

Theorems 11.1 and 11.2 are due to Rozanov (see Volkonskii and Rozanov [1]). Rather close results were obtained by Ibragimov [1].

Various sharpenings of the central limit theorem (asymptotic expansions and large deviations) were given for completely regular processes by Statulyavichus [1].

Important results of a concrete nature (regarding geodesic flows on surfaces of negative curvature) have been obtained by Sinai [1].

BIBLIOGRAPHY

General Literature

Akhiezer, N. I., *Lectures on the Theory of Approximation*, Moscow-Leningrad 1947 (English translation: Ungar Publishing Co., New York, 1956).

Cramér, H., *Mathematical Methods of Statistics*, Princeton University Press, Princeton, N. J., 1956.

Doob, J. L., *Stochastic Processes*, John Wiley & Sons, New York, 1953.

Gantmakher, F. R., *Theory of Matrices*, Moscow, 1953 (English translation: Chelsea Publishing Co., New York, 1959).

Gelfand, I. M., *Lectures on Linear Algebra*, Moscow-Leningrad 1948 (English translation: Interscience Publishing Co., New York, 1961).

Gnedenko, B. V. and A. N. Kolmogorov, *Limit Theorems for Sums of Independent Random Variables*, Moscow, 1949 (English translation: Addison-Wesley Publishing Co., Reading, Mass., 1954).

Halmos, P. R., *Measure Theory*, D. Van Nostrand Co., Princeton, N. J., 1950.

Hardy, G. H., J. E. Littlewood, and G. Polya, *Inequalities*, 2nd Ed., Cambridge University Press, London, 1959.

Helson, H., *Lectures on Invariant Subspaces*, Academic Press, New York, 1965.

Hoffman, K., *Banach Spaces of Analytic Functions*, Prentice-Hall, Englewood Cliffs, N. J., 1962.

Kolmogorov, A. N., *Foundations of Probability*, Chelsea Publishing Co., New York, 1950.

Loève, M., *Probability Theory*, 3rd Ed., Van Nostrand Co., Princeton, N. J., 1963.

Pontryagin, L. S., *Continuous Groups*, 2nd Ed., Moscow, 1954 (English translation of 1st Ed., Princeton University Press, Princeton, N. J., 1939).

Privalov. I. I., *Boundary Properties of Analytic Functions*, Moscow-Leningrad, 1950 (German translation: *Randeigenschaften analytischer Funktionen*, VEB Deutscher Verlag der Wissenchaften, Berlin, 1956).

Riesz, F. and B. Sz. Nagy, *Lecons d'analyse fonctionelle*, 3rd Ed., Akademiai Kiado, Budapest, 1955 (English translation: Ungar Publishing Co., New York, 1955).

Yaglom, A. M., *An Introduction to the Theory of Stationary Random Functions*, Prentice-Hall, Englewood Cliffs, N. J. 1962.

Special Literature

Bernstein, S. N.

1. "Sur l'extension du théorème limite du calcul des probabilités aux sommes de quantités dépendantes," Math. Ann. **97**, 1-59 (1926).

Birkhoff, G. D.

1. "Proof of the Ergodic Theorem," Proc. Natl. Acad. Sci. U.S.A., **17**, 656-660 (1931).

Blanc-Lapierre, A. and R. Fortet,

1. *Théorie des fonctions aléatoires*, Masson et Cie., Éd., Paris, 1953.

Bochner, S.

1. "Integration von Funktionen, deren Verte die Elemente eines Vektorraumes sind," Fund. Math. **20**, 262-276 (1933).
2. "Monotone Funktionen, Stieltjessche Integrale und harmonische Analyse," Math. Ann. **108**, 378-410 (1933).

Cramér, H.:

1. "On the Theory of Stationary Random Processes," Ann. Math. **41**, 215-230 (1940).

Dolph, C. L., Woodbury, H. A.

1. "On the Relation between Green's Functions and Covariances of Certain Stochastic Processes and Its Applications to Unbiased Linear Prediction," Trans. Amer. Math. Soc. **72**, 519-550 (1952).

Doob, J. L.

1. "The Elementary Gaussian Processes," Ann. Math. Statist. **15**, 229-282 (1944).

Gebelein, H.

1. "Das statistische Problem der Korrelation als Variations und Eigenwert Problem und sein Zusammenhang mit der Ausglechsrech," Z. Angew. Math. Mech. **21**, 364-379 (1941).

Gladyshev, E. G.

1. "On Multi-dimensional Stationary Random Processes," Theory of Probability and its Applications, **3**, 425-428 (1958).

Grenander, U.

1. "Stochastic Processes and Statistical Inference," Ark. für Mat. **1**, No. 3, 195-277 (1950).

Grenander, U. and M. Rosenblatt.

1. *Statistical Analysis of Stationary Time Series*, John Wiley & Sons, New York, 1956.

Hanner, O.

1. "Deterministic and Non-deterministic Stationary Processes," Ark. für Math. **1**, 161-177 (1950).

Helson, H. and D. Lowdenslager.

1. "Prediction Theory and Fourier Series in Several Variables, I," Acta Math. **99**, 165-202 (1958), "II," Acta Math. **106**, 175-213 (1961).
2. "Vector-valued Processes," *Proceedings of the Fourth Berkeley Symposium on Mathematical Statistics and Probablity*, Vol. II, 203-212, University of California Press, Berkeley and Los Angeles, 1960.

Helson, H. and G. Szegö.
1. "A Problem in Prediction Theory," Ann. Mat. Pure Appl., **51**, 107–138 (1960).
Ibragimov, I. A.
1. "Some Limit Theorems for Strictly Stationary Random Processes," Dokl. Akad. Nauk SSSR **125**, 711–714 (1959).
2. "On the Spectral Functions of Some Classes of Stationary Gaussian Processes," Dokl. Akad. Nauk SSSR **137**, 1046–1048 (1961) [English translation: Soviet Math.-Doklady **2**, 403–405 (1961)].
Karhunen, K.
1. "Über lineare Methoden in der Wahrscheinlichkeitsrechnung," Ann. Acad. Sci. Fenn. Ser. AI. **37**, 3–79 (1947).
2. "Über die Struktur stationären zufälligen Funktionen," Ark. Mat **1**, 141–160 (1950).
3. "Zur Interpolation von stationären zufälligen Funktionen," Ann. Acad. Sci. Fenn. Ser. AI. **142**, 3–8 (1952).
Khinchin, A. Ya.
1. "Zur Birkhoffs Losüng des Ergodenproblems," Math. Ann. **107**, 485–488 (1932).
2. "Korrelationstheorie der stationären stochastischen Prozesse," Math. Ann. **109**, 604–615 (1934).
Kolmogorov, A. N.
1. "Sur l'interpolation et extrapolation des suites stationnaires," C. R. Acad. Sci. Paris **208**, 2043–2045 (1939).
2. "Stationary Sequences in Hilbert Space," Bull. Moscow State Univ. **2**, No. 6, 1–40 (1941).
3. "Interpolation and Extrapolation of Stationary Random Sequences," Izv. Akad Nauk SSSR. Ser. Mat. **5**, 3–14, (1941).
4. "A Simple Proof of the Ergodic Theorem of Birkhoff and Khinchin," Uspehi Mat. Nauk **5**, 52–59 (1951).
Kolmogorov, A.N. and Yu. A. Rozanov.
1. "On Strong Mixing Conditions for Stationary Gaussian Random Processes," Theory of Probability and its Applications **5**, 204–208 (1960).
Krein, M.G.
1. "On an Extrapolation Problem of A.N. Kolmogorov," Dokl. Akad. Nauk SSSR **46**, 306–309 (1944).
2. "On the Basic Approximation Problem in the Theory of Extrapolation and Filtering of Stationary Random Processes," Dokl. Akad. Nauk SSSR **94**, 13–16 (1954).
Kryloff, N. and N. Bogoliouboff.
1. "La théorie générale de la mesure dans son application a l'étude des systèmes dynamiques de la mécanique non linéaire," Ann. Math. **38**, 65–113 (1937).
Loève, M.
1. "Sur les fonctions aléatoires stationnaires de second ordre," Rev. Sci. **83**, 297–303, (1945).
Masani, P.
1. "Sur les processus vectoriels minimaux de rang maximal," C.R. Acad. Sci.

Paris. **246**, 2215–2217 (1958).
2. "Sur la fonction génératrice d'un processus stochastique vectoriel à densite' spectrale non bornee," C.R. Acad. Sci. Paris. **246**, 2337–2339 (1958).
3. "Sur la fonction génératrice d'un processus stochastique vectorial," C.R. Acad. Sci. Paris. **249**, 260–362 (1959).
4. "Sur les functions matricielles de la classe de Hardy H_2," C.R. Acad. Sci. Paris. **249**, 906–907, (1959).

Maruyama, G.
1. "The Harmonic Analysis of Stationary Stochastic Processes," Mem. Fac. Sci. Kyushu Univ. Ser. A. **4**. 45–106 (1949).

Matveev, R. F.
1. "On the Regularity of Multi-dimensional Stationary Processes with Discrete Time," Dokl. Akad. Nauk SSSR **126**, 713–715 (1959).

von Neumann, J.
1. "Zur Operatorenmethode in der klassischen Mechanik," Ann. Math. **33**, 587–648 (1932).

Obukhov, A. M.
1. "Normal Correlation of Vectors," Izv. Akad. Nauk. SSSR, Otdel. Matem. i estestv. Nauk., No. 3, 339–370 (1938).

Pinsker, M. S.
1. "Theory of Curves in Hilbert Space with Stationary nth Increments," Izv. Akad. Nauk SSSR Ser. Mat. **19**, 319–345 (1955).

Pisarenko, V. F., and Yu. A. Rozanov.
1. "On Some Problems for Stationary Processes Which Reduce to Integral Equations Related to the Wiener-Hopf Equation," Problemi Peredachi Informatsi **14**, 113–135 (1963).

Potapov, V. P.
1. "The Multiplicative Structure of J-contractive Matrix Fuctions," Trudy Moskov. Mat. Obšč. **5**, 125–237 (1955) (English translation: Translations Amer. Math. Soc., Ser. 2, **15**, 131–244).

Rokhlin, V. A.
1. "Selected Topics from the Metric Theory of Dynamical Systems," Uspehi. Mat. Nauk. **4**, 57–128, (1949) (English translation: Translations Amer. Math. Soc., Ser. 2, **49**, 171–240).

Rosenblatt, M.
1. "A Central Limit Theory and a Strong Mixing Condition," Proc. Nat. Acad. Sci. U.S.A. **42**, 43–47 (1956).

Rozanov, Yu. A.
1. "On the Linear Interpolation of Stationary Processes with Discrete Time," Dokl. Akad. Nauk SSSR **116**, 923–926 (1957).
2. "Spectral Theory of Multi-dimensional Stationary Random Processes with Discrete Time," Uspehi Mat. Nauk **13**, 2 (80), 93–142 (1958).
3. "The Linear Extrapolation of Multi-dimensional Stationary Processes of Rank 1 with Discrete Time," Dokl. Akad. Nauk SSSR **125**, 277–280 (1959).
4. "On the Extrapolation of Generalized Stationary Random Processes," Theory of Probability and its Applications **4**, 426–431 (1959).
5. "A Central Limit Theorem for Additive Random Functionals," Theory of

Probability and its Applications **5**, 221-222 (1960).

6. "On Stationary Sequences Forming a Basis," Dokl. Akad. Nauk SSSR **130**, 1199-1202 (1960) [English translation: Soviet Math.—Doklady **1**, 155-158 (1960)].
7. "On the Interpolation of Stationary Processes with Discrete Time," Dokl. Akad. Nauk SSSR **130**, 730-733 (1960) [English translation: Soviet Math.—Doklady **1**, 91-93 (1960)].
8. "Spectral Properties of Multivariate Stationary Processes and Boundary Properties of analytic matrices," Theory of Probability and its Applications **5**, 362-376 (1960).
9. "An Application of the Central Limit Theorem," *Proceedings of the Fourth Berkeley Symposium on Mathematical Statistics and Probability*, Vol. II, 445-454, University of California Press, Berkeley and Los Angeles, 1960.

Sarmanov, O. V.

1. "Maximal Coefficient of Correlation," Dokl. Akad. Nauk SSSR **120**, 715-719 (1958).

Sinai, Ya. G.

1. "A Central Limit Theorem for geodesic Flows on Manifolds of Constant Negative Curvature," Dokl. Akad. Nauk SSSR **133**, 1303-1306 (1960) [English translation: Soviet Math—Doklady **1**, 983-987 (1960)].

Statulyavichus V. A.

1. "On the Sharpening of Limit Theorems for Weakly Dependent Random Variables," Trudy IV All-union conference on Probability theory and Mathematical Statistics, Vilnyus, 1962.

Szegö, G.

1. "Beiträge zur Theorie der Toeplitzschen Formen," Math. Z. **6**, 167-202 (1920).

Vinokurov, V. G.,

1. "Conditions for the Regularity of Random Processes," Dokl. Akad. Nauk SSSR **113**, 959-961 (1957).

Volkonski, V. N. and Yu. A. Rozanov.

1. "Some Limit Theorems for Random Functions. Part I.," Theory of Probability and its Applications **4**, 178-197 (1959).

Wiener, N.

1. "Differential Space," J. Math. Phys. **2**, 131-174 (1923).
2. *Extrapolation, Interpolation, and Smoothing of Stationary Time Series*, Technology Press and John Wiley & Sons, New York, 1949.
3. "On the Factorization of Matrices," Comment. Math. Helv. **29**, 97-111 (1955).

Wiener, N. and P. Masani.

1. "The Prediction theory of multivariate Stochastic Processes, I Acta Math. **98**, 111-150 (1957); "II," Acta Math. **99**, 93-137 (1958).
2. "On Bivariate Stationary Processes and the Factorization of Matrix-valued Functions," Theory of Probability and its Applications **4**, 300-308 (1959).

Wold, H.

1. *A Study in the Analysis of Stationary Time Series*, 2nd Ed., Almqvist and Wiksell, Stockholm, 1954.

Yaglom, A. M.

1. "On the Problem of Linear Interpolation of Stationary Random Sequences and Processes," Uspehi Mat. Nauk **4**, No. 4, 173–178 (1949).
2. "Extrapolation, Interpolation, and Filtering of Stationary Random Process with Rational Spectral Densities," Trudy Moskov. Mat. Obšč. **4**, 333–374 (1955).
3. "Effective Solutions of Linear Approximation Problems for Multivariate Stationary Processes with a Rational Spectrum," Theory of Probability and its Applications **2**, 239–264 (1960).

Zadeh. L. and R. Ragazzini.

1. "Extension of Wiener's Theory of Prediction," J. Appl. Phys. **21**, 645–655 (1950).

Zasukhin, V. N.

1. "On the Theory of Multi-dimensional Stationary Processes," Dokl. Akad. Nauk SSSR **33**, 435–437 (1941).

INDEX